ECOHOLIC
BODY

YOUR ULTIMATE

EARTH-FRIENDLY GUIDE

TO LIVING HEALTHY

AND LOOKING GOOD

ADRIA VASIL

BASED ON THE POPULAR NOW COLUMN

ECOHOLIC
BODY

VINTAGE CANADA

VINTAGE CANADA EDITION, 2012

Copyright © 2012 Adria Vasil

Published in Canada by Vintage Canada, a division of Random House of Canada Limited, Toronto, in 2012. Distributed by Random House of Canada Limited.

Vintage Canada with colophon is a registered trademark.

www.randomhouse.ca

This publication contains the opinions and ideas of its author. It is intended to provide helpful and informative material on the subjects addressed in the publication. It is sold with the understanding that the author and publisher are not engaged in rendering medical, health or any other kind of personal professional services. *Nutritional and other needs vary depending on age, sex and health status. If you suspect that you have a serious medical problem, the author strongly urges you to consult your medical, health or other competent professional for treatment.*

Library and Archives Canada Cataloguing in Publication

Vasil, Adria
Ecoholic body : your ultimate earth-friendly guide to living healthy and looking good / Adria Vasil.

Includes index.

Issued also in electronic format.

ISBN 978-0-307-35715-1

1. Hygiene products—Canada—Environmental aspects—Handbooks, manuals, etc. 2. Green products—Canada—Handbooks, manuals, etc. 3. Beauty, Personal—Canada—Environmental aspects—Handbooks, manuals, etc. I. Title.

RA778.5.V37 2012   613.'4   C2011–904093-X

Cover and text design: Kelly Hill with Erin Cooper
Cover images: (photography) Dustin Rabin, (icons) Dreamstime.com
Interior images: Dreamstime.com and Shutterstock.com

Printed and bound in the United States of America

2 4 6 8 9 7 5 3 1

For my brother Nick, who led the way

INTRODUCTION 1

Body Care Basics 3

Skin Care 21

Body Maintenance 57

Makeup 95

Hair Care 123

Sex and Contraception 153

Health 171

Natural Health Products 227

Environmental Health 261

Health Care System 281

Clothing 293

Footwear 341

Jewellery and Accessories 353

Kids and Babies 367

Big Issues 395

RESOURCES 409

GLOSSARY 441

ACKNOWLEDGEMENTS 457

INDEX 460

CONTENTS

 DIY Do it yourself (easy-peasy).

 Sniff out questionable green marketing claims (a.k.a. greenwash) by tracking down this symbol.

 Follow this birdy and you'll find more money in your wallet.

INTRODUCTION

Wake up. Hop in the shower. Throw on some clothes. Pop a few vitamins, maybe, and off you go into the world. It's all so routine, we tend to drift into autopilot (if they ever need an extra for a zombie flick about making toast, I'm so there). But while we're all dozing on our feet, boy, do we ever manage to do a lot of collateral damage. Every day in our households, there's an oil spill in our bathroom, a chemical spill in our closets and a drug lab flushing down the drain. Yes, sir, we take in and pump out a hell of a lot of pollutants in the name of looking and feeling good, and to be honest, it's not our fault. If it's on shelves and in stores, it should be safe. Period. But we're starting to notice that a lot can lurk behind a pretty package. And we're beginning to see that *we're* the guinea pigs when it comes to testing the long-term chronic health impacts of all the chemical substances in our shine-boosting shampoos, wrinkle-retarding clothes and pain-killing pills. (Funny, I don't recall signing a release form, you?)

As the bigger picture comes into focus, we're waking up to the fact that we're not only making ourselves sick, we're making the planet sick too. Because, though it often feels as if our bodies are bubble-wrapped islands unto themselves, there's actually an invisible umbilical cord tying our bellies to the earth, and when the mother on the other end of that cord gets sick, so do we all. That means that when the products we use hurt Mother Earth, oh baby, it gets personal. Our choices boomerang right back at us, knocking us upside the head like a five a.m. wake-up call from Gaia. Just skip ahead to chapter 9, Environmental Health: What Goes Around Comes Around, to get an inside peek at some of the illnesses coming back to haunt us. Kenya's late, great, kick-butt Nobel laureate and green revolutionary Wangari Maathai boiled it all down for us in one simple phrase: "To destroy what is essential to life is to destroy life itself."

Truth is, all this disconnection from the world around us is dragging us down, making us anxious, making us sick. If this were a self-help book, I'd tell you the key to a better, healthier body, a better, happier life and a better, greener world is simple, it's easy, and it won't cost you a penny (well, other than the low one-time cost of buying this book, in three easy instalments, on sale for you today only). It comes down to peeling back the bubble wrap that separates us from the world and connecting the dots. Connecting the dots between the lungful of air you're inhaling at this very moment and the park full of trees quietly exhaling crisp, fresh oxygen just up the street. Connecting the dots between the bodies we haul around this earth every day and the spewing chemical industry that makes all those products in our bathrooms, medicine cabinets and closets. Connecting the dots between us and the great web of nature all around us that sustains us, that *is* us. No, you don't have to hug a tree to do it—but you can rub a homegrown pumpkin mash onto your face (page 34) or drizzle some honey onto a wound (page 197) to put you in touch with nature's built-in remedies. It's time to knock down that wall of toxic products between us and nature and have a spoonful of planetary harmony. Call it *Chicken Soup for the Earth-dwelling Soul*.

Ecoholic Body will tell you exactly how to do your part to live more sustainably while protecting yourself from toxins—all while dodging phony greenwashed products, of course. We'll also connect the dots between those toxins and the people that put them there, and I'll tell you just how to harass your politicians and the companies making these goods into prioritizing our health—and the health of the planet. If enough of us do it, we'll eventually have a better world to call home. Until then, *Ecoholic Body* is here to arm you with the knowledge you need to keep you and your family healthy, happy and green— inside and out—and, yes, still looking, smelling and feeling good along the journey.

Cosmetics Regulation	5
Conventional Body Care Products	6
Mean 15	8
Body Care Labels	13

BODY CARE BASICS

Beauty and the Beasts

I would later deny it, but I was a total
girlie girl growing up. By the age of nine I was covertly
smearing my legs with Nair hair dissolver, and by the time I
turned twelve I had a weird nail-drying machine and elaborate
makeup kits in my arsenal. Then, sometime in my teens, things
changed. I started reading labels. I couldn't help but notice a
hell of a lot of unusual chemicals in everything from my
toothpaste to my shampoo. Soon enough I was putting my
busgirl-earned dollars towards health store finds and banana
Body Shop shampoo. Okay, so not all those products ended up
being as pure as I'd hoped (see The Body Shop, page 65). But
all in all, it felt right. It felt political. Like I was voting for
green pastures, clean rivers and happy bunnies with every
dollar I spent. And we are. More and more Canadians are
asking why exactly we need carcinogens in our body wash and
estrogen mimickers in our soap. That's exactly why you'll see
more drugstore brands that say they're free of parabens. Hell,
we did that. We're demanding change. Unfortunately, the toxic
journey doesn't end there.

COSMETICS REGULATION

In an ideal world, you and I would be able to walk into a drugstore, pick any product off the shelf and assume it was totally free of harmful ingredients. Wait? Can't we do that today? Sorry, no, that's life in a parallel universe called Canada the Good. That world could easily exist if Health Canada were doing its job of protecting our health by getting tougher on body care chemicals. Oh sure, they've phased a few bad guys out lately, but we need to dig deeper. At this point, our big safeguard is Health Canada's "List of Prohibited and Restricted Cosmetic Ingredients" (a.k.a. the Cosmetic Ingredient Hotlist). It sounds like serious business, as if it might actually keep harmful chemicals far away from our bodies. What a pity it's got minimal legal teeth and no one's really policing it. Let's get real here: five years after my first *Ecoholic* book complained about this, there's still no one pre-screening products to make sure they're free of cancer-causing or long-term-health-disrupting chemicals. No wonder the David Suzuki Foundation and Réseau des Femmes got all up in Health Canada's grill in 2011 and filed a petition asking why Canada isn't enforcing a prohibition on estrogen-mimicking substances in personal care products such as shampoos, lotions, deodorants and makeup. If it did, junk like phthalates, parabens, siloxanes and dodgy preservatives like BHA (see Mean 15, page 9 for more info) wouldn't be in the vast majority of body care products. But peekaboo, there they are! And how protective can a system be when a company doesn't even have to submit its ingredient list to the feds until ten days *after* its product is on the market? Is that a joke? We're certainly the punchline when, as both Environmental Defence and the David Suzuki Foundation so aptly point out, the list only applies to ingredients that are intentionally stirred into cosmetics and says absolutely nothing about all the toxic by-products that, oops, appear in the final product while companies look the other way. If a Hotlist chemical happens to be found in that bottle of shampoo or body wash as a *contaminant,* Health Canada won't say a word. To add insult to injury, what does Health Canada recommend a company do if one of their products contains a Hotlist ingredient? Not remove it, nuh-uh. According to the advice posted openly online: "Consider marketing the product as a drug or natural health product." Turns out, if there's something medicinal in your product, you can avoid the Hotlist altogether (not to mention the fact that the ingredients don't have to be listed). That's great, Health Canada—glad to see you nudging corporations to use a dodgy loophole that increases secrecy.

So what can you do to protect yourself and others (apart from sharing a copy of *Ecoholic Body* with everyone you know)?

- Tell the health minister in no uncertain terms that you'd like to see our cosmetics laws strengthened. Tell him/her that the items on the Hotlist should be illegal whether they're ingredients or by-products, and that you'd like the list expanded to ban all substances banned in Europe. (Europe's restricted over 1,300 substances from personal care products. Canada? Around 500.)

- Tell the feds we have a community right to know what toxins are hiding in our products. Until all cancer-causing, mutagenic, hormone-disrupting toxins are banned, we should have California-style warning labels on products informing us when there's a known toxin lurking inside. That's what the Canadian Cancer Society is asking for.

- For more information on what's wrong with our system and how to get involved in changing it, check out Environmental Defence's Just Beautiful campaign (justbeautiful.ca) and the David Suzuki Foundation's What's Inside? That Counts (davidsuzuki.org).

CONVENTIONAL BODY CARE PRODUCTS

The beauty biz is a clever bunch. Big players know which buzzwords to plant smack dab on the front of their labels and which ones are raising shoppers' eyebrows. Shrewd drugstore, department store and salon brands know they'll get some mileage with the health-conscious set if they can say they're free of SLS (sodium lauryl sulphate) and parabens in particular. But what exactly are they replacing them with? Basically, it's goodbye parabens and sulphates, hello shady strangers. Just remember: being free of two chems doesn't a safe and natural product make.

Preservatives: Let's first recap the good news: estrogen-mimicking parabens are getting the boot from more and more products! The Debbie Downer bad news? There are plenty of other dodgy preservatives out there to avoid, including BHA, BHT, and formaldehyde-releasing diazolidinyl urea and imidazolidinyl urea, to name just a few. By 2010, many paraben-containing brands (including Aveda, Herbal Essences and most drugstore labels) had shifted their preservatives to a lesser-known combo of methylisothiazolinone (MIT) and methylchloroiso-thiazolinone (MI), both of which are considered such irritants that they're on Health Canada's Cosmetic Ingredient Hotlist (see page 5). When used together, they can't be more than 0.0015% of the product. Did I mention that early evidence suggests prolonged low-level exposure to MIT may damage to the nervous system? We just can't win for losing, can we?

Even a "safer" substitute—phenoxyethanol, common in health store products—isn't totally worry free. In 2008, the U.S. Food and Drug Administration issued a warning about nipple cream containing the stuff, saying the chem "can depress the central nervous system and may cause vomiting and diarrhea, which can lead to dehydration in infants." If not swallowed, it's mostly classified as an irritant. Some organic certifiers stand by its safety (such as Ecocert and the U.K.'s Soil Association), though Germany's BDIH certified natural cosmetics label doesn't allow it and neither does the USDA National Organic Program.

I have to admit: finding a totally harmless preservative that gives you some shelf life is tough. An ingredient that's considered safe today could get the proverbial skull and crossbones tomorrow. Anyone hoping for something in the middle will have to keep researching new ingredients as they pop up.

- **Definite No's:** parabens (especially butyl-, propyl-, methyl-, ethyl-), BHT, BHA, formaldehyde-releasing quaternium-15 (biggest culprit), imidazolidinyl urea, DMDM hydantoin, diazolidinyl urea.
- **Emerging concerns:** methylisothiazolinone (MIT) and methylchloroisothiazolinone (MI; irritants linked to allergic reactions, first one is a possible neurotoxin), phenoxyethanol (a shadowy figure even though it's approved by Ecocert and the U.K.'s Soil Association).
- **Not so bad:** sodium benzoate, benzyl alcohol (though both may trigger skin reactions in some), sorbic acid
- **Best:** rosemary (rosemary oil extract/rosemary oleoresin), tocopherol (vitamin E), citric acid, ascorbic acid.
- Oil-based products such as body balms and butters don't need preservatives (unlike water-based products), so they shouldn't come with any.

ECOHOLIC'S MEAN 15:
TOP BODY CARE INGREDIENTS TO SHELVE FOR GOOD

Here, ladies and gents, are the most common bad guys you'll see on shelves. Sadly, there are so many blasted estrogen mimickers, endocrine disruptors, carcinogens, and water and wildlife polluters in our body care, it's hard to narrow the list down. The Mean 15 include originals from my "top ten ingredients to avoid" from the first *Ecoholic* book, mixed with some suggestions by the godfather of green, Mr. Suzuki, as well as some growing eco-villains, such as palm oil. It's certainly daunting to think that 12 of these are found in 80% of the over 12,000 products the David Suzuki Foundation surveyed, and the others (such as palm oil) are likely to be found in even more. But don't worry, that still leaves a growing chunk of products that are in the clear. The following chapters will spell those out for you, complete with product reviews and testing.

For a **printable pocket-sized guide** to the Mean 15, check out **ecoholic.ca**.

#1 BHA and BHT: These preservatives are suspected endocrine disruptors, and in California, BHA has to come with a warning label about cancer. Both are bad news for aquatic life and have the potential to bioaccumulate, so we don't want them going down the drain.

#2 DEA (diethanolamine): Reacts with preservatives in cosmetics to form nitrosamines, which may cause cancer. Why can't we limit this contaminant the way Europe does? Avoid MEA (air pollutant in ammonia-free products) and TEA too, since both can be contaminated with DEA. Cocamide DEA is a coconut-oil sudsing allergen that contains diethanolamine..

#3 Formaldehyde-releasing preservatives (DMDM hydantoin, diazolidinyl urea, imidazolidinyl urea, methenamine, quaternium-15 and Bronopol, a.k.a. 2-bromo-2-nitropropane-1,3-diol): You don't need your cosmetics continually off-gassing low levels of known human carcinogen- and allergy-linked formaldehyde, do you? Restricted in Europe—but here? Nope.

#4 Oxybenzone (BP-3/ benzophenone) and **octinoxate** (octyl methoxycinnamate): Two of the worst sunscreen chems. Oxybenzone, found in 97% of us, is a potential hormone disruptor tied to lower birth rates in baby girls as well as allergic reactions. Octinoxate is another suspected endocrine disruptor and mild estrogen mimicker linked to thyroid changes, so don't be misled by mentions of it being derived from cinnamon. For more info, see Sunscreens, page 44.

#5 Palm oil (or anything with "palm" or "palmate" in its name, like sodium palmate): This replacement for petrol-based ingredients isn't a health concern as much as an ecological nightmare, tearing up the rainforests and savannas of Malaysia and Indonesia. For more, see Palm Oil, page 12.

#6 Parabens: This estrogen-mimicking family of preservatives raised questions when one preliminary study found it in breast cancer tissues. Several studies have found that various parabens may also interfere with male reproductive functions. By early

2011, Denmark became the first EU country to take the precautionary approach and ban the biggest suspects, propyl- and butylparabens, from body care products for kids under three. See Preservatives, page 7.

#7 Parfum/fragrance: Any synthetic fragrance will feature a whole host of unwanted chemicals, including several hormone disruptors, carcinogens, as well as allergy- and asthma-triggering ingredients (see Perfume, page 83). Some natural Euro brands with "parfums" are made with natural essential oils (it should say so on the label), though these can still aggravate the scent sensitive.

#8 PEGs (polyethylene glycol compounds, and anything with "-eth" in its name): These are often contaminated with 1,4-Dioxane, which is classified as a probable human carcinogen. For more on ingredients containing 1,4-Dioxane, see page 125.

#9 Petrolatum/paraffin/mineral oil/petroleum distillates: Who wants to smear their face/hair/lips with a product that supports the climate-cooking, war-ravaging, ocean-spilling impacts of petroleum? Can be contaminated with carcinogenic polycyclic aromatic hydrocarbons. In Europe, petrolatum is restricted in cosmetics unless the manufacturer provides a full refinery history to prove it's not a carcinogen. Not here. For tips on avoiding petrochemicals, see page 24.

#10 PPD: Sorry, all permanent hair dyes, even the health store ones, contain cancer- and non-Hodgkin's lymphoma–linked phenylenediamine. Very toxic to fish. Can also be called p-Aminoaniline; 1,4-benzenediamine; p-benzenediamine CI 76060; p-Diaminobenzene; 1,4-phenylenedia-mine; 1,4-diaminobenzene;

4-aminoaniline. For more, see Hair Colouring, page 136.

#11 Phthalates: You won't spot these on most ingredient lists since they're hidden behind the word "fragrance," but you can and should look for the phrase "phthalate free." Dibutyl phthalate (DBP) and diethylhexyl phthalate (DEHP) are two of the phthalates that have been banned from toys but are still found in cosmetics here. The European Union has restricted several phthalates from cosmetics. See Nail Care, page 116, and Perfume, page 83.

#12 Retinyl palmitate: This one's great for smoothing out skin as well as combating acne and wrinkles, but maybe not so great if you plan on combining it with something you're exposed to every day—sunlight. Retinyl palmitate seems to speed up the carcinogenic effect of UV rays in mice. Not good when UV rays already increase your skin cancer risks. Stay out of the sun with this ingredient. See Sunscreens, page 44.

#13 Siloxanes: Pass on cyclo-ingredients that end in "-siloxane" or "-methicone." Cyclotetrasiloxane (D4) and cyclopentasiloxane (D5) are siloxanes (silicone-based polymers) that have been recognized as toxic to fish and aquatic life and stay in the environment for way too long. Cyclomethicone is a mixture of D4, D5 and D6 siloxanes. Environment Canada is in the process of restricting them, but it could take years, so do your own screening. Look for silicone/siloxane-free products.

#14 Sodium laureth sulphate: Foaming agent that, like PEGs, is often contaminated with carcinogenic 1,4-Dioxane. Sodium *lauryl* sulphate used to get a lot of bad press, but it's mostly just an irritant. For more info, see page 125.

#15 Triclosan/triclocarban: This antibacterial bad boy is a suspected thyroid disruptor and may contribute to antibiotic resistance. It's highly toxic to aquatic life and is turning up in dolphins at levels known to disrupt development in other animals. See pages 33 and 81 for more on antibacterial acne and hand-washing products.

11

Palm Oil: Think palm trees are all fun and games, there to dot the vacation beaches of our minds? Think again. Palm oil is a serious business. Malaysia alone exports $20 billion worth a year. Business has been booming since the price of crude skyrocketed a few years back and companies such as Procter & Gamble announced they'd be using more palm oil instead of petroleum oils in their shampoos and detergents. Actually, palm oil–based chemicals are everywhere, at both the drugstore and the health store—in lotion, hairspray, soap, shaving gel, self-tanners, mascara, foundation. It wouldn't be an issue if the ingredients derived from palm weren't so ecologically calamitous. The drive to plant what's known as oil palm trees to harvest palm oil (from the pulp of the fruit) and palm kernel oil (from the seeds)—all to supply consumer products—has led to the mass clear-cutting of Indonesia's and Malaysia's old growth rainforests and vital peat lands, to the point that enviro groups such as the Rainforest Action Network say the days of endangered Sumatran orangutans, tigers and elephants are numbered. Sadly, even industry greening efforts like the Roundtable on Sustainable Palm Oil have been slammed for failing to enforce minimal standards amongst their members.

The Body Shop was the first big cosmetics company to commit to sourcing only sustainable palm oil for its soaps, but it landed in hot water in 2009 when it was revealed that its organic Colombian palm oil wasn't so ethically sourced after all. The U.K.'s *Guardian* newspaper outed The Body Shop's Colombian partner, Daabon Organic, for evicting a farmers' co-op to make way for a palm plantation, and by late 2010 The Body Shop dropped Daabon. Clearly, palm oil is a messy business. Who needs that much bad karma first thing in the morning?

- Read the ingredient lists on your body care products to make sure you don't see anything with "palm" in its name (like sodium palmate or retinyl palmitate). The tricky part is that a good dozen ingredients, including glycerine, coco-betaine, coco-glucoside, cetearyl alcohol and glyceryl laurate, are often but not always palm oil derived (and not from organic sources), but the label doesn't necessarily tell you that. Luckily, many brands will list palm as the source in brackets after the ingredient in question, so you can avoid it.

- Look for palm oil–free brands. **Ella's Botanicals, Rocky Mountain Soap Company, Hempen Stuff** and **Mountain Sky Soaps** are all essentially palm oil–free Canucks. Also free of palm are **Val's Veggie Bars** (this one's got a great three-for-one price; though it's not locally made, it is made close to its olive oil source, in Greece) and, as of 2009, all **LUSH** products.
- If there's palm oil in there somewhere, make sure it's certified organic. Companies that use organic palm oil include **The Botanical Soap Shop** and **Druide** (which uses Brazilian certified-organic palm oil). The Rainforest Action Network says it's no guarantee against forest destruction, but it's certainly an improvement.

SO YOU SAY IT'S "NATURAL"? PROVE IT!

Whether you're strolling through a shopping mall or outdoor fair, you'll stumble across more and more exuberant salespeople who will tell you with full conviction that their oh-so-amazing product line is fabulously all natural. It may very well be. But before you buy it hook, line and sinker, ask them to prove it. Often the sales clerks have no clue what they're selling. Scan for Mean 15 ingredients and look for third party certification seals (see Label Decoder, page 411). Tiny, independent brands with homemade products may not have expensive seals but they should have ingredients you'd be willing to swallow, wholeheartedly.

BODY CARE LABELS

What, you don't crack codes for a living? Picking out a genuinely natural or organic skin care product requires serious analytic capabilities or some sort of divining rod. How else are you supposed to know that a moisturizer with the word "natural" or "organic" built into its name may have next to no natural or organic content? The Canadian government finally got its butt in gear and started a national organic certification system in early 2009 but, oops, they forgot to include beauty care. Actually, they intentionally dodged the whole minefield. Until we get our bleep together and crack down on misleading natural and organic labelling in body care, here's a mini-guide to decoding the labels you'll spot on shelves.

Natural: What sort of "natural" are we talking about here? Natural looking? Natural feeling? If a product's brand name, label or packaging tries to imply that the ingredients come from Mother Nature herself, take a second look. No one's regulating this term, so, well, naturally it's highly abused. Double-check ingredient lists to see if you recognize what's inside. Does it actually sound natural to you? Truth is, it's not strictly accurate to call a product natural unless its ingredients come direct from nature with zero processing. That's the rule for food labelled "natural," so that should be the rule for body care as well. Case in point: coconut oil is natural; cocamidopropyl betaine, not so much. Unless you recognize the contents as coming straight from a farm, a tree or the earth, chances are higher that the ingredient is more accurately "naturally derived," if it's natural at all. Ecocert and Natural Products Association (below) both certify products as natural/naturally derived and screen out certain ingredients.

Naturally Derived/Plant based: Also unregulated, but this label is more accurate than "natural" in most cases since so many plant-based ingredients in a shampoo or whatnot have been lab altered and synthesized. Remember, just because it's plant based doesn't mean it's sustainable (case in point: palm oil–based ingredients), nor does it mean you want it on your skin. Sodium laureth sulphate, for instance, often comes from coconuts and can therefore count as "naturally derived" or "plant based," but it's also often contaminated with carcinogens. (See page 11 for more on sodium laureth sulphate.) Cocamidopropyl betaine (from coconuts) was voted 2004 allergen of the year by the American Contact Dermatitis Society. LUSH probably has the most honest perspective on this. Here's what their website says: "Some ingredients which we label as synthetic are derived from plants but go through such a lot of processing that they become unrecognizable; for example, sodium palm kernelate (in vegetable soap) is derived from palm trees but we think it is more realistic to describe it as a synthetic than to claim it is natural."

NOTICED GREENWASHING? CALL THIS NUMBER

If you spot a product that you think is fudging its green cred, don't be shy, call the Competition Bureau. Their job is to ensure truth in advertising. They need just half a dozen complaints about a company before they have to investigate, so get your friends to complain, too. Call the bureau at 1-800-348-5358 or fill out a complaint form at **competitionbureau.gc.ca**. And for those of you who prefer snail mail:

Competition Bureau
50 Victoria Street
Gatineau, Quebec
K1A 0C9

Natural Products Association Certified: This label tells you a product is at least 95% naturally derived (see above), excluding water. It screens out red-flag ingredients such as parabens, phthalates, synthetic fragrance, chemical sunscreens, petrolatum, siloxanes, formaldehyde-releasing ingredients, ethoxylated ingredients (see page 125) and much more. The seal doesn't signal that the ingredients are in any way organic (i.e., farmed without pesticides), but it does tell you that a lip balm, eyeshadow or foot cream is largely plant or mineral based. This label doesn't call for sustainable manufacturing as Ecocert does, only greener packaging. naturalproductsbuyersguide.com

Ecocert: You'll spot this French logo on a growing number of products. Certifies both "natural" and "natural and organic." Both have to be 95% or more "of natural origin" (see Naturally Derived, page 14). While plain "natural" products have to have at least 5% organic content, the certified-organic ones need to be only 10% organic. Why so low? It's partly about semantics. Unlike other certifiers, Ecocert includes water in the percentage count, whereas others don't (so if a product is mostly water, it still has to be 10% organic). That's lower than the new European Cosmos Organic standard, which says a watery product still has to be 20% organic. On the bright side, whatever is plant based in a certified-organic product has to be 95% organic. But what about the parts that aren't plants or water? It's all very confusing.

Reasons to like Ecocert: it bans synthetic scents and colours, petrochemicals, and dodgy processes such as ethoxylation (which leads to 1,4-Dioxane, see page 125), nano tech and genetic engineering, and it calls for greener manufacturing practices, so it's still a good standard if you aren't annoyed by their muddled labelling. Regardless, it's being phased out by 2015 to merge with the unified Cosmos standard (see Cosmos, opposite). ecocert.com

Organic: This doesn't mean diddly-squat without the seal of a third party, such as USDA Organic or Ecocert.

USDA Organic: La crème de la crème. This is considered the top seal on the market since body care brands that use it follow USDA Organic rules for food, making a moisturizer or lip balm technically edible. You'll see this seal on lotions and beauty potions that are at least 95% certified organic. There are now about 50 body care companies that have at least one product that meets this standard but note that the seal may apply to just two or three of their products, not the whole line. ams.usda.gov/nop

Made with Organic Ingredients: This exact wording is only okayed by certifiers such as USDA for products that contain 70% to 94% certified-organic content.

OASIS Organic: In 2008, about 30 companies (including Aveda, Juice Beauty, Hain Celestial—maker of Jason, Avalon and Alba—Origins and L'Oréal, owner of The Body Shop) banded together to form their own organic labelling standard called OASIS (Organic and Sustainable Industry Standards), which by 2012 was to allow products to label themselves "organic" if they were 95% certified organic. OASIS pegged itself as "the first organic standard for the beauty and personal care market," which had organic advocates seriously peeved since the tougher USDA Organic seal can be and has been applied to beauty products that meet top-grade food standards. The Organic Consumers Association slammed OASIS as a "bogus" standard. Regardless, it's all moot now since the seal has withered thanks to lack of funding and support from the brands that created it.

COSMOS: This brand new European standard is really the beefed-up amalgamation of Ecocert, BDIH, Cosmebio (France), Soil Association (U.K.) and others, and will replace all those by late 2015. Basically, it'll ensure a product is biodegradable, free of nano, GMO and officially endangered ingredients, as well as animal testing and ingredients from slaughtered animals. No PVC packaging, either. Of the agricultural ingredients, at least 95% must be certified organic, and when you count water and minerals, a product will have to contain a minimum of 20% organic content (with exceptions such as rinse-off products, as well as products high in mineral content, which can be as little as 10% organic). That's better than the old Ecocert standard. By the way, COSMOS also forbids the use of "organic" in the brand name unless the product is actually high in organics. Petrochemical solvents are allowed under restricted conditions for the first five years of the standard. cosmos-standard.org

17

BDIH Certified Natural Cosmetics: Well-respected German label tells you a cosmetic product is free of synthetic fragrances, ethoxylated raw materials, silicone-based and genetically modified ingredients, dead-animal by-products, organic-synthetic dyes, paraffin and other petroleum derivatives. It also has standards for eco-friendly manufacturing, packaging and biodegradability. By the way, the EU asks brands to label essential oil fragrance blends as "parfum/ fragrance," which confuses the toxicity scorers at cosmeticsdatabase.org, who automatically assume any scent labelled "fragrance" or "parfum" is a dodgy synthetic. Spot this one on quality European brands including Weleda, Lavera, SANTE Naturkosmetik and prized Dr. Hauschka; U.S.-based Aubrey Organics carries the seal too. Will be phased out by 2015 and merged with Cosmos standard (see Cosmos, above). kontrollierte-naturkosmetik.de

Naturally Sephora: This in-store seal appears on 1,400 products on Sephora shelves. It's pretty vague, though, calling for "high concentrations" of natural ingredients and "fewer to no" bad guys. Basically, products have to exclude a minimum of six of the following where viable alternatives exist: GMOs, parabens, petrochemicals, phthalates, sulphates, synthetic fragrances, synthetic dyes and triclosan. I've still seen products with this seal that contain Mean 15 ingredients as well as estrogenic sunscreen chems such as octinoxate. Be wary of greenwash.

For more labels see Label Decoder, page 411.

? CRACKING DOWN ON ORGANIC BODY CARE

You don't expect the definition of "organic" to change substantially when you go from the veggie aisle to the bread aisle, so why should it become a free-for-all when you saunter over to the body care aisle? Good question. In 2010, the Consumers Union (authors of *Consumer Reports*) and the

Organic Consumers Association put that question to the Federal Trade Commission in the United States, petitioning them to take action on misleading organic labelling in body care products. Unfortunately, they got nowhere. Then, by the summer of 2010, Whole Foods announced that they would be cracking the personal care whip in their own stores. Toothpaste or body wash manufacturers that make organic claims at American stores had to get certified by the toughest organic beauty standard around (USDA) by June 2011 if they wanted to sell their goods at the popular health food chain. (The standard is eventually making its way to Canadian stores.) That means that if a product wants to call itself straight-up organic, it has to be 95% certified and the other 5% has to be okayed for use in organic edibles. Otherwise, it can say "made with organic ingredients" if it has at least 70% organic content. Failing that, it can say simply "contains organic aloe/lavender/or whatnot," but even those have to be certified. And if you can't meet any of those standards, fine and dandy—just don't call yourself organic or you'll get the boot.

The biggest change of all is that companies with the word "organic" embedded in their brand name (such as Aubrey Organics or Giovanni Organic Hair Care) literally have to change their name on products that fail to meet the tough 95% organic standard. And surprise, surprise, instead of a whack of new super-pure organic products appearing on the market, brands such as Giovanni and Nature's Gate dropped the word "organic" from their brand names like a hot potato.

The thing is, not everyone cleaned up their act. So, in June 2011, California's Center for Environmental Health sued 26 companies for violating a little-applied California law that says a personal care product can't call itself organic unless it's at least 70% certified pesticide free. That same year, CEH joined a class action suit against Hain Celestial (maker of JASON, Alba, Avalon Organics, Zia and more) for mislabelled products. Fingers crossed, all this legal action will spawn a new wave of clarity on shelves. Let's just hope Canada doesn't become a dumping ground for old products that can't be sold in California or at Whole Foods.

COSMETICSDATABASE.COM VS GOODGUIDE.COM

Want to get a clearer picture of how your personal care products rank? You've got two main online choices: you can punch in one of tens of thousands of brand name products at cosmeticsdatabase.com or goodguide.com. So, what's the difference and why don't their scores match up? Well, Environmental Working Group's cosmeticsdatabase.com rankings focus strictly on the toxicity of a product's ingredients. They cross-check ingredients against nearly 60 health and chemical databases, government regs around the world, industry panels and academic studies. By contrast, goodguide.com doles out three scores, for the product's health rating as well as the company's environmental and social performance.

EWG is way tougher on products than goodguide.com, so an antiperspirant with controversial but inconclusively harmful aluminum as well as synthetic fragrances (typically containing hormone-disrupting ingredients) would get a mid grade at EWG versus quite a good health grade with goodguide.com. On the other hand, EWG is pretty spotty at keeping product ingredient lists current (a problem when many companies reformulate continually to remove naughty chemicals) and will slam a product for, say, having "fragrance" in its ingredient list even when that fragrance is naturally derived from essential oils. Don't rely on either score as gospel, just use them as a rough guide and check to see when the product was filed so you know whether it's up to date.

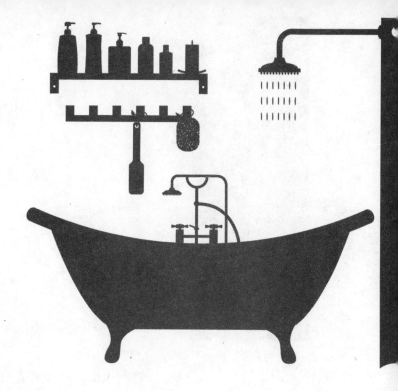

Soap and Body Washes	23
Moisturizers	25
Facial Cleansers	32
Acne Washes and Gels	33
Anti-Aging Creams	36
Scar-Fading and Skin-Lightening Creams	43
Sunscreens	44
Spas	54

SKIN CARE

What Lies Beneath

It's not often we get judged on the

beauty of our organs. No one bats a lash at the healthy sheen of
your spleen, and when your liver takes a beating, you can mostly
keep it to yourself (depending on how much you had to drink the
night before). On the other hand, when our skin ain't happy, the
whole world knows it. Zits, dark circles, rashes, all reveal more
than we'd like: how little we've slept, how stressed we are, how
much junk we've eaten. Our soft outer layer, your body's largest
and most public organ, bears the visible brunt. I know, as soon
as I start tossing and turning, my skin turns a lovely ashen
shade and black moats form under my eyes (I'm waiting for
crocodiles to set up shop). That epidermis also takes a whooping
every time we step outside and soak up the sun or stroll through
a smog zone. Sure, we try to keep it happy by scrubbing and
rubbing it with drugstore lotions and potions, but we're only
loading it down with petrochemicals and Mean 15 ingredients
(see Mean 15, page 8). Here are some ideas for being good to
your skin and the planet in the same stroke.

SOAP AND BODY WASHES

How did something as simple as a bar of soap get so complicated? All we used to need to make a bar was some sort of oil (animal or vegetable) and a little ash. Nowadays, if you were trying to make your own soap using conventional ingredients, you'd have to stop by an oil refinery for an armload of petrochemicals, fly 18 hours to the South Pacific for some unsustainable palm products (see Palm Oil, page 12), load up a sack full of beef tallow and glycerine from a factory farm, and make a pit stop at a few international mines for ingredients such as talc and titanium dioxide. You'd also have to befriend a chemist who could stir in up to a hundred chemicals to create your signature scent. And that's before you've even added any fancy ingredients like formaldehyde-releasing preservatives or any of the carcinogen-contaminated ethoxylated ingredients you find in body wash (see Mean 15, page 8). You'll notice ingredient lists get way longer when you liquefy soap, and even health store brands start pumping up the "naturally derived" synthetics. But come on, do we really need all these synthetics when even body wash lovers can get all the lather they crave from castile soap (which is really just saponified vegetable oil such as coconut or olive oil)?

If you want a super-sudsy, all-natural body wash made with the highest organic content, **Dr. Bronner's Magic "All-One!" Organic Fair Trade Shikakai Soap** (or just use their cheaper **18-in-1 Hemp Pure Castile Soap**) and **Val's Liquid Castile Soap** are the way to go. While not organic, B.C.'s **Mountain Sky Soaps'** liquid soap is another true castile-based body wash made from coconut oil with entirely natural ingredients (mountainskysoap.com). Ditto for Alberta's **Rocky Mountain Soap Company Hand & Body Wash** (rockymountainsoap.com). For a Canadian body wash that is not quite as pure but still safe and naturally derived, check out certified-organic **Green Beaver Body Wash** or **Gluten-Free Body Wash** (greenbeaver.com) and **Ella's Botanicals** liquid soap (ellasbotanicals.com). To go back to basics with bar soap, wash up with great palm oil–free Canadian brands such as **Rocky Mountain Soap Company**, Saskatchewan's **Hempen Stuff** (hempenstuff.com), **Mountain Sky Soaps** and **Ella's** (by the way, the palmarosa in Ella's is a type of lemon grass, not a palm derivative).

OIL SPILL IN THE BATHROOM

After months of watching the Gulf of Mexico drown in oil, millions of North Americans started flipping the channel. Why? Disaster fatigue. Most people were at a loss as to how to get involved and be part of the solution (outside of packing bags and heading to the Gulf). Think outside the well. Skim off some oiliness from your everyday life. Obvious enough when it comes to prioritizing cycling and subways over gas-powered transport, but can you get through the rest of your week without buying a single item of plastic (from shampoo bottles to dental floss)? That's a pretty tough assignment, though you can look for health stores that offer refillable shampoos and lotions. Next, can you steer clear of petrochemicals altogether? The Alberta government says petrochemicals have woven their way into 10% of all the products we consume. Purging them means no synthetic fragrances, no synthetic shampoos, and no synthetic fabrics or processed foods either. Try it for a day and you'll see how intricately linked our daily lives are with BP, Esso, Shell and every other oil driller on 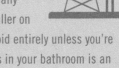 the planet. Their by-products are impossible to avoid entirely unless you're Amish, but reaching for petrochemical-free options in your bathroom is an honest start. Stay away from:

- ✗ paraffin (common in moisturizer, lipstick, mascara)
- ✗ mineral oil (ointment, baby oil, lotion, cosmetics, shaving cream)
- ✗ petrolatum (lip balm, petroleum jelly, soap, lotion, hair pastes)
- ✗ isopropyl alcohol (rubbing alcohol, nail polish)
- ✗ microcrystalline wax (big in lipstick, gloss, sunscreen)
- ✗ synthetic wax (mascara, foundation, concealer)
- ✗ propylene glycol (deodorant, lube, eyeshadow)
- ✓ For big picture ways to help, see page 395.

MOISTURIZERS

Canadian skin does a lot of suffering. Call it the martyr of the epidermis world. Half the year we face frigid, face-slapping winds and bone-dry homes, then in summer we expose our reptilian flakes to megadoses of UV. So be good to your epidermis and avoid the typical drugstore petrol pump that is moisturizer. Most conventional lotions are loaded with petroleum-based ingredients such as mineral oil and petrolatum, which can suffocate the skin. Your basic St. Ives/Lubriderm/Jergens/Curel/Keri Lotion/Vaseline Intensive Care is also chock full of other Mean 15 ingredients. Plus, if your lotion has any sunscreen properties, the manufacturer is likely using junky hormone-disrupting chems such as octinoxate and oxybenzone (see Sunscreens, page 44). So what should you be slathering on your skin? Well, depends how thirsty your epidermis is.

Lighter Lotion: If wallet-friendliness is what you're looking for, you've probably been tempted to reach for tubs of Kiss My Face/JASON/Alba/Nature's Gate. Know that you're slathering a lot more synthetics on your bod than with other health brands. The biggest, best-priced bottle is **EveryDay Shea**'s 950-millilitre pump (everydayshea.com). The shea is fair trade; the palm is from small, organic Togo farms. If all you're looking for is a light, all-over Lubriderm-style unscented lotion, **Curelle**'s B.C.-made hand and body lotion is a great basic. Unscented **Nature Clean Moisturizing Lotion** and organic **Green Beaver Body Lotion** are both fairly priced and grease free (naturecleanliving.com; greenbeaver.com). If you're ready to go up in price and performance, **John Masters Organics**' divinely scented **Blood Orange & Vanilla Body Milk** and **Bare Unscented Body Lotion** create a surprisingly long-lasting moisture barrier (johnmasters.ca). If you want more variety of delicious all-natural scents (think dark chocolate or honey pear) with high organic content, hunt down **100% Pure**'s super-silky line (100percentpure.ca). Easy-to-please scent lovers looking for something that's a little better priced will like Canadian **Ella's Botanicals'**

palm-free creams (ellasbotanicals.com). **Dr. Bronner's** lotions are tops for purity, being USDA certified and therefore 95%+ certified organic (I like the lavender coconut one), but are quite watery.

You might be trying to shop for petrochemical-free soaps and shampoos, but those products are still shipped around the country on gas-gobbling trucks. No matter how you pump it, tar sands oil is more polluting and carbon intensive than other sources of fuel, so with the encouragement of ForestEthics (the peeps who convinced Victoria's Secret to stop pimping out the boreal forest for their famous catalogues), about two dozen large companies have committed to reducing the environmental impact of their transportation by giving oil sands fuel the cold shoulder. Maybe it's not so surprising that more conscious brands including LUSH and Whole Foods committed to stop using tar sands fuel wherever possible, but we were definitely slack-jawed when straight-laced Avon and Bed Bath & Beyond asked their transportation partners to, according to Avon's VP, "avoid high-impact, high-carbon fuels such as those from the tar sands." Might not be a popular move in parts of Alberta, where anti-Avon campaigns were subsequently launched and spin doctors are trying to market Alberta's oil as "ethical." But just because workers are well paid doesn't mean we should ignore the pollution it creates, the land it devastates and the health risks to surrounding Native communities (see Big Issues, page 395).

Just keep in mind that the PR moves by Avon and others are largely designed to boost their green image and don't mean that the companies have removed petrochemicals from their ingredient lists. See Oil Spill in the Bathroom, page 24, for some ideas on going petrol free.

Richer Cream: On the thicker side, you can get more for your money with well-loved **Green Beaver Winter Body Lotion** or **Boreal Body Lotion** (greenbeaver.com). Though less local, **Alaffia's Neem & Shea Butter Therapeutic Body Lotion** and **Cocoa Butter Intensive Body Lotion**, both with certified fair-trade shea butter, are awesomely rich and great for winter (alaffia.com). **Weleda** makes all kinds of beautifully hydrating creams and lotions rich in biodynamic and organic ingredients as well as moisture-locking lanolin. Its **Skin Food** cream is particularly good at relieving dry spots with anti-inflammatory camomile and calendula and antiseptic pansy extracts (weleda.com). If you're looking for some naturally scented options, **Ecco Bella Herbal Body Lotion** makes a hydrating, vegan formula that's 70% organic (though last checked it had retinyl palmitate, which you won't want to expose to a lot of sun, see Sunscreens, page 44; eccobella. com). Wanna stop cold-weather itching? Pick up a bottle of Quebec-made **Druide's Karite Raw Shea Butter Lotion** for very dry skin (druide.ca). Probably the mother of nourishing creams for those with a little more cash to spare is **John Masters Organics' Cacao and Cupuacu Hand & Body Butter**. Wow, is this USDA organic–certified product ever rich (johnmasters.ca).

Balms/Salves/Ointments: When my eczema flares up, my hands are begging for a healing balm. Honestly, the best place to track down a salve for itchy skin is the baby aisle of your local health store. There you can find balms with calendula, comfrey, camomile and other super-healing ingredients. **Matter Company** (mattercompany.com), **Lunar Eclipse** (lunareclipse-babies.com) and **Butterfly Weed** (mattercompany.com) all make great antiseptic, anti-inflammatory and anti-itch balms. I love, love **Sigrid Natural Skin Care's Healing Salves** (sigridnaturals.com). **Green Beaver Boreal Hand Balm** isn't as healing herb–heavy but it's 96.5% certified organic.

If you've got psoriasis, rosacea or more serious eczema, and are looking for a natural, animal-free alternative to skin-thinning hydrocortisone creams (made of, ick, animal hormones from adrenal glands), check out **DermaMed All Purpose Skin Ointment** and **Psoriaderm** cream (dermamed.com). Plant-based Florasone is another popular pick, though it has some junky fillers like mineral oil. I much prefer two all-natural Canadian-made picks: **St. Francis Herb Farm's Red Clover Plus Salve** with organic anti-inflammatory ingredients (stfrancisherbfarm.com) as well as **Clef Des Champs Organic Skin Conditions Ointment** for eczema (clefdeschamps. net). You'll fork out a little more to get celeb-endorsed **Egyptian Magic**, but the bee propolis and olive oil salve has a massive following among psoriasis and eczema peeps; egyptianmagic.com). **Tamanu oil** (from the seed of a cultivated South Pacific evergreen tree) is another hot solution, with super-healing powers for inflamed or damaged skin.

Dry Skin Tips:

- Rub a small palmful of straight olive, jojoba, grapeseed, almond or, my fave, coconut oil on your skin. My mom uses straight safflower on her legs to soothe razor rash. Oils are probably the purest (especially if you buy organic), most nourishing and value-friendly moisturizer for basic dry skin woes. Do it when your skin's still wet after your shower for best results.
- Swallow nutritional oil supplements that feed the skin, such as primrose, borage, flax and sustainable fish oils (see Fish Oils, page 245), to keep your outer layer happy.
- Dump your chemical laundry detergent, add a chlorine filter to your shower head, switch to a gentler body wash and get a good humidifier (with a humidistat) for your bedroom in heating months and your skin will be thanking you in no time.
- Soak in oats. Skip the Aveeno bath oils and foams, which look super natural because they contain soothing oatmeal but also pack a ton of Mean 15 ingredients. Instead, grind your own oats in a food processor or coffee grinder till they're super fine. You can also sprinkle some itch-soothing baking soda and, if you

have some, milk powder in the tub. I like to pour in a little almond, jojoba or any other good oil in there too. If you don't like the mess of the oats, tie them into a cheesecloth bundle.

EMU, MINK AND WHALE OILS? OH MY!

I know dedicated fans of emu oil will curse me for calling this oil out, but with all the fabulous and effective plant-based products on the market, there is really zero need for emu oil in lip balms, soaps, hair oil, makeup remover and countless other natural and not so natural body care products. Ditto for oil scraped from the hides of farmed minks (garnering only a few grams of oil per mink, according to one manufacturer).

That means you should pass on weird nail-salon drying sprays made with mink oil (see Nail Salons, page 119). Make sure any squalene in your beauty product is olive or plant based and not whale derived, too (see Face Creams, below). Those wanting to avoid all animal-derived ingredients should go to **peta.org/ living/vegetarian-living/animal- ingredient-guide.asp**.

Face Creams: Looking for a good face cream? Welcome to GougeLand. Brands, both natural and not, know they can charge women through the nose to moisturize that very appendage. As with anti-aging products (see page 36), you'll find all kinds of bizarre ingredients in some, from bird poop to snail slime (no kidding), though luckily most major beauty brands stopped using shark oil–based squalene in their moisturizers and serums after facing heavy protests in 2008. Still, who wants to slather petrochemicals, formaldehyde-releasing preservatives and endocrine disruptors into their T-zone? Time to drop them all and reach for straight oils. If you're shaking your head thinking, nuh-uh, my face can't handle any oil, think again: any bad experiences with oily lotions arise because oil-based creams are loaded with too many fillers. As a former breakout queen, I'm telling you, start by just using them at night and see if you like it. They can be applied in the day too, but more so in colder, drier months. You should be wearing moisturizer with sunscreen in the day, really (see page 44 for suggestions).

So which oils should you buy? A hot commodity in many medicine cabinets is pure organic **rosehip seed oil** (see page 34 on making it yourself). Always look for the certified-organic variety, which tells you it's cultivated and grown without chemical pesticides. It's wonderfully rejuvenating for your skin and should reduce any redness. Though some with acne love it, it's not really recommended for those with extremely oily skin. In that case (or if you have rosacea), you should really try organic **sea buckthorn seed oil**, which will also help heal any scarring or burns, as rosehip does. Organic **jojoba oil** is a good basic because it's considered the oil most similar to that produced by humans and may help balance out oil production. **Skin Essence Organics** (skinessence.ca) and **Pure + Simple** (pureandsimple.ca) both offer great blends of fine organic facial oils. Keep in mind that all of these oils are quite economical because you really do use only a drop or two compared to regular moisturizer. Your best locavore oil, by the way, is Canadian-grown organic hemp oil (see The Great Canadian Beauty Oil, page 31).

If you're looking for lightweight and fluffy with a sweet silky finish and you have a decent budget, hunt down U.S.-made **100% Pure**'s face creams (100percentpure.ca). They're purer and more affordable than Aussie-based **Jurlique**'s much-loved, lightweight but super-hydrating Day Care line (jurliquecanada.com). Jurlique has been critiqued for adding a few more synthetics such as PEGs in recent years, though Jurlique maintains that their products always contained certain synthetics but they are now listing them to follow "global norms." Their day creams are PEG free. One of my long-time faves for super-simple, top organic summer moisture is **Terressentials Fragrance-free Organic Facial Lotion**. It's got clean, all USDA organic–certified ingredients and is great for summer or day use for normal or even oily skin (terressentials.com). Also high in organic content, **Seaflora** makes more high-performance, lightweight moisturizers out of hand-harvested B.C. seaweed and sea mud (seafloraonline.com). Want to keep things low cost? If you're not seeking anything fussy, **Green Beaver Daily Facial Moisturizer** is a decent pick for just $12. For a little extra performance, Manitoba-based **Pure Anada's Hydra Lotions** should win you over (thepureboutique.com). Lightweight, Quebec-made **Druide Pur & Pure Face + Body Lotion** can be used head to toe. Note: a bottle of 100% pure organic **aloe vera gel** makes a great serum, without all the silicones and synthetics found in, say, The Body Shop's Aloe Protective Serum. It works really well as a super-light, healing summer moisturizer in sweaty weather, too.

For heavier-weight creams, for normal to dry or mature skin, **Weleda's Wild Rose Smoothing Day Cream** (weleda.com) has a lot of fans and is better priced than **Dr. Hauschka**'s beloved skin care lines, though **Hauschka's Rose Day Cream** is richer and many proholistic aestheticians still consider Hauschka superior (drhauschka.ca). **NeoBio** makes a whole range of fawned-over mid-weight creams for a range of skin types, though it does contain palm (neobio.de). Readers have praised **Evan Healy's Rose Vetiver Day Moisturizer** (evanhealy.com) and 85% organic **Kibio Intense Moisturizing Cream** (kibio.com; available at Shoppers Drug Mart). An affordable local? Lovin' **Green Beaver Après-Ski Boreal Face Cream**. For anti-aging creams, see page 36.

THE GREAT CANADIAN BEAUTY OIL: HEMP

It seems that every beauty ingredient in every product in every aisle comes from lands far, far away. Isn't there a Canadian beauty ingredient that can rescue us? Enter hemp oil. This Canadian-grown, naturally low-water, low-pesticide crop is even greener when you get it certified organic (see **Hempola** or **Manitoba Harvest**). Just keep a bottle of this essential fatty acid–packed, noncomedogenic (meaning it won't clog pores) oil in your fridge and put it everywhere—face, hair, body. For real. Optional: drizzle in Canadian lavender oil from **bleulavande.ca** (QC), **greatlakeslavender.com** (ON) or **lavendercanada.com** (NS).

31

Eye Creams: Most women equate their eye creams with liquid gold. The problem is, they cost a small fortune and most of them feel like they're doing diddly-squat. Want a goody? **Devita Revitalizing Eye Life Crème with Polypeptides** is loved by everyone who tries it. With dark circle–combating vitamin K, this light cream also lifts, moisturizes and helps plump skin to fill out wrinkles thanks to hyaluronic acid. Plus, a $20 bottle should last you a year (devita.net). **Dr. Hauschka Eye Contour Day Balm** for cold winter months forms an excellent barrier around your delicate skin (though it can be greasy for day use). For puffy, baggy eyes, **Dr. Hauschka's Daily Revitalizing Eye Cream** would do a better job (drhauschka.ca). Both will set you back about $50. Want something made closer to home? **Skin Essence's Ocular Serum** uses all certified-organic oils, making it a good night pick (skinessence.ca).

FACIAL CLEANSERS

If your skin is sensitive, finding the right cleanser can take a lot of experimentation. I've tried dozens and my skin always seemed to break out at some point or other. On my old student budget, I controlled breakouts with less pure but still decent **Earth Science's Clarifying Facial Wash**, though it's a little drying (earthsciencenaturals.com). **Green Beaver Daily Facial Cleanser** is another popular, affordable option that also happens to be Canadian but again, it's a foaming cleanser. The problem? Holistic aestheticians will tell you to avoid foaming cleansers like the plague because they're too stripping, but I'm a huge fan of **100% Pure's Facial Cleansing Foam** (100percentpure. ca); it kept my annoying combination skin happy and breakout free for the whole, long-lasting bottle. Sure, Jurlique has great non-drying cleansing foams too, but for double the price (jurlique.ca). Otherwise, though, you should listen to the pros and stick to creamy cleansers. No need to strip your skin. Mature skin will definitely thrive better, as a whole, on cleansing milks, but even acne patients will benefit (see page 33 for more on acne). Earth Science's gentler, bestselling **A-D-E Creamy Cleanser** is a great, wallet-friendly pick for all sorts of skin types and washes off heavy makeup, too. Right now my fave top-notch price-conscious pick is **Andalou Naturals Apricot Probiotic Cleansing Milk**, which is beautifully nourishing and heavenly apricot oil–scented for under $10 (feels like a much more expensive product (andalou.com). For bigger budgets, Hauschka and Weleda make some great creamy cleansers though locavores will dig B.C.'s **Seaflora's Sea Foam Cleansing Concentrate** and **Potent Sea Kelp Exfoliator** with certified-organic hand-harvested B.C. seaweed—though foam does contain some palm derivatives (seafloraonline.com).

WASH YOUR FACE WITH . . . OIL?

There's a whole secret society out there of people who wash their face not with cleansers or foamers but with straight oil. They use what's called the OCM (Oil Cleansing Method) and it involves slowly massaging a blend of castor oil and olive, jojoba (or all-Canadian hemp oil) into your face in circular strokes then washing it all off with a damp, hot face cloth, lifting out the impurities. Not good daily for everyone but devotees love it (often in combo with steam).

ACNE WASHES AND GELS

Guffaw, do *I* know acne? When I was a zitty 11-year-old, my grade school crush told me I should wash my face more, when I was already scrubbing it twice a day with medicated acne wash. Yep, mortification is the word. I had it so bad and so young that I was my dermatologist's youngest patient to be on full-time antibiotics—tetracycline. (For more on internal acne medications and strategies, see page 192.) I still have to be careful about what I put on my face, but these days I make a point of not stripping my skin with drying treatments that would just kick my oil glands into high gear.

How do you keep your acne fight clean and green? Why, you steer clear of zit-busting soaps such as Clearasil and Clean & Clear that contain body- and planet-contaminating triclosan (see Antibacterial Hand Soap, page 79). Besides the triclosan, the naughtiest zit zappers, such as Murad Acne Body Wash and Neutrogena's Oil-Free Acne Wash foaming scrub, have ingredients including formaldehyde-releasing DMDM hydantoin or diazolidinyl urea and polyethylene, which is all too often contaminated with carcinogenic 1,4-Dioxane. Pretty well all acne products contain salicylic acid, which Environment Canada says is turning up in water bodies such as the St. Lawrence River, though that's mostly because salicylic acid is also a metabolite of pain relievers like Aspirin (translation: we pee it out; see Pain Relievers, page 195). Many natural acne washes also contain salicylic acid; it's hard to avoid since it's so effective. It's safe enough as long as you don't swallow it, but what are your alternatives?

- Stop stripping your skin! Using oil-free products actually pushes your oil glands into overdrive. Try using a cleansing cream such

GROW YOUR OWN COSMETICS!

Tired of products that advertise their natural aloe and avocado oil content, then drown them in crappy, unnecessary fillers? Time to reclaim what nature has given us and bypass the pre-packaged, watered-down versions pawned on us. Yes, friends, it's time to grow our own body care ingredients.

- **Aloe**: Keep a potted aloe plant in a bright spot and break off a little hunk whenever you need its skin-healing properties (the plant will heal itself, too).
- **Roses**: With a rosebush in your yard, you can make your own rosewater, a.k.a. hydrosol mist (quick way: **tipnut.com/how-to-make-rose-water-4-recipes/**; original way: **care2.com/greenliving/rose-water-how-to-make-your-own.html**). Once the roses fall off, gather the rosehips to make your own rosehip seed oil in a slow cooker! Here's how: **garden-guides.com/86407-make-rosehip-oil.html**.
- **Cucumbers**: Got puffy eyes or dark circles? Grow some cukes for your own homegrown under-eye circle/bag deleters.
- **Pumpkin**: Time to start a little pumpkin patch so you can make your own super-nourishing beta carotene—and vitamin A—rich mashed pumpkin and honey mask! Mix the mash with sugar and you've got a killer body scrub.

as **Earth Science A-D-E Creamy Cleanser** (which is pretty affordable at under $10; earthsciencenaturals.com), unless you have cystic acne, which author Kristen Ma, author of *Beauty Pure + Simple* and co-founder of Pure + Simple spas, says is the only type of acne that requires you to reduce oils on the skin's surface.

- Banish bacteria the natural way. If you've got pus-y whiteheads, you'll need an antibacterial treatment, so try something with 5% diluted tea tree oil (which some studies have found to be as effective as benzoyl peroxide) or gentle lavender oil instead of eco-headache triclosan. Lotions with 2% or more antibacterial green tea extracts have been found to be effective on mild to moderate acne. You can even try rubbing crushed naturally antibacterial garlic cloves on zits at night . . . seriously! Just wash it off after a few minutes.

- Get toned. Straight witch hazel is an excellent breakout-controlling toner. When my skin was at its worst, straight witch hazel (from the health store or drugstore) really helped keep it in check. Note: if you buy Thayers blended witch hazel, get the alcohol-free kind. Hydrosols (a.k.a. floral waters made from steam distillates) such as rosewater are great too. To minimize cotton ball usage, spritz it on instead.

- Try moisturizing with super-healing oils such as antioxidant-rich tamanu oil (from the tamanu nut) or sea buckthorn oil, both of which are fantastic for acne-prone and all sorts of problem skin.

- The acids in drugstore and prescription peels may be naturally derived, but the chemical fillers on the ingredient lists aren't. Since acid peels can be effective for controlling acne and improving scars, try a health store alternative made with natural alpha-hydroxy acids like sugar cane–based glycolic acid or lactic acid (see Anti-Aging Creams, page 36). Try your own homemade mask with the natural healing acids in yogurt, lemon juice and naturally antibacterial honey.

- Consider whole-body reasons for your breakouts. Skin guru Kristen Ma says that if you're bunged up, stressed out, have some sort of liver imbalance or are low in pantothenic acid, it could be taking its toll on your face. For must-try acne diet tips, see Acne, page 33.

ANTI-AGING CREAMS

I swear there should be a reality show called *Fear Factor: Aging Edition.* Injecting botulism toxins in frown lines—why not? Wrinkle fillers made from babies' foreskin? Sign me up! There are creams out there made with snake venom, guano, aborted fetal skin cells (which has pissed off some pro-lifers), you name it. The more they charge for it, the more we believe it might just turn back the clock. Case in point: some women are paying through the nose for creams made with afterbirth womb-linings, a.k.a. placenta (mostly from humans, cows or sheep), especially since celebs including Jennifer Lopez and Eva Longoria are purported to swear by them. Okay, yes, fetal placenta is about as youthful an ingredient as you can get, but placenta produces estrogen and other hormones. The use of placenta-heavy hair-straightening products was inconclusively linked to frighteningly early breast and pubic hair development in young black girls in the '90s. Some companies claim their particular placental extract is hormone free, but come on, it's still creepy and excessive (and are women really signing over their placenta to skin care companies on the delivery table?).

No matter what the active ingredient, nearly every anti-aging product you find on shelves is filled to the brim with your usual garbage, such as tissue-clinging triclosan, formaldehyde-laced DMDM hydantoin, unsustainable, pore-clogging petroleum products, as well as bad-news BHA and BHT and other Mean 15 ingredients (see Mean 15, page 8). And they're often topped off with estrogenic sunscreens such as octinoxate and oxybenxone (see Sunscreens, page 44).

Regardless of what they're made of, *Consumer Reports* tested nine anti-aging creams and serums (including Lancôme, Vichy, Neutrogena, Olay Regenerist and Burt's Bees) and found that after 6 to 12 weeks' use "even the best performers reduced the average depth of wrinkles by less than 10 percent, a magnitude of change that was, alas, barely visible to the naked eye." To complicate matters, performance varied from person to person: "every serum we tested produced a visual change in wrinkle length or depth for at least one person and did nothing for others." Ditto for face creams. Most notably, they found zero correlation between price tag and efficacy. In fact, they found the $200-an-ounce cream performed worse than the competition. I would have liked to see them test infamous La Mer moisturizing cream which, at $250 a bottle, is really just petroleum with seaweed and vitamins. *Consumer Reports* tested only one natural product, Burt's Bees Naturally Ageless Intensive Repairing Serum, and unfortunately found it slightly less effective than all the others. Though it and Burt's Bees Naturally Ageless Skin Firming Night Crème still has a legion of fans online, however. Goes to show you how subjective all this stuff is.

I considered getting cross-generational pals to help me with a product ranking of natural wrinkle creams, but since results vary so much from person to person, I'm leaving this one open-ended. Sorry, gang—you'll have to do your own experimenting.

Mainstreamer naturals like JASON's Ester-C anti-aging cream as well as Avalon Organics' Co Q10 anti-aging system didn't do much for my skin, but Nature's Gate Oh What a Night was pretty good for a pseudo natural. Regardless of the cream/serum/potion, let's be realistic here, people: no product is going to work as a permanent magic eraser on wrinkles or hike up your jowls like a pair of suspenders.

- Fine lines are nourished and much less visible after the use of straight oils, such as skin-rejuvenating **rosehip seed oil,** which has gathered a huge following with women of all ages or **tamanu oil** for problem, mature skin. For more on oils, see page 28.
- Looking for more oomph than you can get from an oil? Aging skin will tend to love many of the richer facial moisturizers I listed on page 31, such as Dr. Hauschka's Rose Day Cream. But if you want some specialized age-combatting ingredients, well-reviewed health store standards include the **Dr. Hauschka Regenerating** line (you'll pay double for it, though), **Jurdique Purely**

Age-Defying (also costly), as well as beloved new import on the block, **Antipodes** (at Whole Foods) and the relatively more accessibly priced **Weleda Pomegranate Line**. DeVita's whole anti-aging line gets high praise from holistic aestheticians, but **DeVita Optimal Rejuvenation** serum, with DMAE (Dimethylaminoethanol), green tea extract and alpha lipoic acid is an award winner (devita.net). One more affordable cream that's won over a lot of fans at my neighbourhood health store is **NeoBio Red Clover Day Cream** for demanding (that's to say, mature) skin. Too bad it's harder to find across Canada (neobio.de).

- Get your natural firming action from the true north strong and free! Just make sure it's really as pure as it claims. Jouviance EcoRejuvenation Anti-Aging Cream has been getting a lot of positive attention and is free of parabens, silicones and artificial fragrances, but it still contains a fair amount of petrochemicals and ethoxylated ingredients (see page 125 for more on ethoxylation). In the premium range, a more natural Canadian bet would be B.C.'s own **Authenta's Skin Renewal Cream,** which is loaded with a long list of excellent anti-aging ingredients including alpha lipoic acid, DMAE and plumping hyaluronic acid (authentaskincare.com). Very nourishing. If you're looking for an organic version of La Mer's petrochem rip-off, Canadian-made **Seaflora** offers a range of lightweight and lovely skin care options that are 70% to 94% certified organic. They even harvest their own certified-organic seaweed and ocean mud off the coast of B.C. and their skin serum has been called the "Dom Pérignon of seaweed-based skin care"(seaflora.com).

- Want Canadian on a budget? Under $25, **Awaken My Senses Organics' Aging Gracefully Fine Line Vanishing Cream** is quite nice (awakenmysenses.com). Also, check out Manitoba-made **Pure Anada Revive Serum** with hyaluronic acid, firming resveratrol and the antioxidant coenzyme Q10 (thepureboutique.com).

- For straight-up line-filling for your big night out, **Andalou Naturals' Deep Wrinkle Dermal Filler** is a more natural way to go for just $20 (andalou.com).
- If you're not primed to have a romantic liaison and are willing to tape sticky paper to your forehead to smooth out lines while you sleep (seriously), get yourself some **Frownies** (frownies.com). These guys have been in business since 1889 making patches for foreheads, eyes/mouth corners and under the eyes, and those who use them swear by them (including friends who shall remain nameless).

Here's a breakdown of some of the major anti-aging ingredients on shelves, and healthier alternatives:

Acids: Skin-peeling alpha-hydroxy acids such as glycolic acid are great at sloughing off dead layers, and you know what? They're actually made with fruit sugars. The only thing is, they can be awfully hard on your skin, causing increased sensitivity, redness, itching and dryness. Sure they can help get rid of sun damage, but they'll also make you more susceptible to further damage. Lactic acid (derived from milk) is the gentlest of the AHAs, and still reduces the appearance of fine lines and boosts collagen. No matter what acid you pick, stick to all-natural brands including **Pure + Simple's Lactic Acid Original 5% or 10%, Reviva Labs' 5% or 10% Glycolic Acid Cream** and **Devita's 2-Step Alpha Beta Home Peel Kit** (pureandsimple.ca; revivalabs.com; devita.net). Not all acids are peeling. Alpha lipoic acid is more of an antioxidant that diminishes fine lines and fights free radical damage, while hyaluronic acid is tops for hydration and plumping.

DMAE (Dimethylaminoethanol): This is a natural amino alcohol that you'll find naturally in small fish like sardines and anchovies. I wouldn't go so far as to buy claims that it's a "facelift in a jar" but it does have some good firming effects.

Retinol A (Vitamin A): This is one of the only compounds proven to clinically reduce fine lines over time. The big problemo is that it can aggravate sensitive skin and it will sensitize you to the sun, making you prone to further skin damage (including skin cancer) if you're not careful to stay out of the sun. In fact, there's early evidence that it may accelerate tumours on skin exposed to sunlight. To avoid the chemical fillers usually paired with retinol A, stick to all-natural products that contain the stuff, and wear them at night only. Make sure you're well defended with a top-quality sunscreen during the day (see Sunscreens, page 44).

Collagen: As we age, we lose our natural collagen and elastin reserves and our skin eventually sags (and that, Johnny, is how jowls are born). Hence the fact that so many products claim to boost your skin's collagen and elastin levels. Just be aware that most of the stuff on the market is made from boiled cow or pig skin. Some face-filling injectables actually contain genetically engineered human collagen made from lab-grown human skin. Sure, no animal died for it, but still kind of creepy. If you aren't averse to fish oils, your best option is actually marine collagen, made from fish skin or scales—by-products of the fishing biz (in other words, they're not killing a fish just to provide you with oil). Don't assume it can slow the rate of collagen loss (sorry), but its hydrating power will help you stay supple. There's been a lot of hype out there around drinking liquid collagen as a miracle anti-aging cure and, yes, specific forms of collagen supplements (mostly from chicken and bovine joints) can be great for arthritis sufferers (see Arthritis, page 205), but there's no independent science backing the fountain-of-youth claims. At $175 for a 30-day supply of Toki powder, for instance, you might want to reconsider.

Cosmeceuticals: Cosmetic products that claim their coffee, green tea or goji berry extract has medicinal properties are huge in the anti-aging world, and it's fantastic to see natural ingredients so glamorized, but there are two things to keep in mind here. One: lots of miracle-promising cosmeceuticals have conventional crappy chemical ingredients (such as Cindy Crawford's melon extract–based Meaningful Beauty line). And two: nothing's ever going to perform the miracles you're hoping for—pill, food or beverage. After resveratrol was profiled for its "life-extending" powers in mice on *60 Minutes* and elsewhere, sales of the supplement spiked 400% in a two-year window, according to SPINS market research—all this despite the fact that no research on humans had ever been conducted. As Consumer Lab points out, to apply the mice findings and dosages to humans, "this would be equal to a daily dose of about 1,500 to 28,000 mg of resveratrol, which is far more than that provided by most supplements." Pending more long-term safety testing on humans, keep in mind that one study on multiple myeloma patients had to be suspended after they developed kidney problems, and that this ingredient is mildly estrogenic and has blood-thinning properties, so it certainly isn't for everyone.

BRAINS BEFORE BEAUTY: NATURAL ANTI-AGING TIPS

Tired of emptying your purse for promising creams that never deliver? Here are some tried-and-true ways to turn back the hands of time—or at least slow down the ticking.

- **Put your vice on ice.** Hate to be the party pooper, but yep, you've got to give up smoking (and excessive drinking too)—unless you strive for "smoker's face" complete with grey, dull skin and wrinkled lips. Drinking a glass of red a day, on the other hand, isn't so much a vice as a proven longevity booster. Phew.
- **Hit the snooze button.** Well actually, going to bed half an hour earlier would probably be wiser career-wise, but either way, the body benefits of sleeping a solid eight hours do transfer to your skin.
- **Zen out.** Daily meditation, yoga or some kind of de-stressor will help keep your woes from weighing on your skin.
- **Slather on the antioxidants.** From creams to snack foods, anything high in antioxidants can be beneficial. In skin care, antioxidants such as green tea,

41

grapeseed extract, pomegranate, vitamin C and coenzyme Q10 are important for repairing pollution and sun damage.

- **Chow down on anti-aging foods.** No fad dieting here, just lots of anti-inflammatory, antioxidant-rich foods such as bright fruits and veggies, whole grains, sustainable coldwater fish (see **seachoice.org** for a pocket guide to eco-safe seafood), beans, nuts, as well as probiotics and lots of water and green tea. In food form the antioxidants will help keep age-related diseases including heart disease and cancer at bay. And if you pick local, organic options, you'll be keeping the planet happy, too. By the way, don't be fooled by all the marketing-hyped nutricosmetics available today (foods or drinks pushing cosmetic properties). You shouldn't put too much stock in, say, vitamin drinks that claim to fight wrinkles or lighten skin with natural licorice extracts.

- **Pick a sunscreen that actually works.** This is easier said than done when so few sunscreens are both safe AND effective (see Sunscreens, page 44). Once you find a good natural one that is free of estrogen mimickers, make sure you're applying a quarter-sized squirt for each limb.

(DIY) ANTI-AGING FACE MASK

My mom has applied an egg yolk mask to her face once a week for the last, oh, 40 years, and she looks amazing. Just crack an organic egg (rich in vitamins A, D, K and E), separating out the yolk into a bowl, drizzle in a little skin-plumping honey, whisk it, apply, and let dry for 10 to 15 minutes before removing with a damp face cloth. Your skin will love, love, love it. To add some skin-rejuvenating lactic acid to the mix, stir in a little yogurt.

SCAR-FADING AND
SKIN-LIGHTENING CREAMS

I've got a fifteen-year-old gash on my thigh that looks like I was stabbed in a bar brawl, but if you've got scarring or skin you'd like to lighten, please, please, please resist the temptation to reach for chemically potent faders. Most contain ultra-risky hydroquinone (a.k.a. 1,4-benzenediol), which is outlawed in Europe and was nearly banned from over-the-counter sales in the United States because of evidence of cancer risks, genotoxic effects and the onset of a disfiguring skin-darkening condition called ochronosis. The ban never went through; the U.S. Food and Drug Administration says it's awaiting the results of human studies, so in the meantime it's still allowed on shelves on both sides of the border. Canada has actually declared hydroquinone officially toxic but somehow still allows higher levels—up to 4% creams—to be sold over the counter (technically, if it's 1% or higher, you have to ask the pharmacist for it behind the counter). Weirdly, where creams labelled as drugs are capped at 2% hydroquinone, Health Canada has approved natural health products with up to 4% hydroquinone; no word on why the discrepancy. Also, be aware that skin-lightening creams around the globe have been found to contain mercury. Yes, that heavy-duty neurotoxin that's found in old thermometers. It's illegal here but has been found in cheap imports pretty regularly. To be safe, avoid buying lighteners when you're overseas. If you want to lighten age spots, look for **Zax's Original Darkspot Cream** (zaxhealth.com).

(DIY) NATURAL SCAR TREATMENT

Skip the Bio-Oil, which contains dodgy BHT and several petrochemicals and make your own scar treatment with a few capsules of vitamin E, some rosehip seed oil, a smear of calendula and a couple of capsules of beta carotene from the health store. **Aloe** makes for a great scar preventer when you've got ongoing skin issues such as acne (I use straight aloe as a light restorative summer moisturizer). Switch to super-healing **sea buckthorn seed oil** or **tamanu oil** in the winter.

SUNSCREENS

You know those gorgeous movie stars who swear that the secret to ageless beauty is staying out of the sun? Okay, so maybe they're not sharing all the ins and outs of their Botox habit, but all that aside, I've always envied anyone with the determination to keep UV rays from their skin at all costs. I, on the other hand, have roasted myself like a chicken on a beach spit with zero, yes, *zero* protection far too many times. I still like tapping into my half-Greek heritage and getting brown, but I do it much more cautiously in my mid-thirties than I did in my twenties. I actually own sun protection now and use it. Well, after allowing myself a decent dose of vitamin D, of course. The big question is, which sunscreen should you choose? And how bad are those chemicals we smear on our skin all summer, and increasingly all year long? Enough to make you red in the face, especially when you find out how poorly they actually do their job.

In its 2011 sunscreen report, Environmental Working Group (EWG) found only one in five of the beach and sport sunscreens they evaluated both safe (health-wise) and effective. Most sunscreens mainly prevent sunburns and fail to block cancer-causing, wrinkle-inducing UVA rays. Things have got slightly better over the last few years, but still, in 2011, 60% of sunscreens labelled SPF 30 or higher offered weak UVA protection that wouldn't meet European standards. The United States is finally bringing in new sunscreen regs to boost UVA protection and Health Canada is likely to follow suit. While Canada already had some of those rules in place (like not allowing products below SPF 15 to make anti-cancer claims), Health Canada may still drop the maximum SPF on labels to 50 (any higher is meaningless), tighten UVA standards and outlaw waterproof claims to harmonize with the States.

Sunscreen Ingredients: Efficacy notwithstanding, sunscreens' chemical contents can be pretty frightening. Oxybenzone (in 60% of all sunscreen) is a weak hormone disruptor that's found in the urine of 95% of six-to-eight-year-old girls tested, as well as in waterways and soil samples. Scientists at University of California, Riverside, reported that

IS YOUR SUNSCREEN KILLING CORAL REEFS?

Snorkelling is an incredible way to take in the beauty of the world's oceans. Too bad your sunscreen could be responsible for accelerating the die-off of coral reefs! A study published in *Environmental Health Perspectives* found that chemical sunscreens can play a big role in bleaching coral reefs by triggering viral infections in the reefs.

Chemicals of particular concern include oxybenzone, ethylhexyl-methoxycinnamate (or octinoxate), 4-Methylbenzylidene camphor and the especially worrisome preservative butylparaben, being banned in Denmark. You can swim guilt free by reaching for biodegradable, all-natural sunscreen.

two-thirds of the male turbot and sole gathered near a sewage pipe a few kilometres off Huntington Beach had ovaries growing. The only real suspect they found in the gender-bending fish was, you guessed it, oxybenzone. Luckily, from 2008 to 2009, 19% fewer sunscreens contained oxybenzone, but it's still found in far too many products, especially when several studies have cautioned against its use in children in particular.

The list of freaky ingredients goes on: estrogenic octinoxate (a.k.a. octyl methoxycinnamate), hormone-disrupting and potentially thyroid-suppressing 4-Methylbenzylidene camphor (a.k.a. 4-MBC or Parsol 5000), and the weak hormone disruptor homosalate. You'll even find some of these sunscreen chemicals in some health store brands, including most Kiss My Face sunscreens and tinted moisturizers, some of JASON's Sunbrellas as well as Nature's Gate regular Face Block/ Kid's Block/Aqua Block/Sport Block sunscreens.

There are a handful of excellent active chemical sunscreen ingredients out of Europe (Tinosorb M or S, Mexoryl SX/Ecamsule) that have no hormone-disrupting properties and pose fewer health risks. It's just a shame that they're almost always combined with troublesome ingredients such as nasty parabens, environmentally persistent siloxanes and problematic sunscreen chemicals like octinoxate, which means I can't really recommend any products to date that contain them (such as RoC Minesol, Ombrelle and La Roche-Posay Anthelios). Sorry.

Natural Sunscreen Ingredients: As chemical sunscreens get an increasingly bad rap, more and more brands are offering mineral sunscreens made with zinc oxide and titanium dioxide. Really, these physical (as opposed to chemical) sunscreen ingredients are considered your strongest bets since they're stable in the sun and provide good UVA and UVB protection. It's unfortunate that zinc mines and titanium dioxide production are both pretty polluting (think open-pit/strip mining), but your enviro-sound sun-blocking alternatives are few and far between. Just keep in mind that a growing number of drugstore sunscreens now add titanium dioxide and/or zinc to their formula to bump up their UVA protection, but the rest of the ingredients are the same junky chemicals and fillers as before. Aveeno's Natural Protection Mineral Sunblock (for adults and babies) says it's made with 100% naturally sourced *active ingredients,* but what about the non-active ingredients? The baby version contains Mean 15 preservative BHT as well as petroleum by-products (for more on kids' sunscreen, see page 376).

Of course the water gets even murkier when you consider the controversy around nano particles. Mineral sunscreen producers often use freakishly minuscule nano versions of titanium dioxide or zinc oxide because this helps eliminate any white residue that comes with mineral sunscreens. These understudied particles are one-billionth of a metre wide and have the potential to mess with the environment and seep past skin cells. It's largely been held that the two nano minerals are non-toxic and will, for the most part, not penetrate unbroken skin, but a couple of Australian studies have found that nano zinc can indeed penetrate healthy skin. Researchers still say the body can handle a little zinc (hell, we take supplements with the stuff) and not to fret, though evidence is emerging that swallowing nano versions of zinc and nano titanium dioxide isn't a good idea. And what are the environmental effects of these nano ingredients washing off into the water? Hard to say at this point, though early studies—including one that looked at the impact of nano zinc on zebra fish, published in the *Journal of Environmental Monitoring* in 2011, and a 2009 University of Toledo study on the impact of nano titanium dioxide on microbes—do raise warning signs. Despite all this, since the two nano minerals are so much more effective than sunscreen chemicals at preventing sun damage and still carry no firmly established health or environmental risks, EWG and others say nano TD and zinc remain your best choice.

Regardless, a growing number of health brands are backing off nano sunscreens and shifting in particular to zinc that is the next size up from nano: a micron (100 nanometres). Now, most of the titanium dioxide on the market is still nano, but some are figuring out ways to minimize the whitening of larger nano-free versions (Pure + Simple uses nano-free TD). Ditto for nano-free zinc. **Badger** (badgerbalm.com), **DeVita** (devita.net) and **Green Beaver** (greenbeaver.com) use non-nano, uncoated zinc (smaller nano zinc and titanium particles are often silicone coated, purportedly to keep your body from absorbing them).

Some health store brands still contain a PABA derivative called Padimate-O (or PABA ester). It's safer than its older brother but can release cancer-linked free radicals and has been tied to DNA damage in some studies. Plus, some people are just as allergic to it as they are to PABA.

Ecoholic Sunscreen Tips:
- Avoid sunscreen that's got retinyl palmitate, since early evidence shows that it may accelerate skin damage and tumour growth when it's exposed to UV sunlight. For all the dirt on why, spend a few minutes at ewg.org/report/ what-scientists-say-about-vitamin-sunscreen.
- Don't fall for sunscreens claiming over 50 SPF protection. They suppress sunburns but give people a false sense of security. FYI, 60 SPF is not double the protection of 30 SPF but just 2% more effective at blocking UVB.

- Stay away from sprays! These make it super easy for you to inhale sunscreen chemicals and nano minerals (see page 47).
- Most of us seriously under-apply sunscreen, thereby cutting its SPF. How much is enough? Half a teaspoon on your face and a shot glass full for the rest of your body.
- If you want to be really responsible, wear a hat and long sleeves. You can even get yourself some UV-resistant clothing. **Patagonia's Sol Patrol** line is so tightly woven it has a UV protection factor of 30 to 40 (patagonia.com). Better still, sit in the shade.

Sunscreen Testing: Cosmeticsdatabase.com does a solid job of ranking sunscreens for efficacy against UVA and UVB rays, nano content (labelled as < 100 nm, or nanometres) and stability in the sun, and it tells you if other health concerns are low. Not all natural sunscreens make the cut. Take, for example, Aubrey Organics' Blue Green Algae line with PABA-derived Padimate-O, and chemical sunscreen–laced Alba Botanica's Hawaiian aloe line. But keep in mind that the database still green-lights some products you might want to avoid (drugstore mineral sunscreens such as Aveeno, which still contain BHT and other Mean 15 ingredients; see page 8), so do your own ingredient scan to be sure. FYI, most health store sunscreens with titanium dioxide and zinc oxide will leave a very faint white residue, to some degree or another. In truth, that residue provides an important physical barrier between you and the sun's rays, but don't worry: not every natural sunscreen has it. To be sure, I asked one of my girlfriends of Indian ancestry to test 'em out with me. Top scorers also had to survive my boyfriend's stubble (a lot of mineral sunscreens look fine on hairless, paler skin but they turn my somewhat ruddy-skinned man into a purple-skinned, white-haired monster).

Here are ones considered safe by Cosmeticsdatabase.com that I've ranked for purity and performance. (P.S. I've factored in reformulations not noted by EWG.)

GREEN SCREEN

Hold your sunscreen, this is way too whitening! Tinted version looks like sickly pink calamine lotion.

LAVERA

Disastrous. Paste left white armour behind. Now nano free.

HARA

Cakey, pasty and meh. Left a white mask on my Indian friend.

❀ HEIKO

This chalky paste left a faint white residue on my skin and a major white mask on my brown-skinned pal. Smells awfully medicinal. At over $30 a bottle, best to reach for DeVita.

CARIBBEAN SOLUTIONS

Company says it's nano free, but with particles well under 100 nm this is definitely nano. Still leaves white residue, which got horribly stuck in boyfriend's stubble. Smells delish though.

LIVESTRONG

Lance Armstrong lovers are snatching this non-nano sunscreen up and it's all-around okay. Super thick and all right for pale faces but not fab on darker skin.

TROPICAL SANDS

Light and watery going on and it's a solid performer if you're light skinned, but dock a point if you're darker complexioned (it used to have retinol A, so check your bottle).

BADGER — Bonus points for high organic content, as well as non-nano, non-coated zinc from recycled sources purified to pharmaceutical grade. This would receive four green thumbs if it weren't so whitening on those that aren't alabaster white to start with. Smells like cocoa butter, yum.

UV NATURAL — This unscented option goes on like glue, is a little greasy and takes some rubbing but it did vanish on darker skin with no ghostly residue.

SOLÉO ORGANICS — Nano-free zinc. Slightly better than UV Natural. Heavy, pasty but no grease and no big white residue except a little in beards.

ALL TERRAIN — Old bottles had oxybenzone and retinyl palmitate, but it's been reformulated. Now nano-free zinc oxide. The spray version is aloe and jojoba based and leaves no white trace.

GODDESS GARDEN — Much lighter than most with no oily residue. This popular pick didn't leave white residue on my tanned skin though it did make my friend slightly paler. Wasn't great in stubble.

🍁 **GREEN BEAVER**	Great value, 100% non-whitening. Original formula is too oily for many (the oils help make it water resistant); new lighter lotion/spray moves it into five thumb territory. Non-nano, non-coated zinc with organic sunflower oil and organic B.C. raspberry seed oil.	
DEVITA	Nothing but rave reviews here. Non-greasy, beautiful texture, no white residue, non-nano, uncoated zinc. Love it. At $35 a bottle it's pricey, but what an excellent performer.	

👍 Green Thumb legend   1 = Might as well hide in the shade   2 = Sorry excuse for sunscreen   3 = Decent UV buster   4 = Great, green sun-brella   5 = Ombrelle's green sister

DON'T GET BURNED COMBINING DEET WITH SUNSCREEN

Come summer, Canadians face two threats: sunburns and bug bites. To face both head-on, we often slap on sunscreen and insect repellent in a one-two punch. The trouble is, researchers out of the University of Manitoba discovered that doing so seriously increases the amount of DEET that seeps into your body and also reduces the efficacy of your sunblock. Applying repellent spray on top of chemical sunscreen lotion meant 10 times more of the bug-repelling neurotoxin was absorbed. And sunscreen on top of DEET will spike your absorption by a shocking 47%! The researchers cautioned that you should wait at least a half-hour after applying sunscreen before reaching for the DEET. Or just skip the chemical sunscreen altogether and consider natural bug blockers (see page 87).

Moisturizer with Sunscreen: Basic health store sunscreens do have a tendency to turn you a little whitish or else go on super thick/oily, which is okay if you're going hiking or swimming but it's just not

51

cool for a daily moisturizer. So I'm putting these to the test. By the way, in the sweaty depths of summer, spritz a little toning rosewater (organic) on your face before applying your moisturizing sunscreen.

BURT'S BEES RADIANCE DAY LOTION SPF 15	Cakey and white, nuh-uh. Will clump under foundation or flake if you rub too much.	👎
THE BODY SHOP VITAMIN E/VITAMIN C SPF 15 MOISTURIZER	Goes on nicely but come on, Body Shop, why are you using estrogenic octinoxate as your main sunblocker, not to mention enviro-persistent siloxanes? I don't think so.	👎
SANTE	The driest finish, thanks to alcohol in here, which some may want, but not if you're brown skinned. My girlfriend looked like the Phantom of the Opera with this on. It also pills.	👎👎
JURLIQUE SUN LOTION	Light consistency but not worth the price or the estrogenic oxybenzone and octinoxate (which it lists as ethylhexyl methoxycinnamate).	👎👎
❧ **HEIKO**	At $45, skip and buy DeVita. Too oily for summer faces, and micronized zinc does leave a little white residue/visible barrier.	👎👎
CARIBBEAN SOLUTIONS	Decent price for a face cream and with a lot of rubbing should vanish from fairer skin, but like cottage cheese in long stubble. Ads say they're nano free but president informed me particles are well under 100 nm.	👎👎

AVALON ORGANICS ESSENTIAL LIFT MINERALS	Unlike some of their other SPF products, this one is free of chemical sunscreens. While thick, there's no residue left behind. Matte finish.	👍👍👍
LAVANILA SPF 40 FACE CREAM	Not quite as pure as some but still has decent organic content. It's pretty thick going on, though, with natural vanilla extract (yum) and skin-plumping hyaluronic acid.	👍👍👍👍
ECCO BELLA DAY CREAM	This one's kind of matting, so good for oily skin. With a little rubbing, white residue vanishes.	👍👍👍👍
DESERT ESSENCE	Good-value face cream with SPF. Dry skin day cream pick is nicely moisturizing and friend says "it doesn't feel like sunscreen."	👍👍👍👍
🍁 PURE + SIMPLE	Great ingredients, nano free, nice and light going on and disappears 99% on tanned skin, but it is a little whitening in stubble.	👍👍👍👍
🍁 GREEN BEAVER SPF 15	Totally non-whitening without the greasiness of original Green Beaver sunscreen. Great pick.	👍👍👍👍👍
100% PURE FRUIT PIGMENTED TINTED MOISTURIZER WITH SPF 20	So sheer and lovely! Nano free, vanishes on all skin tones, top ingredients. Maybe a little oily going on in heat wave, but it sinks in eventually and nourishes nicely.	👍👍👍👍👍

| DEVITA SOLAR PROTECTIVE MOISTURIZER SPF 30+ | Tops! Love this one! Lightweight, no residue, and non-nano zinc oxide. Plus hyaluronic acid for skin plumping. | |

🍃 Green Thumb legend   1 = Might as well hide in the shade   2 = Sorry excuse for sunscreen   3 = Decent UV buster   4 = Great, green sun-brella   5 = Ombrelle's green sister

Bronzing Lotions: Who would have thunk it but all the self-tanning creams on the market get their faux glow from a pretty natural ingredient, dihydroxyacetone (DHA). DHA is actually derived from beet or cane sugar, and its effect is analogous to a browning apple when it interacts with the proteins in surface skin cells. Still, most of the self-tanners in beauty aisles are loaded with a litany of unscrupulous chemicals, including environmentally persistent Mean 15ers cyclopentasiloxane, estrogenic sunblocks, parabens and worse (see Mean 15, page 8).

Tree-hugging tanorexics can find largely natural self-tanners in health stores. **Lavera** makes a safe 'n' green award-winning self-tanning cream for body and face that's also certified natural (lavera.com). U.S.-based **True Natural Anti-Aging All Natural Self Tanner** is high in organic ingredients (truenatural.com). **Nature's Gate** isn't quite as pure, but it offers a sunless tanner that clings to your skin for a week as well as a tinted Glow Lotion that moisturizes while gradually boosting your hue, also with DHA. Natural skin care king Dr. Hauschka also makes a beeswax and rose petal–based tinted moisturizer called "toned day cream" to give pale skin a warm glow. I personally add a drop of **Dr. Hauschka's Transluscent Bronze Concentrate** to my regular moisturizer when I want a little boost. Otherwise I dab **Revolution Organics Freedom Glow Beauty Balm** all-in-one stick on my face. It's 85% organic oils (revolutionorganics.com).

SPAS

If I had a dollar for every time a spa brochure mentioned the words "botanical" and "organic" without actually using genuine natural

products, I'd own my own oceanfront retreat by now. Despite all
the angelic whale music and seaweed wraps, and the claim made by
nearly every spa that it uses potions made from herbal ingredients, if
you look past the leafy marketing you'll realize you're being slathered
in petrol-heavy synthetics, honey. There are, blissfully, a growing
number of spas that offer genuine natural and/or organic products,
including spa lines like USDA-certified **Eminence Organics**
(eminenceorganics.com) or B.C.-made **Seaflora** (seafloraonline.
com). It would be impossible to mention every (mostly) natural spa
in Canada, but here's a taster: **J-Spa Organic Skin Care Spa** in
Vancouver (j-spa.ca), **Kolya Naturals Wholistic Skincare & Spa**
in Edmonton (kolyanaturals.com), **Riverside Spa** in Calgary
(riversidespa.ca). Moving east, **Elixir** and **Pure + Simple** are two of
the longest-running organic spas in Toronto (elixirspa.ca, pureand-
simple.ca). **Spa Dr. Hauschka** and **Espace Nomad Holistic Spa** are
good ones in Montreal, and **Spirit Spa** in Halifax has some organic
treatments (spadrhauschka.com; espacenomad.ca; spiritspa.ca).
If you don't live near any of those, here are some things to look
for at your next spa visit.

- Seek out spas that feature and utilize top-quality natural
  products with certified-organic ingredients, from companies
  such as **Dr. Hauschka** (drhauschka.ca), **Eminence Organics**
  (eminenceorganics.com) and **Jurlique** (jurlique.ca), and that
  have clear-cut environmental mandates posted on their websites.
- Ask to see the actual products before treatment, and scan
  ingredient lists before you get steamed/wrapped/baked/
  massaged with a product. You may be too relaxed to remember
  all the ingredients that need to be avoided, but at least steer
  clear of parabens or products that are clearly petroleum based
  (i.e., mineral oils, paraffin or petrolatum).
- If you're getting your makeup done professionally at a spa, look
  for one that uses natural brands such as **Jane Iredale**, **Hauschka**
  or even **Aveda** (for more on Aveda Salons, see page 147).

HOW DO I GET RID OF PARTLY USED
CONVENTIONAL BODY CARE PRODUCTS?

What happens when you decide your body's had enough sweetly scented toxins for one lifetime and you want to make the switch to more natural personal care products? This is a tough one, since they're not considered hazardous waste—although in many municipalities, aerosol cans can be brought to your town's haz waste depots. What do you do otherwise? Please, don't just dump it all down the toilet. We don't need more trace PPCP pollutants in our water supply (that's Pharmaceutical and Personal Care Product contaminants for those of you not monitoring water quality issues for a living). You could dump the contents into a leak-proof bag and put them in the garbage and then recycle the container or better still, send the offending product back to the company that made it and tell them you want ingredients of concern phased out.

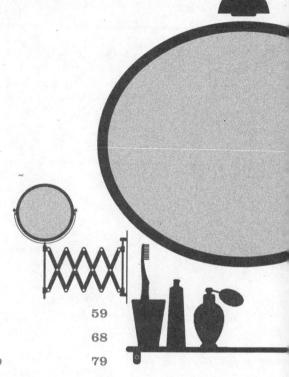

Body Odour Control   59

Dental Care   68

Hand Sanitizers and Hand Soap   79

Perfume, Cologne and Scents   83

Bug Repellent   87

Menstrual Products   90

BODY
MAINTENANCE
The daily show

Maintaining our bodies is a bit like

maintaining a good home: we're forever fighting weird odours,
struggling to keep bugs out and trying to ensure that surfaces
are sanitized. But while Canadians are switching to, say,
greener cleaners for our homes in record numbers, too many of
us are still reaching for chemical antiperspirants, toxic bug
sprays and synthetic scents on a daily basis. Truth is, we may
be happy to try out organic lotion or natural lip balm, but when
it comes to personal care products such as deodorant, toothpaste and bug spray, or even perfume, we want them to really
get the job done. But if you're going to detoxify your body,
you've got to go all the way, baby. Can you do it and still stay
stink, cavity and bug bite free? Hell, yeah. You just have to
know which natural products actually work, and that happens
to be my specialty.

BODY ODOUR CONTROL

No one wants to be that person who stinks up a room/cab/gym (call it olfactory pollution), so we reach for sticks that promise to keep us nice 'n' odourless. I know lots of organic food junkies who stash a drugstore deo somewhere in the house for emergencies. But I wouldn't raise my hand to defend the safety of the stench-stopping agents found in conventional deodorants and antiperspirants. Here's the rundown on what to avoid.

Say no to:

- **Aluminum**: This pore blocker can make up anywhere from 8% to 25% of the product; it literally clogs the pores to stop you from sweating. Pretty neat trick. The thing is, the ingredient remains controversial in alternative-health circles since aluminum, a known neurotoxin, is found at greater levels in the brains of Alzheimer's patients. To be clear, there is no conclusive evidence linking aluminum to Alzheimer's, and the U.S. Food and Drug Administration (FDA) considers the link "not resolved." Still, it acknowledges that "a small amount" of aluminum can be absorbed through the skin and that those with kidney problems can have trouble excreting aluminum from their kidneys, so they should consult a physician before using antiperspirant. Kidney disease or not, many people prefer to avoid antiperspirant altogether.
- **Antibacterial triclosan**: This one's found in regular deodorants — not to mention in breast milk, waterways and dolphins. Many major brands have phased out this ingredient but it's still in some Right Guard, Adidas and Soft & Dry deos.
- **Aerosols**: Both aerosol deodorants and antiperspirants are heavy in petrochemicals such as butane, and release smog-inducing, lung-irritating VOCs (volatile organic compounds). In fact, the makers of Axe Body Spray were fined $1.3 million in 2010 for selling body sprays that failed to meet California's air quality standards!
- **Talc**: The process of bringing this stuff up out of the ground is devastating for the environment. In 2010, opponents of 19 talc mines in Bhutan noted that local talc mining caused more damage to the environment than revenue generated. Closer to

home, Canada Talc Mines faced charges in 2008 for lying about dumping pollutants directly into local waterways for years. Thanks to potential asbestos contaminants, cosmetic-grade talc is supposed to be purified (though Korean talc was found to be laced with asbestos in 2009).

- **Synthetic fragrance**: I know they mask your BO, but say no to synthetic scents, as they're loaded with hormone-disrupting phthalates and other dodgy chems (see Perfume, page 83).

DIY DEODORANT

Try straight-up baking soda on your pits. You can mix a tiny bit with a dab of water; use it dry with a powder puff; or make a bigger batch, cut with cornstarch and a few drops of essential oil, shake, then apply with a damp face cloth. Some DIYers like to make this recipe with vegetable glycerine. Not for heavy stinkers, but works on some.

Deodorant Testing Guide:

Nothing like a heat wave to put your natural deodorant to the test. I've tried a couple that barely survived a short bike ride downtown — and it's flat the whole way! Since dead-end deodorants only give natural products a bad name (and natural body care enthusiasts a bad smell), I thought I'd spare you the agony of testing these yourself. Keep in mind that plenty of "natural" deodorants contain synthetic ingredients such as skin-irritating, fossil fuel–based propylene glycol (Tom's says they tried to remove this antifreeze ingredient but customers complained so they put it back in their formula). And also note that while I tested these on multiple friends, everyone's body chemistry is different, so what works for me might not work for you. Always, always, always keep a stick of naturally scented deo in your bag for reapplication. Also, since lots of natural deos seem to mysteriously stop working for some people after a month or so, have a couple on hand and rotate them to keep yourself fresh.

KISS MY FACE'S ACTIVE ENZYME

Totally bites. Died after 20 minutes on the bike. 👎

🍁 **TERRA NATURALS**

This product used to claim success with 94% of users, but that sticker is gone. Wise move, since time and again it failed me, though the (synthetic) acai scent is a temporary masker. 👍👍

TOM'S OF MAINE

Long-lasting protection? Puh-leeze. It barely survived a sedentary summer workday typing at my computer. I wouldn't subject others at the gym to this one. 👍👍

ALBA CLEAR ENZYME

Enzymes sound effective, but I had to reapply before and after exercising and still reeked at the end of the night! Sticky, too. 👍👍

JASON

Fine until I finished working out, when emerging BO made me switch to another brand post-gym. What's the point? Full of chems, too (though JASON says it's since taken some out). 👍👍

🍁 **GREEN BEAVER**

I'm no athlete, but I can say their "sport 24" deo only survived physical exertion when freshly applied (it held up well through a hot summer run but started to fail six hours after application during a mellow evening bike ride.) This may not be 24-hour protection, but it's not bad, relatively speaking. The wild yam and lemon stick totally failed me though. 👍👍👍

NATURE'S GATE (non-organic)

While the Organic Fruit Blend line is honestly about as good as smearing mayo under your arms, the non-organic one has solid masking powers (one of the few that can cover up existing stink). Unfortunately, it's also heavy in propylene glycol and cocamide DEA.

EARTH SCIENCE LIKEN PLANT

Feels smooth going on but leaves a sticky finish. Still smelled lovely after biking around the city all day. Almost gave it four stars, but it didn't hold up past eight hours. You'll need to reapply. Has propylene glycol.

AVALON

Goopy roll-on needed time to dry (try a fan). Nice mint-thyme scent faded but still kept me smelling perfectly clean right through my evening run. Woke up 24 hours after application smelling minty fresh! However, it left weird yellow stains on my boyfriend's shirts. Like others, it stopped working for me after a month, so I'm docking it a point.

HUGO NATURALS

Why do I smell cleaning products? Oh, wait, that's me. The Mexican Lime scent smells like a freshly cleaned toilet, but it carried me through a power walk, an hour-long gym session and a sweaty walk home in 30-degree humidity. A good masker, it actually lasted a whole summer, but then failed me at my little brother's fall wedding. Almost gave it a 4.

CRYSTAL

The sweaty boyfriend's favourite (until he dropped it and it cracked). You have to apply it on clean, freshly showered armpits. You need to wet it then rub, like, 25 strokes per pit for it to work. No tarty fragrance, no goop, no residue. FYI, this type of aluminum (potassium alum) isn't supposed to penetrate skin and gets green-lit on **Cosmeticsdatabase.com**, but it's still a mineral and thus polluting to source.

LAFE'S ROLL-ON

A couple of months in and this liquid crystal is still mostly working for me and my guy if applied on freshly washed skin (you'll need to shower in the morning). Performs better than other liquid crystals by Rocky Mountain Soap Company or Naturally Fresh.

TERRESSEN-TIALS

Top-notch purity and performance. This product used to leave a serious chalky residue, but that's mostly improved over the years. Watery going on, so you'll need time to air-dry. A little pricey too.

✤ DRUIDE

I have to confess this really runny lemon meringue–scented roll-on failed me the first time I tried it. *But* since it has so many fans, I tried it again a year later for six weeks in summer and it proved to be a good stink-controller. I'm converted.

WELEDA

Alcohol base means it's a bad idea for anyone who shaves every day or so (it'll burn!). Otherwise a solid performer, especially on clean skin, though the sage-scented version can smell kind of funny (warning: never spritz the sage on existing BO!). Go for the lemon or rose instead.

LAVANILA

If you'd rather smell like baked goods than BO, this is a solid champ. It costs a small fortune at $23, and you can only get it at one of the Sephora stores in five provinces, but it's a gem for most people most of the time. Still, it failed on me a few times, so no 5 stars.

DR. MIST SPRAY

This one worked like a charm for a month, then it started conking out on me, although I've had a 240-pound guy tell me he'd been using it for two years and had zero stink issues. A crowd favourite (though my mother-in-law calls it Dr. Missed). Worth a try.

🍁 SAVON-NERIE DES DILIGENCES

This weirdly gritty handmade stick from Quebec is a no-go for anyone with hair there, but when applied on clean, wet skin and rubbed in, this stuff will go the distance.

DR. MIST ROLL-ON	Survived 30-degree gardening days followed by one night on a steamy dance floor. I wouldn't say I smelled like roses, but I smelled like . . . nothing much, and happily waved my arms in the air like I just didn't care. The 48-hour claims are a stretch, but at least you'll wake up in the 24th hour without stench, unlike with most of the competition.	

Green Thumb legend   1 = Did something die in there?   2 = Sorry excuse for a deodorant
3 = Decent odour buster   4 = Gets you through a day without stink   5 = Secret's green sister

? HOW GREEN IS MY BEAUTY BRAND REALLY?

LUSH: A blindfolded man could find a LUSH store from three blocks away thanks to the overpowering aroma of these soap shops. Yes, they do stuff their vegetarian beauty collection with some natural ingredients, though many of LUSH's products contain disconcerting sodium laureth sulphate (see page 125), a few parabens, artificial dyes, and pretty overwhelming synthetic, albeit phthalate-free, fragrances (if the word "perfume" is listed in green ink, it means it's all natural). Still, they have fewer synthetics, product for product, than The Body Shop, and in 2009 LUSH ousted palm oil from all of its products (see Palm Oil, page 12). Lots of packaging-free options. All products sold in North America are made in Vancouver and Toronto. It's independently owned, to boot. **lush.ca**

The Body Shop: If you probe, even Body Shop clerks will tell you their products aren't all natural, they're mostly just "inspired by nature." But while they still contain synthetics like sodium laureth sulphate (often contaminated with 1,4-Dioxane), phthalates were banished from their scents by 2009, which is very good news. The Body Shop switched to "sustainable" palm oil in 2007 to avoid the eco-nightmare of Asian palm products, but complications continued (see Palm Oil, page 12). The Body Shop was a pioneer in profiling fair-trade ingredients, and it finally came out with its first certified-organic skin care line, Nutriganics, in 2009 (it's Ecocert-certified which means it can be as little as 10% certified organic when you count in water; see Ecocert, page 16). It vowed to be the first carbon-neutral retailer by 2010. Too bad The Body Shop (now owned by L'Oréal) cancelled their bottle refilling program. **bodyshop.ca**

Aveda: A few years ago I would have slammed Aveda with more vigour. Their ingredient lists used to be not unlike synth-drenched conventional brands, though with a few more botanicals tossed in. They have since phased out a few high-profile ingredients of concern, such as phthalates, EDTA, parabens, formaldehyde-releasing ingredients and most silicones, and they keep greening their ingredients. Not bad at all for an Estée Lauder–owned corporation, but this isn't an organic brand by any means. Good news: 90% of their essential oils are now certified organic, their packaging is high in recycled content, products are 50% plant derived and Aveda offsets its headquarters and manufacturing facility with wind energy credits (see Aveda salons, page 147). **aveda.com**

Burt's Bees: A lot of alt-brand lovers dropped their beloved Bees balms like a hot potato after Clorox bought the company, but did the move make Burt's any less green? The company certainly keeps churning out the green headlines—BURT'S BEES ELIMINATES LANDFILL WASTE in 2010, BURT'S BEES CUTS WATER USE BY 20% in 2008—plus, it pledged to cut its U.S. greenhouse gas emissions by 35% per dollar sales from 2006 to 2011. One thing's for sure: Clorox has exposed Burt's to way more consumers who might never have wandered into a health store to buy lip balm. Still, not everyone's happy that Burt's goes all the way to Africa to source its beeswax, cancelled its lip balm tube recycling program and has synthetic (albeit phthalate-free) fragrances in many of its products (they'll be all natural by 2020), or that profits feed into the whole Clorox bleach-making machine. But hey, Burt's is still a solid gateway product with no major red-flag ingredients (beyond the fragrance thing). Plus, Burt's has pushed Clorox to get a little greener in places too. Largely Natural Product Association certified (see page 15 for more info). **burtsbees.ca**

Arbonne: The Avon of so-called "natural" beauty companies. Their motto is "inspired by nature, enhanced by science," but a look at the ingredient lists on some of their products reveals way more lab-based synthetics than genuinely natural ingredients, though they have reformulated over the last few years to eliminate petrolatum, phthalates, formaldehyde-releasing preservatives, DEA and more. Plus they finally ousted parabens from their entire product line in 2011. Be sure to scan ingredients on their website before you buy. Some products are more natural than others. Beyond a vague commitment to responsible ingredients and soy inks, sustainability practices are thin. **arbonne.com**

Origins: Similar slogan to Arbonne—"powered by nature, proven by science"—except these guys have a legit organic line. Origins Organics is actually certified by the USDA, so these products are, at a minimum, 95% certified organic. Okay, so it's only a handful of items, but it's a start. Even the non-organic products are free of parabens, phthalates, propylene glycol, mineral oil, petrolatum, paraffin, DEA and animal ingredients. **origins.com**

Kiehl's: This brand coasts on a pseudo-natural reputation but still has far too many Mean 15 synthetics such as parabens, PEGs, siloxanes and more, though at least they have an Ecocert-certified organic line. They also reward customers for bringing their empties in for recycling. **kiehls.com**

DENTAL CARE

We put most body care products *on* our bodies, but this category goes straight inside us, right to our mucous membranes. It's like getting mouth-to-mouth from the chemical companies. Be sure to let only truly natural products in to kiss and tell.

Fluoridated toothpaste: Okay, time for a partial retraction — call it eating my words. In my first *Ecoholic* book I told you guys to stay away from fluoride toothpaste, then gave you all the reasons why fluoridated water is a bad idea. I still stand firmly behind the studies and researchers that don't recommend fluoridated water. Heavyweight dental experts like the University of Toronto's head of preventative dentistry, Hardy Limeback, suggest fluoridated water (whether flowing out of the tap or bottled) is a bad idea for the whole health of our bodies. For a copy of Limeback's letter "Why I am now officially opposed to adding fluoride to drinking water," see Fluoridealert.org/limeback.htm. In it, he points to increased bone fractures and dental fluorosis (white or dark spots on enamel). One Harvard study noted an increased risk of a rare bone cancer in boys. In 2011 alone, a couple dozen North American communities decided public water fluoridation just wasn't worth the risks. When StatsCan compared cavity rates in Ontario, where the water is heavily fluoridated, versus essentially fluoride-free Quebec, the difference was minimal; Quebec had less than half a cavity more per child on average.

Hardy Limeback and others have been very clear that fluoride's benefits come from putting fluoridated products straight on your enamel, not in your body. It's undeniably a wicked cavity fighter when brushed directly onto your teeth. That's why I'm giving my thumbs-up only to *natural* fluoridated toothpastes that are free of all the synthetic sudsers, cancer-linked saccharin and antibacterial chemicals that are found in conventional toothpaste (see below) and still give you proven cavity-fighting potential. If you're interested in otherwise natural fluoridated options, JASON, Tom's of Maine and Dr. Ken's offer both the fluoride and fluoride-free kind. Natural or not, keep in mind that fluoridated toothpastes shouldn't really be swallowed, hence why parents are told to put a pea-sized amount on their kid's brush and advise their young ones not to swallow. Still, a study in *Nature* found that two-and-a-half-year-olds swallow, oh, 72% of the paste on their brushes. Look for one of the many fluoride-free children's toothpastes available at health stores. Green Beaver, JASON, Earth's Best, Weleda and others all make kids' versions of their pastes.

Antibacterial toothpaste: Yes, we all have bacteria in our mouths—800 different kinds, actually. Some of them are good and some of them are bad. Keeping them in balance is key to whole-body health. But is it really necessary that we boost the bacteria-banishing power of our paste by turning to a persistent chemical that's lingering in 75% of North Americans? There's no denying that triclosan—the stuff in Colgate Total—is damn good at killing bacteria. Studies prove it's better at killing bacteria than regular fluoride toothpaste (although, to be fair, fluoride's main boon isn't bacteria killing but enamel strengthening). It's also true that studies have raised concerns about the potential long-term risks of triclosan toothpaste creating antimicrobial-resistant bacteria in our mouths. What's the point when a Swedish study found that brushing with a triclosan/polymer toothpaste and a fancy electric toothbrush for three years "failed to prove additional benefits" compared to brushing well with regular fluoridated paste and a manual brush? So put the Colgate Total down. This is the only toothpaste line with triclosan in it, but it's in a heck of a lot of bathrooms. Yes, I see it there on your sink!

However, you definitely want to kill the bad bacteria; not only does it lead to bad breath and cavities, but scientists are now tying mouth bacteria to heart disease and other illnesses. But if you're avoiding antibacterial triclosan, how do natural health store toothpastes compare? A 2004 study pitting the antibacterial power of herbal pastes against Colgate Total named Nutribiotic's Dental Gel as the all-round "herbal" winner for combating four harmful strains of bacteria. The thing is, its active ingredient, grapefruit seed extract (GSE), comes with its own mouthful of controversy (see page 194 on grapefruit seed extract). So which natural toothpaste battles bacteria without resorting to synthetic bug fighters? According to the herbal toothpaste study published in the *Journal of the American Dental Association,* Peelu, Weleda's Pink toothpaste with Myrrh, Herbal Brite and Dental Herb weren't great at the task, and against one oral bacteria linked to heart disease you can also toss out JASON's NutriSmile. But **JASON's Healthy Mouth, Auromère, Nature's Gate Natural Toothpaste** and **Tom's of Maine** (non-fluoridated) all had solid results.

Remember, dentists have long advised us to keep bacteria in check with two simple steps: brush well twice a day and floss once. Colgate's own website points to a third cavity-busting tip: reduce the amount of fermentable carbs you eat (such as sweets, chips, crackers, sticky fruit like raisins). Gargling with essential oil–based mouthwashes heavy in menthol, eucalyptol and thymol has also got the clinical thumbs-up.

Toothpaste Testing Guide:

If you're going to spend a couple of bucks extra on a natural toothpaste, you want it to a) taste better than chalk; b) leave your breath fresh for more than five minutes; and c) take the furry slippers off your teeth. So how do natural brands measure up?

🍁 **JEVATEE**	Ick. The label says mint, but all I taste is the Himalayan salt brine and cloves. Not my idea of a good time in the morning.	👎
KISS MY FACE	Whitening aloe gel version tastes too much like Aspirin. Wimpy Tartar Control version was equally disappointing: teeth felt furrier than without brushing.	👎👎

NEWCO Albertans may want to support this brand (if they're on the locavore diet), but it's one of the weakest toothpastes on the list. Sorry.

GREEN BEAVER It doesn't foam much and it feels kind of weak, but it does have good abrasive power. Note: the mint is more effective than the licorice.

TOM'S OF MAINE Too chalky for my liking, and the super-sudsy SLS irritates my gums, but this Colgate-owned top seller is one of the few that offers fluoride. The peppermint and licorice flavours are good picks.

DR. KEN'S I like that they offer a fluoride option, but I found it a little too sweet. Could have more lasting power after brushing.

DESERT ESSENCE Their natural tea tree oil and neem paste is decent, but nowhere near top performing.

DRUIDE This Quebec-made paste is a little gritty and comes in interesting flavours (such as minty lemon) that aren't for everyone, but I like 'em. Could be a little stronger, but it works.

NATURE'S GATE Solid, economical amount of foaming, no bad aftertaste. Gets the job done with no complaints. Hooray.

| LUSH DIRTY TOOTHY TABS | I love these weird tabs (and their cardboard box packaging), but only with electric toothbrushes so you can avoid your gums (otherwise it's way too abrasive). Super smoothing. At $4 for 40 tabs and with some sensitizing ingredients like cream of tartar this isn't a daily use kind of thing but great once in a while. | 🖐🖐🖐🖐 |
| JASON'S POWERSMILE | Top performer by far. Lasting freshness and you can pick the fluoride option if you prefer it. Good whitening power to boot. | 🖐🖐🖐🖐🖐 |

🖐 Green Thumb legend 1 = Might as well brush with ash on a rag 2 = Weak excuse for toothpaste 3 = Decent dental polisher 4 = Your mouth is in good hands 5 = Colgate's green brother

Toothbrushes: Back in the day, the English used to brush their teeth with soot and salt on a rag. I'm going to refrain from making any jokes about British dental care and just take a moment to say how grateful I am that the brushing of teeth has advanced since then. Still, do we need to be throwing away plastic sticks every few months? Oh, I know, your toothbrush looks small, but we have enough plastic throwaway items in our lives. Undoubtedly, the toothbrush is the one invention none of us would really want to live without, but we can green the whole experience by looking for more planet-friendly brushes.

- **Reach for replaceable heads: Eco-DenT**'s **TerraDent** makes some simple replaceable models for kids and adults. Something about its bristle design earns this toothbrush the honour of having the lowest bacteria count amongst conventional toothbrushes. eco-dent.com
- **Blue-bin it:** Actually, your local recycling system won't accept toothbrushes, but you can buy a **Preserve** toothbrush made of yogurt cups and then send, say, a year's worth back to the company

to be recycled into more toothbrushes (preserveproducts.com). Just skip their toothbrush subscription system since it takes way more carbon to ship one toothbrush to one door than it does to send a crateful to your local health store.

- **Go *au naturel*:** For those trying to minimize plastic from their lives, natural bristles are an option. Weirdly named **Fuchs** are best known for their natural boar bristles (the company says the German boar are sheared like sheep—unlike boar bristles from China, where they're killed for their meat). Their rippled V bristles are a nice switch from the basic flat-topped bristles all too common on health store shelves, though the handles are plastic and it's too bad they only offer replaceable heads on synthetic versions. On the flip side, **The Environmental Toothbrush** is made with a bamboo handle but polymer (plastic) bristles (theenvironmentaltoothbrush.com)—all in a cardboard box. If you want to go all natural, harder-to-find **Ecologic** makes an Italian maple wood brush with natural bristles.

- **Go for plant-based plastic: Clean Idea EcoBrushes**, head-quartered in North Vancouver, makes toothbrushes for adults and kids out of certified compostable plant-based plastics (though at this point, it's tough finding facilities that will compost them). These brushes, made from corn, potato, wheat and tapioca, also come with ridged bristles, which I like (cleanideadental.com). Celeb-favoured **Radius** brushes have a super-ergo design made of cellulose, a plant-based plastic. The thing is, the head is damn large and isn't for everyone. Its Intelligent model has a smaller head and a two-minute timer (useful for anyone who stops brushing after 30 seconds), though the mini batteries have to be recycled. I like the Source model, which also has a more compact, replaceable head and a handle filled with old newspapers (though I still find the head a little too large). Original models don't have replaceable heads (radiustoothbrush.com).

- **Mull over antibacterial action:** Norwex's Silver Care antibacterial toothbrushes with replaceable heads plated with pure silver (not dodgier nano silver, according to the company) has been shown to reduce three kinds of bacteria on your brush and in your mouth by releasing silver ions, which the company says fall below accepted ingestion levels for silver. It adds that your body excretes most of that silver anyway, but still, doesn't this mean that the antibacterial silver ends up in our waste water? Germophobes will love it, but you can also just soak your toothbrush in alcohol once in a while.

- **Forgo toothpaste:** I wouldn't recommend this unless you get a fancy high-tech Soladey toothbrush from Japan, which has a light-activated titanium rod inside the handle which releases negatively charged ions that blend with your own saliva to draw out and bust up the positive ions in your plaque acid (soladeycanada.com). It's supposed to disintegrate plaque, thereby preventing cavities, and there's some published peer-reviewed research to back up this claim. However, a study by the University of Saskatchewan published in the *Journal of Clinical Periodontology* found it was much better at reducing plaque on the front surfaces of the teeth than the back surfaces, maybe because of light-activation.

Electric Toothbrushes: I always thought electric toothbrushes were for lazy people—until I tried one and my teeth seemed as smooth as a freshly Zambonied ice rink. Now, serious environmentalists will wag their fingers and tell you there is never an excuse for using a plug-in gadget where a manual option exists, and I see what they're saying. But I like going electric now and then. If your dentist insists on it or you're dead set on using one, you can make the whole experience greener. For one, pick a brush that actually works. Turns out most cheaper electrics do the same job as good old-fashioned muscle power if you're manually brushing and flossing properly (as in, brushing for longer than the typical 30 to 60 seconds most North Americans do). Lazy manual brushers will do well with timed electrics (which is partly why parents give electrics to kids).

- The only kind of power brush that beats a manual, according to the non-profit oral health organization Cochrane Oral Health Group, is the rotating oscillating brush (which, as you may have guessed, rotates and oscillates, versus those that spin just one way, vibrate or have side-to-side action). The rotating oscillating kinds may do a better job of keeping plaque and gingivitis in check, but these are not $15 battery-operated sticks. Top-scoring **Oral-B ProfessionalCare SmartSeries** brushes cost over $100.
- Keeping an electric toothbrush powered up generates 48 grams of climate-cooking CO_2 a day (or 17 kilograms a year), according to the UN. You can extend the overall life of your battery and reduce your energy-sucking time (a.k.a. phantom power) by unplugging the brush between charges and letting it drain before plugging it back in. By the way, pricier models can hold a charge for two weeks if you don't store them on the charger, so you can get your brushing-related CO_2 output down to 1 kilogram a year.
- Consider, gasp, sharing a unit. Sounds icky, but you don't actually share bristles, just the handle.
- The biggest problem with the rechargeable systems is that once the battery finally dies (three to five years in, according to manufacturers), the whole handle has to be tossed (and the battery safely recycled at your local hazardous waste depot). You can't just pop a new rechargeable battery in there like you can (and should) with the cheapies. Well, you can, but Oral-B Sonic instructions for doing so involve a soldering iron. Way too Bob Vila for most of us.
- If you use a disposable battery–powered toothbrush, make sure you swap your batteries for the rechargeable kind. You'll only have to pop them into the charger now and then.

Tooth Whitening: Is it just me or has everyone had their teeth whitened? I remember when it was just professionally capped celebrities who flashed impossibly white pearls every time they mugged for the camera. Now, unless your teeth are already the colour of a sheet of photocopy paper, your dentist has probably tried to upsell you on a lightening procedure. Most of the at-home whitening systems on the market get their Wonder Woman white power from carbamide peroxide, hydrogen peroxide and/or sodium hydroxide. All three are corrosive at higher concentrations (the last one is actually used in drain clearing), and any whitening system that contains any of them is very likely to increase tooth sensitivity and irritate your gums while you're using it. Some, in combo with pro light treatments, have caused burns and sores. There are still no good long-term studies giving us a clear picture of the impact of using whiteners year after year. All I can say for sure is that pregnant and lactating women, kids under 16, and those with gum disease, eroded enamel or untreated cavities are advised to stay away from whiteners until more is known. Whatever you do, avoid chlorine dioxide–based whitening treatments available at spas and clinics. The British Dental Association has warned there's no proof they work, and the treatments can seriously damage your enamel.

- Look for a toothpaste that lightens not with bleaches but with a mild abrasive like hydrated silica, such as **Kiss My Face Whitening** or **JASON's PowerSmile All Natural Whitening Toothpaste,** which also uses calcium carbonate and bamboo powder. I won't lie and tell you they offer the same brightening power you get from a tray or a strip, but both products do take a little of the tarnish off your teeth. Lots of Crest- and Colgate-style whitening toothpastes also get their power from silica, but they're loaded with chemical fillers.
- Try some toothy tabs now and then. **Lush's Toothy Tabs** (see Toothpaste, page 68) contain some classic whitening ingredients like baking soda and cream of tartar, though they can heighten tooth sensitivity, so don't use often.
- Regardless of whether you settle on a pro job or an at-home system, tooth whitening is never permanent. Keep swilling black tea and Bordeaux and you'll be daydreaming of dental strips in as little as a month.

Mouthwash: Funny thing about drugstore staple Listerine: it gets its plaque- and gingivitis-fighting abilities from essential oils such as thymol, menthol and eucalyptol, but then sabotages its natural potential with coal tar dyes and lots of PH-screwing alcohol. In the '90s, studies linked alcohol-based mouthwashes to oral cancer, though other studies have countered those findings. Whatever the case, best to gargle with something a little more natural. By the way, Tom's of Maine and The Natural Dentist mouthwashes contain petrochemicals poloxamer 407 (like Listerine) and 335 because, they say, they help mix mint oils into water-based solutions better than any other ingredient. Tom's insists they're benign, but if you don't want 'em, pick one of the other ones below.

DR. KEN'S	Gaggingly sweet. No thanks.	👎
JASON	Tried two flavours but both tasted kind of like toilet bowl cleaner/pool water. Sea Fresh version just as nasty as their papaya enzyme one.	👎
DESERT ESSENCE TEA TREE OIL MOUTHWASH	The spearmint flavour can't mask the distinct bitterness. Not much of a deep clean.	👍👍
THURSDAY PLANTATION	Like the light 'n' natural antibacterial tea tree power.	👍👍👍👍
TOM'S OF MAINE	This one really freshens and leaves you with a sparkly mint feeling. I'd give it five thumbs if it weren't for the fossil-fuel poloxamers.	👍👍👍👍

🍁 CAROL'S	Light and refreshing option made by B.C.'s Life Root Healing, with effective gum-soothing herbs. Liked it so much I've bought it a few times. New formulation has good lasting power.	👍👍👍👍
KISS MY FACE	Now we're talkin'! Potent and classically minty—like drugstore brands but without the chems. Too bad the $9 bottle is so small my household of two used it up in two weeks.	👍👍👍👍👍

👍 Green Thumb legend 1 = Might as well swish with tap water 2 = Meh, not worth the money
3 = Decent mouth cleaner 4 = Now that's fresh! 5 = Listerine's green brother

(DIY) MOUTHWASH

💲 If you're a big swisher, natural mouthwash can be an expensive habit—unless you make it yourself. Just put half a teaspoon of baking soda in 1/3 cup of warm water, add a few drops of organic mint oil, swish and spit. For mouth sores, add a splash of pure witch hazel (not the kind that has alcohol in it).

Floss: Floss much? You can brush and gargle all you want, but you're still going to get cavities if you don't start getting on top of this habit. Flossing once a day with petroleum wax–coated string can be a bit of a turnoff, though. Most flosses from the health store are still made of nylon, but they're naturally waxed with stuff like beeswax (as **Tom's**, **Spry** and **Dr. Tung's** flosses are). Vegans and packaging haters alike will prefer **Eco-DenT**'s jojoba and candelilla wax–coated floss that comes in a cardboard casing. Don't want any petroleum product between your teeth? Your only nylon-free option comes from **Radius** organic silk floss; the silk itself is fair-trade USDA-certified organic. If you've got wider spaces between your teeth, **Desert Essence Tea Tree Oil Dental Tape** is a good pick.

HAND SANITIZERS AND HAND SOAP

More than spiders and underwear bombers, Canadians fear eensy-weensy germs. We used to touch bathroom taps and subway poles with abandon, but now we do elaborate dances with our elbows to exit a restroom without contact. We used to lather up no matter how grimy or sliver-like the wedge of bar soap in a public loo, and now we insist on hands-free pumps of antibacterial soap.

Antibacterial Hand Soap: It may seem perfectly reasonable to want to kill every germ that comes in contact with your body, until you ask the people in charge of health in this country: Health Canada. According to them, "anti-bacterial soaps are not recommended because they destroy good bacteria as well as bad and can add to the problem of antibiotic resistance." Translation: they can breed supergerms. And upping our antibacterial soap usage in winter to avoid colds and flus seems absolutely loony when you listen to what the chair of Health Canada's Advisory Committee on Animal Uses of Antimicrobials and Impact on Resistance and Human Health has to say: "Colds and the flu are caused by viruses, and antibacterials don't work on viruses!" So why the hell are we washing with antibacterial soaps come flu season? Marketing.

Our antibacterial obsession goes well beyond wanting to avoid getting a runny nose. Antibacterial protection in toothpastes, deodorants, moisturizers, towels and even hair accessories is now commonplace, and antibacterial chemicals can be spotted in every aisle of the drugstore (and grocery store). No wonder the level of antibacterial triclosan coursing through our bodies has jumped by 50% since 2004, according to the Centers for Disease Control and Prevention. It's in our blood, urine and breast milk. Just a few short years ago, companies (even some health store labels) insisted that triclosan was harmless and would break down quickly when flushed down our drains, but we now know that triclosan keeps doing its job—killing bacteria—even after it leaves water treatment plants and is released into waterways. We've also learned from the University of Toledo that when we spread triclosan-laced sewage sludge on crops such as soybeans (as communities all around the world do), the triclosan is actually sucked up by the roots. Kind of unnerving when you consider that low doses of the chem have been found to act as an endocrine disruptor. None other than the Canadian Medical Association asked the feds to ban it from consumer products in 2009. By spring 2012, the feds should have decided whether to phase this bad boy out.

- Avoid anything labelled "antibacterial" or "antimicrobial" unless you know the bacteria fighter is a totally natural ingredient such as thyme oil. (Microban is another trade name for

BACTERIA OVERKILL

Here's a list of some of the heaviest triclosan/triclocarban users:

Dial antibacterial liquid soap, bar soap and body wash
Balea antibacterial hand soap
Bath & Body Works antibacterial hand soap
Tersaseptic
Cetaphil Antibacterial Gentle Cleansing Bar
Clean & Clear Oil-Free Foaming Facial Cleanser
Colgate Total toothpaste
Right Guard Total Defense Power Deodorant
Adidas 0% Aluminum
Soft & Dry Deodorant
Anything with regular Microban, including BioEars earplugs, scünci hair accessories and Canopy towels
Clearasil and Clearasil Stayclear Daily Face Wash (discontinued in 2011 but still on some shelves)
Neutrogena Deep Clean Body Scrub Bar (discontinued but still on some shelves)
Softsoap antibacterial liquid hand soap (discontinued in 2011 but still on some shelves)

triclosan, though Microban does make some triclosan-free options; best to ask.)

- If you want to wash bacteria away from your hands or face or any other body part without resorting to chemicals, try sudsing with any natural soap for 20 seconds (long enough to sing "Row, Row, Row Your Boat" or "Happy Birthday" in your head twice). Just be sure to turn the taps off while you lather.

Hand Sanitizers: Don't you wish you'd invested in hand sanitizer stocks right before news of the swine flu spread? At least alcohol-based hand sanitizers such as Purell don't contain triclosan and aren't linked to supergerms in the way that antibacterials are—but guess what? You don't need all those petroleum-based chemicals and synthetic fragrances floating in hormone-disrupting phthalates either.

- Natural hand sanitizers that contain at least 60% alcohol (or ethanol) kill just as much as Purell (including cold and flu viruses). **EO** makes a whole line of largely natural, organic alcohol–based hand sanitizers from pumps to wipes (though disposable wipes aren't as eco-friendly), with organic jojoba and essential oils (eoproducts.com). Even better, Canada's own **Natureclean** broke onto the hand sanitizer scene with pumps filled with 62% ethanol. They come in unscented and citrus versions and have an even simpler, all-natural ingredient list (naturecleanliving.com).
- Keep in mind that all the hand washing and sanitizing in the world won't keep the flu from spreading from cubicle to cubicle if Barry from accounting launches open-air sneezes like a dandelion in a windstorm. Only a third of flus are thought to be caught via hands (it turns out that cold viruses are way better at living on your hands than flu viruses). So what is a chem-free (and zero-waste) common-sense solution? Simple: sneeze (and cough) into your sleeve.

(DIY) HAND SANITIZER

$$ Make your own hand sanitizer (for real!) by mixing 2/3 cup (150 mL) of
ethanol or grain alcohol, 1/3 cup (75 mL) of pure aloe vera gel and 15
drops of lavender essential oil. Store in a sealable container or empty hand
sanitizer bottle.

Liquid Hand Soap: How did we get to the point where we need a
disposable plastic bottle just to lather up in our own homes? Don't get me
wrong, I kind of like liquid soap in a pump too, but it's totally unnecessary,
especially if you haven't invested $10 into a reusable dispenser. Even if
you recycle the bottle every time, it still takes new virgin plastic to make it
and energy to recycle it, and the pump part just gets landfilled in the end.
Plus, most liquid hand soap has all the same junk that's in conventional
shampoo and body wash (see Mean 15, page 8). Either go back to bar
soap and get yourself a nice, natural, palm-free brand (see Palm Oil, page
12) or stick exclusively to the kind of natural liquid soap that offers refills.
I don't consider Method an all-natural pick; they use potent synthetic
(albeit phthalate free) scents, dyes and preservatives. I love Toronto-based
Natureclean's large 3-litre boxed-bag refill of its hand soap. **Green
Beaver Foaming Hand Soap** refills give 3 bottles' worth.

(DIY) HAND SOAP

$$ Yes, you can make your own. The cheapest way involves grating a bar of any
basic all-natural soap (pure veggie gylcerine bars grate in 10 seconds flat)
and mixing it into a pot of near-boiling water (1.5 L should do). Remove from heat,
stir and let it sit a day before you mix in organic essential oils of your choice. If
it's not runny enough, add more water and let sit again. The lazy but pricier way
involves buying basic castile soap from a bulk or health store, cutting
it with a little water and, if you like, adding your own essential oils
and a dollop of a moisturizer such as jojoba oil or vegetable glycerine.

PERFUME, COLOGNE AND SCENTS

I'm sometimes told that in the good old days people didn't get sick from scents like they do today, that they were stronger, tougher. When that comes up, I always mention my mom. As a young mother of four, she got brutal migraines from perfume—the kind of migraines that would lock her in her bedroom for two days with the lights off and the curtains drawn. But she was quiet about it. Never complained to perfume-wearing friends. The only difference between then and now is that the silence has lifted. There were always people who were sickened by chemical substances; they just kept it in the shadows. Today, there are thousands of hospitals and offices across the continent that declare themselves scent-free zones to protect their chem-sensitive workers.

Still, we tend to be drawn to scents like flies to, well, you know. And while an orchid musk or citrus zing may lure you into buying a particular brand of perfume/deodorant/shampoo, chances are you're taking in a dose of hormone-disrupting phthalates with every squirt/smear/slather, whether the scent aggravates your senses or not. Six phthalates are of such high concern that they've been banned from baby toys in the U.S.A., Europe and most recently Canada, and yet no one's stopping us from misting ourselves in the plasticizers.

As consumers grow wiser to the dangers of basic beauty products, though, corporations seem to be getting the message. In 2002, 72% of the deodorants, perfumes, hairsprays/mousses/gels and lotions tested in a report called "Not Too Pretty" by Health Care Without Harm and Environmental Working Group contained at least one phthalate. In 2005, Greenpeace found phthalates in 35 of 36 perfume samples tested. Then, in 2008, retesting for a report by Campaign for Safe Cosmetics called "A Little Prettier" discovered that companies seem to be reducing the amount of phthalates in their goods. In fact, some had got rid of them altogether: Poison by Christian Dior had some of the highest levels of the dodgy chemicals back in 2002, and in 2008 it had next to none. Ditto for Pantene Pro-V hairspray and Arrid Extra Dry deodorant spray. But the news isn't all good. Charlie Cologne Spray had over twice the phthalates it did in '02.

Others, including Red Door, Trésor, White Diamonds and Wind Song, still had high levels.

Either way, phthalates aren't the only harmful ingredient lurking in synthetically scented products. The word "perfume" or "fragrance" can easily hide 100 ingredients that don't have to be listed on the label. Environmental Defence's 2010 "Not So Sexy" report noted a full dozen different hormone disruptors in the popular perfumes and colognes they tested, ranging from worrisome preservatives such as BHT to estrogenic sunscreen ingredients (including in Hannah Montana perfume aimed at girls). ED also found 24 chemical sensitizers in fragrances that can trigger allergic reactions (from headaches to asthma). Plus, it noted that repeated exposure to the chemical sensitizers in fragrances just increases your chances of developing allergic symptoms later in life. Fabulous.

Keep in mind that lots of "natural"-branded products contain synthetic scents. Even scent ingredients from natural sources, such as limonene (citrus oil) and linalool (from lavender oil), are potent sensitizers that can cause reactions. Actually, limonene can react with ground-level ozone to create hazardous air pollutants. Truth is, whether they're natural or not, scent ingredients give off all sorts of air-polluting volatile organic compounds. All this is why really sensitive Ecoholics will already know they have to stay away from synthetic and natural scents, including essential oils. Anne Steinemann, lead researcher on a University of Washington–led study, says that whether you know it or not, scents affect you at the subclinical level: "People who use them all the time don't realize they're injuring themselves," she says.

Ecoholic Scent Tips:
- Play it safe and reach for entirely fragrance-free products. And use a sniff test to prove there's zero smell: many "unscented" drugstore creams and body care products contain "light" masking fragrances. Totally misleading.
- If you don't want to give up smelling purdy and aren't scent sensitive, at least pick products that get their aroma from natural

DIY ALL-NATURAL PERFUME

$$ Who wants to smell like you just stepped out of a mall wearing the same perfume as 10,000 other people? Make your own signature scent from scratch with organic essential oils. For solid perfume, first grate 2 tablespoons (30 mL) of beeswax (use the end of an old candle or, if you're vegan, soy wax). Melt beeswax in a double boiler along with 3 tablespoons (45 mL) of jojoba oil. Once the mixture is fully melted and blended, remove from heat and stir in 45 drops of the certified-organic essential oils of your liking (such as vanilla, grapefruit, sandalwood—mix and play!) and quickly pour into a small, shallow glass container or cute antique tin. Once it's set, dab and go.

sources, like **Pure + Simple**'s entirely natural concoctions (pureandsimple.ca). Other natural scent purveyors include Australian-made **miessence Botanical Perfumes,** and U.S.-based **Ecco Bella** and **Aubrey Organics**, which is 95% certified organic, petrochemical free and supposedly phthalate free (see below; eccobella.com; aubrey-organics.com). Definitely check out **Tsi-La** scents (tsilaorganics.com) and **Lavanila** offerings (lavanila.com).

- Be aware that even phthalate-free companies have been caught with their pants down. In 2007, a *Consumer Reports* study on perfumes found even Aubrey Organics and Aveda products contained a few different phthalates, despite claims to the contrary. An Aubrey consumer rep says they've since dropped that particular perfume and test their perfumes to ensure they're phthalate free.

- If more natural choices don't get your nose excited, you can try your hand (or neck) at spritzing with partially synthetic fragrances that are free of a chunk of naughty scent ingredients. Though **Pacifica**'s lovely range of solid and spray perfumes is partly synthetic, they are made without phthalates, petrochemicals, nitro musks or animal ingredients. The solid scents come in a base of organic coconut and soy (pacificaperfume.com). Edmonton-based

85

Diva Girl Body's fruity body sprays aren't naturally sourced (Diva reps say it's tough to get such a wide range of scents naturally) but are free of phthalates, harmful VOCs, synthetic musks and parabens (divagirlbody.com).

- If you're an essential-oil lover, ask for high-quality, certified-organic oils that don't use petrochemical solvents. Scent devotees should keep in mind that a genuine essential-oil scent may not be VOC-less, but it should at least be free of the hundreds of other worrisome ingredients found in the thousands of scented consumer products lining shelves. Also, by sticking to certified-organic essential oils, you should avoid the litany of fake scents claiming to be essential oil based.

 KINGS OF GREENWASH

So many body care products claim to be natural and green these days, it's dizzying. Most everyone is stretching the truth at least a little, but these are the top greenwashers on shelves today. By the way, if you're annoyed by greenwash claims, call the Competition Bureau and complain (1-800-348-5358), or complete a complaint form online at **competitionbureau.gc.ca**! That's the only way the government bureau will investigate poseurs. For more on greenwashed body care labels, watch my spot on CBC's *Marketplace*: cbc.ca/marketplace/2011/lousylabels.

Aveeno Active Naturals: Think Aveeno is oh so natural? Sorry, there's very little genuinely natural apart from the oats in most Aveeno products (including the baby line). Their Active Naturals line is a perfect example of a cosmeceutical (cosmetics claiming some medicinal benefit) that mixes natural "active" ingredients with a synthetic base. Mean 15 ingredients (see page 8) abound in anti-aging and sunscreen products in particular. Even found parabens in some. Fresh Essentials' line contains a few more natural ingredients at least.

Organic Surge: The only thing organic about this brand is the essential oils. That's it. Pretty pathetic. The company says it will soon offer some Ecocert-certified organic products, which means they'll have to be at least 10% organic.

Suave Naturals: Fake as it gets. Other than a fruit extract or two and an absence of parabens, this is just suds full of questionable synthetics.

TRESemmé Naturals: This low-sulphate (not no-sulphate) line has a couple of organic ingredients and a little aloe and avocado thrown in, but don't expect it to be truly natural. Better than Pantene NatureFusion, though. Their mousse contains a greenhouse gas (see page 135).

Pantene NatureFusion: Move along. No parabens but plenty of ethoxylated sulphates that are commonly tainted with carcinogenic 1,4-Dioxane, plus other Mean 15 ingredients such as cocamide MEA and bioaccumulative siloxanes in their conditioner.

Down Under Natural's: Oh, puh-leeze. Move on. At least their NUDE line is much greener, has no parabens, phthalates, DEA or SLS, and says it's 98% plant based.

Jergen's Natural: Don't let the beige bottle fool you! This so-called natural line is loaded with formaldehyde-releasing DMDM hydantoin, environmentally menacing siloxanes, petrochemicals, fake scents and more.

Fa Natural & Pure: This one's hilarious since it actually has essentially the same ingredient list as regular Fa bubble bath, which is already free of parabens, but both contain sodium laureth sulphate and lots of other ethoxylated—eths. Did I mention they charge more for the Naturals?

BUG REPELLENT

Going into deep woods or dewy tropics and worried about being eaten alive? Just invite me along! I'm hands-down the single biggest bug magnet in town, so you should be safe standing next to me. After spending a week on one infested beach, I counted over 150 sandfly bites from my neck to my toes, while my man had, oh, four. Now, people will share a million and one dietary tips for repelling mosquitoes naturally, from slimming down (thinner people purportedly emit less bug-attracting carbon dioxide) and eating less meat, dairy and sugar to eating more onions and garlic. Well, I'm a thin, garlic-loving half-Greek and long-term lactose-intolerant vegetarian who gave up sugar a decade ago, and I don't buy it. I take B vitamins, too (B1 is recommended as another strategy), and I can't say that's helped. A good dozen studies have concluded with the same poor showing for B1, but you know what? If you want to try all the above to repel the little buggers, you'll be a healthier person for it, so please, do your own trials and prove me wrong. Personally, I've just accepted that I'm biochemically irresistible and had better load up on the right repellent.

DEET: What I can tell you conclusively is that while DEET works harder and longer than any other repellent available, it's most definitely a proven neurotoxin, meaning it's toxic to the central nervous system. A 2009 study published in the journal *Occupational and Environmental Medicine* found a link between DEET use in the first three months of pregnancy and an 81% increase in hypospadias (where the penis opening is in the wrong place). More research is needed to confirm the findings, but the U.S. Agency of Toxic Substances does confirm that between 1961 and 2002 there were two adult and three child fatalities from DEET applications to the skin and 17 cases of "significant toxicity," mostly in kids. Symptoms included lethargy, headaches, tremors, seizures and convulsions with dermal applications of sprays containing as little as 15% DEET. No wonder Health Canada says "Prolonged use should be avoided in children under the age of 12."

Ultimately, you've got to weigh the risks in your specific geo-graphic location. In your backyard, DEET should be a serious no-no, but if you're trekking through a malaria- or dengue fever–plagued jungle, you might consider an exception for short-term use. What are your DEET-free options?

Citronella: Bad news. Looks like Health Canada is pulling all citronella products off the market by 2013/2014. Shocker, I know. It's true that studies never found it to work all that well (a *New England Journal of Medicine* study I cited in the first *Ecoholic* book found citronella had to be reapplied after as little as 10 to 30 minutes) but still, it was our choice to use it. Why is it being pulled? Health Canada says: "While no immediate health risks were identified with the use of citronella-based personal insect repellents, these products will be phased out unless requested scientific data are supplied." One natural bug spray company I asked about this said they just didn't have the funds to finance a lot of expensive research on the ingredient.

Soybean Oil: Health Canada says a 2% soy oil repellent protects against mozzies for 3.5 hours and against blackflies for 8 hours. And you can use it as often as you like on everyone in the family! For top natural protection, track down something that's soybean oil based like **Green Beaver's Outdoor Lotion**. Or next time you're in the United States, get **Buzz Away Extreme** or **Bite Blocker**. Both have done very well in clinical trials.

Neem/catnip oil: Neem oil is a traditional Indian bug repellent and has performed well in trials done by the Malaria Research Centre in Dehli, India. A 2006 study published by the American Chemical Society concluded catnip oil is a "potent mosquito repellent" though not as long lasting as DEET. **Alypsis Neem & Catnip Outdoor Body Spray** is a good pick, though greasy.

Other Bug-repelling Options:
- Eucalyptus oil–based products have shown some promise.
- Wear long, light-coloured clothing at dusk, tuck in pants to avoid ticks, and bring a bug burka on camping trips. The **Original Bug Shirt Company** has all sorts of clothing to keep you sting free. Stay away from bug clothes dipped in bug-repelling chems like permethrins; they're not permitted in Canada anyway.

- Save your money and skip useless ultrasonic and electronic devices. Bug zappers are also a waste (zappers may catch thousands of bugs per day, but only 6.4% are mosquitoes and of those, only half are the biting females). Citronella candles help only if you're sitting right next to them and the wind is blowing your way.

(DIY) BUG SPRAY

$$ Mix up 1/4 cup (125 mL) of soybean oil (if you can find it, get the organic kind from the health store—Spectrum makes some), 1/4 cup of water, 2 tablespoons (30 mL) of coconut oil, 45+ drops of essential geranium oil, 1 teaspoon of neem oil. Put in a spray bottle, shake well, spritz and rub into your skin.

Itch Relief: If the bugs still get you, try a dab of tea tree oil on bites to stop the sting without the ammonia in mainstream itch stoppers. Rubbing in some itch-busting **Aroma Crystal Gardener's Dream Cream** should calm things down in no time, too (aromacrystal.com).

MENSTRUAL PRODUCTS

I was 11 when I got my first period. I remember it clearly because it was also the day of my very first saxophone lesson, and I was both mortified at the overlap and confused about how to proceed. Regretfully, I had stuck my fingers in my ears and hummed my way through my mother's "talks" on the topic, so I was more or less in the dark about protocol. For months I tried to hide all evidence by flushing my pads down the toilet, which worked like a charm—until our plumbing finally jammed. So what should you do when Aunt Flow arrives? And what can you do to douse the accompanying cramps (another topic I'm painfully familiar with) as well as PMS? Read on.

Pads: Next time you have your period, count how many pads you go through in a cycle, then multiply that by, oh, 35 to 38 years of menstruating and you've got a hell of a lot of plastic on your hands.

Basically, you're lining your underwear with a layer cake of poly-ethylene dry weave, chemically processed wood pulp, strips of SAP (super-absorbent polymer) gel made of, you guessed it, petrochemicals, as well as synthetic latex wings. I personally don't want to be that intimate with the petrol industry. You?

- Look for certified-organic cotton disposable pads. **Natracare**'s are totally plastic free, and are made of 100% organic cotton and totally chlorine-free plant-based cellulose (natracare.com). **Organyc**'s and Whole Foods' **Azalea** pads are also 100% organic cotton and don't bunch as much, according to some users (organic-online.com). **Seventh Generation**'s aren't as green since they contain petrol-based polyolefins and wood pulp (though they are totally chlorine free); however, their absorbent gel is made from wheat, which is better than traditional SAPs.
- Keep your eyes peeled for B.C.-made **Nurture Verde** pads made out of compostable corn-based materials (nurtureverde.com).
- Greener still, try reusable cloth pads. Get dark colours with snappable wings and you're laughin.' **Lunapads** offers some just like that, and I'm a big fan. Their hipster, bikini, brief and, if you go there on your period, thong underwear are pretty awesome because they're designed to add liner inserts (lunapads.com). This Vancouver-based company offers all kinds of kits too, including seven-dayers, teen kits and starter kits, in both regular and organic cotton.

DIY PADS

If you're even slightly crafty, try making your own pads for way less money. For all kinds of patterns and tutorials, check out **alter-eco. info/cloth-pad-patterns.html**.

Tampons: When I was a tween, I remember thinking tampons had to come out every time you peed. Boy, was that inconvenient. Luckily, that's not anatomically necessary, and in my opinion, neither are the ingredients in tampons. The mini-plugs are generally made of a blend of chemically processed and bleached rayon wood pulp and conventional pesticide-demanding cotton. It's true that you should no longer find carcinogenic traces of dioxin in tampons now that elemental chlorine–free—and totally chlorine-free—bleaches are used. The U.S. Food and Drug Administration now asks rayon tampon makers to routinely monitor dioxin levels, which is comforting. But at the end of the month, what do you want inside you?

- It's certainly better for the planet and everyone living on it to rely on certified-organic cotton tampons instead. No "flushable" plastic applicators that pop back up onshore after a storm sewer overflow, thanks. Seabirds end up swallowing those things, for god's sake. **Natracare**, **Organyc**, **Azalea** and **Seventh Generation** all offer pesticide-free organic disposable tampons, with and without cardboard applicators. Try going applicator free to cut back on waste.

Cups: Tired of adding more disposable trash to the landfill but not really a cloth pad girl? Welcome to your tampon alternatives! Women who try reusable cups absolutely love them. **The Keeper**, for instance, is an easy-to-use cup made of natural gum rubber and lasts about a decade (keeper.com). If you're allergic to latex, use the silicone-based **DivaCup** or **Mooncup** (divacup.com; mooncup.com). Emptying takes a little getting used to, but these do rock once you get the hang of them. Just steer clear of drugstore poseurs like Instead Softcup, which looks like a reusable cup but has to be thrown out after one use. Not sure what the point of that one is.

Douching: Can I be frank? Please don't squirt a bunch of unnecessary chemicals up your kooch. You do not need artificial dyes, suspect parabens and synthetic scents in your privates. Actually, you don't need to douche at all. Women have just been shamed by marketers into thinking we're "unclean" down there. And if you do have strong odours, weird discharge and irritation under your hood, douching ain't gonna fix it; go see your doctor or naturopath. Douching can actually disrupt the balance of a healthy vajajay (wiping out good bacteria, leaving bad bacteria to flourish), not to mention the fact that the warning on Massengill boxes says straight up: "An association has been reported between douching and pelvic inflammatory disease ('PID'), ectopic pregnancy ('EP'), tubal infertility, chlamydia and bacterial vaginosis ('BV'). These conditions require immediate medical attention."

Makeup	97
Mineral Makeup and Foundation	100
Concealer	105
Lipstick and Gloss	107
Mascara	112
Makeup Remover	116
Nail Care	116
Tattoos and Permanent Makeup	120

MAKEUP
Toxic cover-up

When style icon (and my secret gay

crush) Tom Ford was asked what's most important about a woman's appearance, he was blunt: "a lot of makeup." Upon hearing his advice, I jotted down a little note to myself: never, ever run into Tom Ford. Now, I may have given up my makeup-kit addiction as a young feminist teen, but I still love my cosmetics basics. That means I ain't leavin' the house without a little eyeliner, a lot of concealer and, depending on where I'm going, some mascara. Those bathroom basics will vary from woman to woman, but even the biggest hippies I know sneak in a dab of under-eye coverage or charcoal liner when no one's looking. Whether you wear a little or a lot, the good news is, there are a growing number of natural cosmetics brands out there that are making it easier for women to amp up their look without loading up on toxins.

MAKEUP

Natural Lash, Natural Match, Beyond Natural: with all the nature-invoking brand slogans on shelves, you'd think you'd died and woken up in a field of unsprayed daisies. Alas, cosmetics purveyors are mostly talking about how well their product will complement your inherent beauty without making you look like a mad orange clown. To further complicate things, there are a growing number of conventional products claiming to be natural or "made from natural ingredients."

Take Covergirl's NatureLuxe line, "luxury touched by nature." The first ingredient in the liquid silk foundation is bioaccumulative environmental polluter and Mean 15 ingredient (see page 8) cyclo-pentasiloxane, with estrogenic octinoxate as one of the SPFs. Sheesh. And what's up with all the petroleum by-products, estrogen mimicking sunscreen and BHT in Sally Hansen Moisture Stay Gloss from Natural Beauty Inspired by Carmindy (of *What Not to Wear* fame)? You have to scan ingredient lists closely (sometimes with a magnifying glass) to see the difference between faux natural and the real thing. Thankfully, it's now mandatory for those ingredient lists to be somewhere on the packaging, which makes sniffing out genuinely natural brands from among all the fakes a little easier.

Natural Makeup Brands: So how do you distinguish true naturals from pseudo-ganics? If you forget your Mean 15 Pocket Guide to toxic ingredients (printable at ecoholic.ca), the easiest way to pick out legit green brands is to look for third-party seals. All the high-end European brands that first proved natural makeup can kick ass carry a seal, such as German-based BDIH Certified Natural Cosmetics (see Body Care Labels, page 13). I'm talking about quality Euro pioneers including **Dr. Hauschka** (drhauschka.ca), as well as **Lavera** (lavera.com), **Logona** (logona.com) and **SANTE Naturkosmetik** (sante.de), all of which offer top-performing, broad-ranging makeup lines.

Ecocert certifies **Organic wear**, which makes some decent, affordable drugstore mascara, eyeshadow and blush, but their powders are pretty cakey. Ecocert also certifies Cargo's **PlantLove**, which does great lipsticks, glosses and eyeshadows (including their massive Green Glamour Kit with 18 shadows for a fantastic price), as well as pressed powders (cargocosmetics.com). Thankfully, PlantLove has phased out some dodgy ingredients they used a few years ago, including BHT and parabens. See page 16 for more on Ecocert standards.

One of the newer seals on the block is Natural Products Association–certified (see page 15). Like Ecocert, a product must be 95% naturally derived, with a long list of no-no's for the other 5%. It's not quite as exhaustive as BDIH and doesn't call for, say, sustainable manufacturing, as Ecocert and BDIH do, but still, it's pretty good. Brands that are NPA certified include **Gabriel/ZuZu** (gabrielcosmeticsinc.com), **PeaceKeeper Cause-Metics** (iamapeacekeeper.com), **Hemp Organics** (colorganics.net), **Burt's Bees** (burtsbees.ca), **Ecco Bella** (eccobella.com), **Suncoat** (suncoatproducts.com) and even some Bonne Bell Lip Smackers. Since only 60% of a brand's line needs to qualify, never assume that a specific product passes without checking.

Organic junkies have probably already noticed that entirely certified-organic makeup is seriously hard to find. Only the smallest minority of makeup brands actually secure full USDA Organic on some items, which basically tells you your makeup is up to the same organic standards as food, containing at least 95% organic ingredients (tough when mineral pigments can't be organic). Aussie-born **Zuii Organic** is one of those to score the seal (as well as the comparable Australian Government Certified seal). Zuii make USDA-certified eyeshadow, foundation, mascara, lipstick and blush that just so happen to perform really well too (zuiiorganic.com). Actually, Australia's the birthplace of several other cosmetics companies high in organic content, particularly direct-to-consumer darling **miessence** (organic foundation, lipstick, mascara and powders) and celeb-endorsed **NVEY ECO** (nveymakeup. com). Not USDA certified but still high in organic content is one of my absolute favourite beauty brands, **100% Pure** out of the United States. Like the three Australian brands, the products aren't necessarily cheap, but every ingredient is essentially edible and the whole line gets

WHAT'S HIDING IN YOUR MAKEUP? HEAVY METAL OFFENDERS

The great Canadian product-testing heroes at Environmental Defence found some pretty disturbing stuff lurking in your makeup bag. The following cosmetics were found to contain the most heavy metals of the products tested in each category. Stay away!

Foundation: Clinique Stay-True Makeup (arsenic, cadmium, lead, nickel, etc.)

Powders: Sephora Sculpting Disk Powder Trio (lead, nickel, berrylium, thallium)

Blush/Bronzer: M·A·C Sheertone Shimmer Blush and Physicians Formula Bronzing and Shimmery Face Powder (lead, nickel, berrylium, thallium)

Mascara: L'Oréal Bare Naturale and Avon Astonishing Lengths (arsenic, cadmium, lead, nickel, etc.)

Eyeshadow: The Body Shop Shimmer Cubes, Almay Intense i-color Trio, Two Faced Eyeshadow Duo (lead, cadmium, nickel, berrylium, etc.)

Eyeliner: Covergirl's Perfect Point Plus, Fashion Flair eyeliner pencil (lead, cadmium, nickel, berrylium)

Lipstick: Benefit benetint Pocket Pal (red) (arsenic, lead, cadmium, nickel, berrylium, etc.)

Source: Environmental Defence, *Heavy Metal Hazard: The Health Risks of Hidden Heavy Metals in Face Makeup,* May 2011.

its colour from fruit and vegetable pigments. You can score their products on The Shopping Channel, too (100percentpure.ca).

Of course, there are plenty of brands that don't have costly certification but are still free of toxins and made of great ingredients.

Manitoba-based **Pure Anada** is one of them that also happens to be more affordable than most green beauty brands and performs really well to boot, especially the mineral foundations, blush, eyeshadow and more (pureanada.ca; thepureboutique.com). I'm also diggin' Ontario-made **LUVU Beauty**'s nicely priced mineral eyeshadows ($8!) and nano-free powders, blush and more (luvubeauty.com). If your budget is tight, Toronto-made **Sula Beauty** offers a whole line of prettily packaged cosmetics including lipsticks, eyeshadows, blush sticks and more that aren't all natural but are free from parabens, phthalates and petroleum by-products—and all for $8 (sulabeauty.com).

What do eco-conscious makeup professionals use? I've spotted TV and movie makeup artists who keep a stockpile of **Jane Iredale**, **Dr. Hauschk**a and **NVEY ECO** in their stash for use on a long list of nature-loving celebs (janeiredale.com; nveymakeup.com).

MINERAL MAKEUP AND FOUNDATION

I'm going to break a lot of hearts here but I have to just say it. The hype around mineral makeup being all natural is, all too often, BS. The yearning for clearer-looking skin without all the crap found in drugstore and department store brands has been a bonanza for mineral makeup marketers. Why? Because marketers have managed to cultivate an aura of earth-derived purity around this stuff when the products aren't even necessarily green or body-friendly. On the environmental front, mining and processing minerals always has a major impact. Take titanium dioxide factories, which have been linked to all sorts of nasty enviro emissions, including dioxins. Oh sure, mineral-based cosmetics can definitely be more natural if they don't have all the added chemicals, dyes and preservatives found in conventional beauty tools. But far too many mineral makeup brands are loaded up with that junk. It's not like anyone is policing terms such as "pure minerals."

Many mineral products are chock full of artificial fragrances and questionable or just plain unnecessary fillers (such as environmentally dodgy talc, see page 59, and lung-irritating silica), as well as that cancer-linked family of preservatives, parabens. Some Pür Minerals, for instance, contain propyl parabens banned from children's products in Denmark. Maybelline Mineral Power powder foundation says it's 100 micro-minerals but the one I found on drugstore shelves contained plastics like polyethylene as well as dodgy Teflon (a.k.a. PTFE)! Physicians Formula Mineral Wear line (available in drugstores) may be touted as talc and fragrance free, but a peek at the ingredients finds those dreaded parabens yet again. And don't trust well-meaning cosmetics clerks who insist a line is all natural. Time and time again, they've pointed me to mineral powders that were loaded with suspect ingredients. Just today, a lovely clerk at Sephora, for intance, told me Tarte offers natural makeup free of parabens but when I actually flipped their mineral powders over while in the store, all I found were plastics and petrochemicals! For god's sake, the first ingredient is polyethylene (plastic), followed by more polymers, nylons, as well as cancer-linked retinyl palmitate and formaldehyde-releasing preservative imidazolidinyl urea. And this brand markets itself as "high performance naturals"? Jokes.

Most mineral makeup brands, including Sheer Cover, Pür Minerals and ColorScience, Marcelle Minerals contain a mineral salt called bismuth oxychloride. It may give your face a nice pearly sheen, but bismuth is a by-product of lead refining. Manufacturers are supposed to make sure the ingredient is lead free, but Canada allows double the amount of lead in cosmetics that California does. For many, though, the bigger concern is that bismuth oxychloride can really aggravate skin sensitivities such as rosacea, contact dermatitis or acne. If you get itchy after sweating in your mineral powder, you're probably having a reaction to it. FYI, Bare Escentuals phased this ingredient out. Marcelle Minerals has it as the first ingredient!

Nano minerals: What's really freaking people out is the sci-fi processing of some of these minerals. To make application smoother and less visible, sunscreen minerals such as titanium dioxide and zinc oxide are often broken down into eensy-weensy particles called microns (one-millionth of a metre) or nano particles (a billionth of a metre). I'm definitely concerned about you inhaling this nano stuff in powder form. Several studies, including one published in *Particle and Fibre Toxicology* and *Environmental Health Perspectives,* have found that inhaling nano particles of titanium dioxide can trigger long-term lung inflammation and oxidative stress. Also, nano particles have been found in the lymphatic system within minutes of being dusted on the skin. There's a lot of debate around what size is safe. The popular assumption is that anything above 100 nanometres is usually considered nano free and thereby safe. Though Friends of the Earth says the benchmark for safety should be anything above 300 nanometres. Concerns are mounting around nano zinc, too, and early evidence that it may damage brain cells.

It gets even more difficult to keep straight who's nano and who's not because mineral and sunscreen brands use totally confusing terminology. When they tell you particles are micronized, you may think that they're the size of a micron (over 1000 nanometres) and thereby totally in the clear, but they're really just talking about the fact that their particles are tiny, and may in fact be nano-sized. Too bad companies don't have to declare the presence of nano particles right on the label, like they will in Europe by 2013. Here in Canada, you'll have to call company hotlines and ask them if their minerals are over 100 nanometres (under 100 and it's nano, baby) or if you're more cautious under 300. For more on nano sunscreen chemicals, including their potential environmental impact, see Sunscreens, page 44. In any event, just because your mineral makeup contains "natural" sunscreen ingredients doesn't make it a great sunscreen replacement. Coverage can be spotty.

Liquid Foundation: Because of the whole "don't inhale nanos" controversy, classic liquid foundations are being seen as the safer option. Though the conventional kind is basically a tinted stew of petrochemicals, parabens and the like. And more and more, we're seeing new-wave foundations with bioaccumulative, environmentally persistent siloxanes. In that category are pseudo-naturals such as Covergirl's NatureLuxe line that I mentioned earlier, as well as Gosh's Natural Touch Foundation "with organic sweet almond oil" (Gosh also has a couple of parabens thrown in for good measure). By the way, Natural FX Foundation is far, far from natural thanks to big baddies like BHT, cyclomethicone, oxybenzone and a wash of petrochemicals.

Natural Mineral Makeup and Foundation: So which mineral makeup is the cleanest and greenest? You can't get away from all the enviro issues (you'll have to go bare skin for that), but read ingredients to scan for genuinely natural brands.

- Manitoba-based **Pure Anada** makes great, inexpensive mineral foundation, finishing powder (their Glow Minerals), primer and corrector, free of nanos (actually their particles are all safely 3 or 4 microns), talc, parabens, cornstarch (which goes on chalky), bismuth oxychloride, GMOs, fragrances, gluten, etc., though like most face powders some of their products do contain silica, which is low on the toxicity scale but hard on the lungs with heavy exposure. Super indie Canuck **LUVU** also does lovely nano-free mineral concealing foundation (luvubeauty.com) for under $18.
- **Jane Iredale**'s mineral line is free of parabens, talc, oils and nano particles and is used by many pro makeup artists. It's also got a great shade range of 24 colours and pressed powders, as well as SPF protection if you want it.
- Shimmery mineral powders tend to magnify pores and wrinkles and only really work on young faces. If you've already bought one, order some 100% **Pure** natural facial primer to diffuse the look of large pores and wrinkles (score some through Shoppingchannel.com or 100percentpure.ca if your local health store doesn't have any).
- Truth is, you can make a more sustainable product that's gentler on the earth if you avoid minerals altogether. I'm a fan of 100% **Pure's Healthy Skin Foundation with Super Fruits** as well as its rice powder–based **Healthy Flawless Skin Foundation Powder,** which contains nothing but edible ingredients, including the only all-fruit-derived pigments on the block. (Though when I need fuller coverage for TV interviews I actually apply their 100% Pure brightening concealer on my entire face.)

- **Zuii Organic Flora Powder Foundation** is another excellent non-mineral pick for any age and any skin type, high in organic content such as plant extracts and a little jojoba oil (zuiiorganic. com). Both Zuii and 100% Pure break out of the mould of natural cosmetics that offer nothing but pinky white tones.
- Keep in mind, if you're looking for heavy coverage, you won't find it in most truly natural products. **Gabriel** makes the only genuinely full-coverage liquid makeup that's natural, *and* it has options for dark skin (don't love the retinyl palmitate in here, though; see page 11). Of drugstore picks, Organic wear's powders are way too cakey and their tinted moisturizer is very, very sheer (translation: no coverage).

TEENAGE BODY BURDEN

If you're a teen, you're probably dousing yourself with way more body care chemicals than your mom. Why? Well, on average, teen girls use 17 body care products a day, compared to 12 for adults. Next time you're getting ready for school, do the math: count up everything from your shampoo and zit cream to your lip gloss and body spray. Not cool when you consider all the crap that's in this stuff. When Environmental Working Group tested the blood and pee (sounds gross, I know) of 20 girls aged 14 to 19, they found 16 chemicals, all of them linked to cancer and hormone disruption (meaning they mess with your body's hormones in one way or another), including dodgy phthalates (in nail polish and anything with a synthetic scent), triclosan (in acne wash and antibacterial products), parabens (common preservatives in almost everything) and musks (in synthetic scents). The findings are even creepier when you consider that teens might be especially sensitive to even trace levels of hormone-disrupting chemicals since your bodies are still growing. Hormones tell your body how to develop from a child into an adult. What happens if you throw in chemicals that mimic or interfere with your hormones? Well, scientists are wondering whether chemicals such as phthalates might play a role in the fact that girls have been developing breasts and pubic hair at younger ages over the last four decades.

It's an unnerving possibility when early puberty has been linked to being at higher risk for things like breast cancer later in life.

To avoid piling suspect chemicals into your system, use fewer products, look for unscented versions, and stay away from permanent hair dyes, skin lighteners, antibacterial acne washes/soaps, and nail polish with formaldehyde. For more information on all this, check out EWG's Teen Cosmetics Study at **ewg.org/reports/ teens**, as well as **femmetoxic.com** for ideas on taking action. By the way, of teen drugstore brands, **Bonne Bell Lip Smacker 100% Natural** and **wet n wild's Natural Blend Lip Shimmers** and **Pressed Powders** have Natural Product Association certification. It's not all natural but **Sula Beauty** is free of big red-flag ingredients and offers punchy modern eyeshadows, lip glosses, blush, eye crayons and more—all for $8 (**sulabeauty.com**). Also online, **LUVU** has tons of shimmery pure mineral shadows, blush and powders from $8 (**luvubeauty.com**). At your local pharmacy chain like Shoppers Drug Mart, you'll find **Organic wear** has 100% naturally derived mascara, eyeliner, blush and bronzer (but skip their foundation).

CONCEALER

There's one piece of makeup I won't ever leave the house without, and that's under-eye concealer. If I do, I'm immediately fielding comments from co-workers and friends about how sick and tired I must be, despite having slept like a well-fed baby. Dark circles run deep in my family, but if your circles are particularly pronounced, you might first want to rule out any health problems: everything from allergies and anemia to B12 deficiencies can cause dark eye circles (in Chinese medicine, dark circles are actually a sign of kidney deficiency). You're most likely lacking vitamin K, so smearing your under-eye area with a cream that contains at least 5% vitamin K will do you good, as will popping vitamin K supplements. You could try daily sessions with potato wedges/cukes/cooled caffeinated tea bags over your eyes (also reduces puffiness), but those solutions are temporary at best.

Concealer Testing: Why am I ranking concealers and not foundations? It comes down to the simple fact that foundations are totally subjective (you may like full coverage and I prefer sheer, you may like powders and I like liquids) whereas concealers aren't: they either hide stuff or they don't. And since I've got plenty of dark shadows under my eyes to hide, let the testing begin. FYI, makeup artists say you should buy two shades and blend 'em. I do ZuZu/100% Pure.

DR. HAUSCHKA	Save your money. This is so thin that it didn't do much to cover my dark rings, and it dries way too fast. Maybe it works better on blemishes since it's so light, but the three pale shades are not enough (unless you're really fair). Dryness highlighted lines.	👎
GABRIEL	Dry, matte and slightly cakey, so it shows off my wrinkles.	👍👍
SANTE	This tidy stick may get the thumbs-up from others because of its heavier coverage, but I'm not a fan of how it yanks on the delicate skin under my eye. Nonetheless, it does the trick, even if I do have to put powder on after to correct the tone.	👍👍👍
LAVERA	Decent performer, and thankfully the price dropped from $30 to $20 on new formula. I need a couple of layers. Pinky corrector tones not for everyone.	👍👍👍
ZUZU LUXE CONCEALER	Thick wand format offers relatively heavier coverage, and there are good options for those with yellow and darker tones in their skin. Highly light-reflective, blends well. One of my go-to faves.	👍👍👍👍

100% PURE	This one is now under $20 (used to be $30 in Canada) and it's my go-to everyday favourite. Not too heavy, not too light, just right, super-clean ingredients with crème to toffee shades. Start on unmoisturized skin or else it can get too oily.	
JANE IREDALE	The vitamin K–enriched Circle\Delete Under-Eye Concealer is about as thick as concrete and does some serious circle deleting, but it's heavy as hell, so you just need a dab (thank god, because it's $35 a jar). I mix it with bronzer because the shades are way too light. The Active Light format is much more light-reflective and lightweight, so it doesn't exacerbate wrinkles.	

Green Thumb legend 1 = Might as well put Crayola under your eyes 2 = Sorry excuse for a concealer
3 = Decent cover-up 4 = Great, green circle deleter 5 = Call this a magic eraser!

LIPSTICK AND GLOSS

Did you hear the one about how women get through hard economic times? They buy more lipstick. No, this isn't the punchline to a sexist joke, but a surprising economic fact. Analysts say that when we can't afford designer shoes, we splurge on cheaper beauty upgrades instead. But no matter what brand you buy, you get more than you pay for when you dole out for lipsticks—red in particular. That's because far too many have tested positive for lead contaminants. The Campaign for Safe Cosmetics has been finding trace lead in the majority of lipstick brands for several years now. With new testing methods, the U.S. Food and Drug Administration found traces of lead in all 20 red lipsticks they tested in 2009 (even Burt's Bees tested positive), and at levels higher than previously detected.

The FDA stands by the safety of lipsticks, because they all fall well below the FDA's 20 parts per million (ppm) standard for cosmetics but

107

the truth is there are no known safe blood lead levels. And when Environmental Defence did makeup testing in 2011, Benefit Benetint Pocket Pal in red totally failed Canada's draft heavy-metal standards for lead of 10 ppm, as well as flunking our arsenic standards. Bottom line, if the Campaign for Safe Cosmetics could find a dozen red lipsticks that had virtually no detectable lead, as they did, then manufacturers should all be capable of making lead-free lipsticks to limit our cumulative body load.

The real shocker in Environmental Defence's test results is that clear glosses were dripping with heavy metals, too. Benefit Cosmetics' Benetint Pocket Pal clear gloss actually contained higher levels of lead than any other makeup tested—a whopping 10 times higher than Health Canada's draft limits on lead in cosmetics! It also totally bombed on arsenic tests, containing nearly 25 times more arsenic than those draft limits will allow. That means you should never assume reds are the only ones causing trouble.

Whether it's a gloss or a stick, don't be dazzled by the presence of a handful of natural ingredients such as jojoba oil or honey in big-name lipstick brands. The majority still contain plenty of Mean 15 ingredients (see page 8) and tend to use iffy endocrine-disrupting sunblock ingredients. Take, for instance, Revlon Beyond Natural Protective Liptint: it has several natural ingredients, including camomile, but it also contains estrogenic skin sensitizer octinoxate as an SPF, as well as petrolatum and other petrol-based ingredients.

Natural Lipsticks: There are so many great natural lipsticks on the market that it's hard to cover them all, but here's an overview. Looking for lipstick you could actually eat and be okay with? If you're transitioning away from M·A·C lipsticks, you'll find comparable colours in health store brands like lead-free vegan **ZuZu Luxe**, **Gabriel** (both at gabrielcosmeticsinc.com) and price-conscious **Honeybee Gardens** (honeybeegardens.com). (Note: ZuZu and Gabriel do have retinyl palmitate in them.) For those who like a little more shimmery frost on their lips, Manitoban **Pure Anada's** lipsticks and glosses are high in organic ingredients and tested to confirm they're lead free and

THINK BEFORE YOU PINK

Most *Ecoholic* readers know all about greenwash (you know, when companies try to convince you they're more planet-friendly than they really are), but what the hell is pinkwash? Well, just think of all those products out there that try to win your heart and cash by being packaged in a breast cancer–friendly shade of pink. Question is, are the products actually good for you? Think KFC's "Bucket for the Cure" (!?) or Think Pink–branded lipstick made with breast cancer–linked parabens. The 10- or 50-cent pink donation is designed to make you feel extra good about your purchase, but doesn't it make more sense to buy a healthier, more natural product and give your bucks directly to charity? **Thinkbeforeyoupink.org** has some great tips for key questions to ask anyone pushing pink:

- How much money from each product sold actually goes to cancer research?
- What's the company's cap on how much money they're willing to donate?
- What programs is the money funding?
- And finally, what's the company doing to make sure their product doesn't contribute to cancer?

Also, you should definitely check out Canadian Breast Cancer Support Fund's **Think Pink Live Green** campaign at cbcsf.ca (which, thankfully, doesn't sell pink blenders, key chains, teddies or guns. Yes, Smith & Wesson makes a pink 9mm Breast Cancer Awareness pistol!). It's Canada's only green breast cancer organization and it promotes non-toxic living while offering financial assistance for struggling women living with breast cancer. Its sister org and for-profit virtual store, **Holly and Ivy**, is a great place to buy genuinely eco-friendly, non-toxic body care, cosmetics, baby care, feminine hygiene products and more—50% of the profits go to the Fund (**hollyandivy. com**). None of this piddly 10-cents-go-to-charity business!

Ontario's **Suncoat** offers lipstick with a coconut oil/beeswax base in a cool bamboo cartridge rather than plastic (thepureboutique.com; suncoatproducts.com). **Lavera** has a subtle shimmer (lavera.com).

For top-of-the-line certified-organic purity and fab hues, look for Australian-made **Zuii Organic** (at Whole Foods and quality health stores) as well as super-chic glosses by **Revolution Organics** (dreamt up by two Ottawa girls and made in the States; revolutionorganics. com or The Shopping Channel). My fave for multitasking is their Freedom Glow Beauty Balm, which you can smear on lips, cheeks, even eyes in five seconds flat. Another excellent pick comes from Toronto-made **Bite Beauty**, which makes creamy lipsticks, glosses and pencils that are marketed as having only edible, often organic ingredients with food grade dyes (available at Sephora.ca). I'm a big fan of **PeaceKeeper Cause-Metics Eco-Moist Lip Paints** (a.k.a. lipsticks) as well as their gloss, particularly since it's an "all-benefit" company that donates all its profits to charity (iamapeacekeeper.com). Plus, it's high in organic content, reasonably priced, and available in eight provinces. You should also definitely check out the gorgeous fruit-derived, yes, fruit-derived hues in **100% Pure Fruit-Pigmented Lip Glaze** with nearly entirely organic ingredients (100percentpure.ca; theshoppingchannel. com). Their glosses are award winning, though not organic.

In the natural but not organic category you'll find **Primitive**, a New York brand with gorgeous all-natural pigments that won Best Lipgloss in 2009, but it's harder to find across the country and unfortunately, contains conventional palm wax (primitivemakeup.com). Palm-free T.O-made **DaLish** offers smart two-in-one Lip Gloss Duos for $22 and $13 lip/cheek balms (dalishcosmetics.com).

Lip Tints: For all-natural lip stains, I know people like their minty **Burt's Bees Lip Shimmers,** but I prefer the high organic content of **Hemp Organics** with organic hemp, castor and jojoba oils, and no drying peppermint oils; they have good deep tints (colorganics.net). If you don't mind a little sparkle, a great local option is **Green Beaver Lip Shimmers**; they're actually made with Canadian-grown carrot and cranberry seed oil (greenbeaver.com). Not sure where the tint is in **Rocky Mountain Soap Company**'s tinted glosses; they leave your lips shiny but colour free.

ALL-DAY LIPSTICK WITHOUT THE MYSTERY CHEMS

There's something freakily intriguing about the idea of lipstick that clings to your lips for dear life through even the sloppiest chewing, slurping, kissing, smoking, pursing and, well, living. I'd much rather see you buy an all-natural lipstick and apply it right for the longest-lasting potential. How, exactly?

- Replace chemical makeup primers with a smear of aloe vera gel.
- Lightly dust a mineral powder, cornstarch or rice flour on your lips.
- Pencil on natural lipliner.
- Use a lipstick brush to apply your natural lipstick of choice.
- Blot your lips with tissue then apply a second coat.

DIY LIP BALM

$$ Forget the petroleum jelly, a.k.a. filtered motor fuel, found in ChapStick, Blistex and LypSyl. (LypSyl touts its pure Swedish beeswax content but still has petrol-based mineral oil, petrolatum and paraffin as its first three ingredients.) That stuff only dries your lips out further and creates a nation of balm addicts. Instead, make your own all-natural stuff.

- Melt (do not boil) 1 teaspoon (5 mL) of grated beeswax in a double boiler on medium (or place beeswax in Pyrex container in simmering pot of H_2O on stove).
- Add 1 tablespoon (15 mL) of quality oil (jojoba, safflower) and one teaspoon (5 mL) of fair-trade shea butter.
- Add a few drops of organic essential oil or natural vanilla extract if you want it scented.
- Want to add a touch of colour? Slice a sliver from a brightly coloured natural lipstick (e.g., deep red, deep pink) and stir it into your mix.
- Stir, pour into containers, let cool *et voilà*. Dab away. Multiply for gifts.

MASCARA

Next to eyeliner, mascara is about as close as you get to poking yourself in the eye with toxins. Okay, so luckily mercury is no longer allowed as a preservative in mascara, but lash coaters pretty much all come with parabens, cancer-linked petroleum distillates and TEA (triethanolamine)—an allergen that forms cancer-causing nitro-samines. Do you really want all that so close to your eyeball? Just don't be confused by pseudo-naturals. Beyond some beeswax and carnauba wax near the top of a growing number of conventional mascaras you'll still find persistent BHT, parabens, siloxanes and lots of petrochemicals. Take Covergirl NaturalLuxe Mousse Mascara, which comes in a leafy green tube. Yes, it's got beeswax and tapioca, but come on, it's also got two types of parabens in there! Their Natural Lash version also has formaldehyde-releasing imidazolidinyl urea. And while L'Oréal True Match Naturale Mineral-Enriched Mascara is actually more natural than some competitors, you'll find BHT and TEA inside. Don't bother when there are plenty of true naturals out there that boost your lashes without the health hazards.

Natural Mascara: First time I tried natural mascara it flaked so badly I looked like I just clocked off a shift as a chimney sweep. But, boy, have they come a long way. I now have no reservations recommending several earth- and body-friendly mascara brands (see testing chart below). The only thing is, tracking down a waterproof natural mascara can be tough. Tarte's Lights, Camera, Splashes! 4-in-1 Natural Waterproof Mascara does get its water protection from natural beeswax; I just wish it didn't contain Mean 15 chem cyclopentasiloxane. Unless you're planning a beach wedding or something, consider skipping the waterproof stuff altogether to minimize your chem exposure. Otherwise, **ZuZu Luxe Mascara** is pretty water resistant.

Mascara Testing: I'm ranking mascaras for you because when natural mascaras go wrong, you'll be left with a face full of flakes and an empty wallet. And I'll be honest with you: you're not going to get the same lash-enhancing shazam you get with those conventional two-step mascaras. The key to getting the most power out of your natural mascara is to apply multiple coats. The more drama you want, the more coats you apply. I do, like, 4 on a regular day and 10-plus on a big night out (all in quick succession—don't wait for them to dry in between). For added oomph, get yourself a lash-curling thingy (warm up the metal a little with a blow-dryer for full curling power). Keep in mind that natural mascaras do tend to fade over the course of the day. Like with conventional mascara, replace your wand every three months—six months max.

ECCO BELLA	Not sure why this so-called natural product has to contain parabens in this day and age. Automatic fail.	
HONEYBEE GARDENS	Ultra-light, even after 10 coats, which is why I was surprised when one cry-fest gave me an instant black eye. Plus, it gets flaky after a couple of months.	👍👍
🍁 **SUNCOAT**	This sugar-based vegan lash stick is maybe the best priced, but it has the lowest wearability—totally flaked off on my cheeks in no time.	👍👍
🍁 **PURE ANADA**	Light, but great pick for everyday use. No smudging, no flaking, most affordable of the bunch at under $10—but I'm docking two points because it contains Mean 15 cyclopentasiloxane!	👍👍
🍁 **EARTHLAB COSMETICS**	Perfect for those locavores who want a very natural look. Doesn't do much boosting, but no flaking, no clumping.	👍👍👍

LAVERA

Nice natural lengthener, but you need more coats to get the same coverage. Even the Intense Volumizing version is quite light. Since it fades with time, you won't wake up with raccoon eyes if you forget to wash it off.

DR. HAUSCHKA

Considered top of the line, and you'll pay through the nose for it, too. Is it worth the price? Not when cheaper competitors do the job as well or better. It still fades over the course of the day. Volume version works best.

ORGANIC WEAR

I'm a big fan of this drugstore purchase. The plump wand is pretty damn effective at separating, lengthening and boosting lashes. Plus, the ingredients are solid (100% naturally derived and nearly 50% organic).

ZUZU

Good wand action with thicker finish than others, this one's great if you want extra oomph. With a dozen coats, this is as dramatic as it gets in the natural world. Quite water resistant.

Green Thumb Legend: 1 = Better off painting your lashes with crayon

2 = Sorry excuse for mascara   3 = Decent lash enhancer   4=Great, green lash booster

5= Great Lash's green sister

WHAT'S UP WITH LASH-GROWING MASCARA?

My baby brother always had big, beautiful lashes that were the envy of my girlfriends. The first time I mentioned it to him, I soon caught him holding a pair of scissors up to his eyes (he was only six at the time and thankfully hadn't snipped them yet). If you, like me, aren't blessed with naturally bountiful eyelashes, you've probably been oddly curious about lash-stimulating products on the market. Some have the appeal of a car accident, kind of compelling but a little terrifying—and I put Latisse in that category. Once it was discovered that this glaucoma drug grew lashes, women everywhere wanted it, and by 2009 it was being re-marketed as a lash extender. All good, except for the potential side effects, including turning your eyelids purple, growing hair in weird places and permanently darkening your iris from, say, blue to brown. All this may be okay if you were first advised of the risks by a physician and had maybe lost your lashes from chemo, but some people are buying this stuff online or from salons without pro advice. Bad idea.

Since then, countless "botanical" eyelash growers have sprouted up online and in drugstores. Some online versions, such as Lashfood and LiLash, cost up to $150 per tube and lean on the "clinical lash-boosting power" of, say, almond or soy peptides (amino acid–based compounds) as well as growth-boosting B vitamins and more. LiLash, in particular, gets rave reviews from those who've tried and swear their lashes are now touching their eyebrows and banging up against their glasses, though many comment on how it weirdly irritates/inflames/darkens/reddens the skin around the lash area. You'll find cheaper versions, made by mainstream beauty companies, at drugstores. Can't promise you they work (reviews are hit-and-miss), but what I can share is my two cents': if their secret ingredient is "botanical" and they promo other natural ingredients such as beeswax, why the hell can't their entire ingredient lists be free of parabens, formaldehyde releasers, cyclopentasiloxane and other health suspects?

MAKEUP REMOVER

You don't want to be rubbing formaldehyde-releasing and estrogen-mimicking ingredients into your eyes, do you? That means it's time to put down the conventional makeup removers. But will natural removers get the job done? Most work well enough on easily removable health store makeup. But I asked a Toronto-based TV host (who has to wear layers of heavy-duty, high-def television makeup) for her input and she said all the natural removers she'd experimented with had failed, except one: **Earth Science's Chamomile Green Tea Eye Makeup Remover**. She gives it five green thumbs-up. Like many removers, it's a little drying and has to be rinsed off, so for lazier, lighter jobs, like getting rid of last night's natural mascara, I prefer **Green Beaver's Eye Make-up Remover**, which is more moisturizing (greenbeaver.com). By the way, my makeup artist pal Margot Keith says **Earth Science's A-D-E Creamy Cleanser** is her go-to product for washing away even stubborn commercial makeup without stripping her skin (earthsciencenaturals.com). It's great for getting acne under control to boot (see Facial Cleansers, page 32).

NAIL CARE

My grandmother was always my number one fan, and I was hers. The fiercely independent senior spat when anyone mentioned Ronald Reagan, practically peed through any joke she told, survived on cold coffee, cigarettes and ice cream—and always, always maintained beautifully manicured nails. She said it was the one vestige of beauty she still laid claim to at age 85, and when I was a tween we bonded over careful nail filing and paint applications. She'd probably roll over in her grave if she saw the chipped, bare state of my nails today, but when I do decide to gussy 'em up, I'm happy to know there's been some good news in the world of nail polish toxin reduction: since 2006, when the Campaign for Safe Cosmetics coalition started aggressively pressing nail polish suppliers to oust the worst of their chemicals, we've slowly been seeing more brands get rid of the three major chemicals. And what are they? Formaldehyde (the carcinogenic hardener), toluene (the neurotoxic smoothener) and DBP, or dibutyl phthalate (the hormone-disrupting wear-and-tear resister)—a.k.a. the Big 3.

Which drugstore and salon brands are Big 3 free, at least in terms of their nail paints? Pretty much everyone these days, from big guns such as Revlon, Rimmel, L'Oréal, Sally Hansen and Maybelline to specialty lines including OPI, Orly, SpaRitual, Zoya and butter LONDON. Now that most anyone with a recognizable name is 3-free, don't assume they're all equally safe. Man, 3-free brands (Revlon, some Sally Hansen, Butter, some Maybelline) still contain hazards including the neurotoxins aluminum powder and/or triphenyl phosphate. Clear polishes, top coats and base coats all rate much lower on toxicity scales.

Almost-natural Nail Polish: So what's a green girl who craves painted nails to do? Nail polish will never be entirely natural, but there are a couple of brands that come close. Two brands you're likely to find in Canadian health stores are **No-Miss** and Canadian-made **Suncoat** (suncoatproducts.com). No-Miss is undeniably the better performer, though water-based Suncoat is the more natural, using entirely earth-based pigments throughout the whole line. No-Miss offers some nail polish hues without synthetic pigments, but the rest blend natural and synthetic cosmetic-grade dyes (it'll say so on the ingredient list; nomiss.com). Other greener picks if you spot them in your local health store include super-slick **Scotch Naturals**, which is tops for trendy shades, as well as the more subdued hues of **PeaceKeeper Cause-Metics Nail Paint** and two-dozen colours from **Honeybee Gardens WaterColors Non-Peel Off Polish** (scotchnaturals.com; iamapeacekeeper.com; honeybeegardens.com). Another water-based pick is Toronto-made **Sula Paint & Peel**. It's extra cool because you don't need any remover to get it off; it literally peels off like rubber, though the top coat is definitely more fume-y (sulabeauty.com). The peel factor also makes it chip-prone, so Sula markets it more for those who want to wear a fun colour for a night or two then peel it off. Note: water-based paints call for long dry time (dries to the touch almost as quickly as regular nail polish but takes four hours to be totally cured), so it's best to do it before bed. Otherwise, like my niece/tester, Brianne, will tell you, it starts to chip super quickly, which failed to impress.

For kids playing dress-up and tweens craving crazy colours, check out odourless, totally non-toxic, water-based **Hopscotch Kids** (hopscotchkids.com), **Piggy Paint** (even its glycol ethers are green-lit by toxicity scorers; piggypaint.com), as well as **Suncoat Girl Water-based Nail Polish** (suncoatgirl.com).

Nail Hardener: While formaldehyde may be vanishing from more and more polishes, it's still par for the course in nail strengtheners. The irony is that it can actually make your nails more brittle over time. Why bother? Instead, treat brittle and peeling nails by rubbing a drop of **neem oil** into your unpolished nails at night. Pop a nail-boosting biotin supplement, too.

Nail Polish Remover: We've all bought acetone-free nail polish remover over the years, assuming it was safer. And yeah, acetone is definitely a lung- and skin-irritating ingredient that can poison a small child if accidentally ingested. But don't assume its replacement ingredients are much safer. In fact, some alternatives have been shockingly dangerous. Medical journals note the death of an infant who fell into a coma and died in 2005 after briefly sucking on two nail polish remover pads that contained gamma-butyrolactone (GBL). According to a report published in *Clinical Toxicology* and elsewhere, GBL is quickly metabolized by the body into GHB, otherwise known as the date-rape drug, and has triggered comas in several children. Incredibly, it was only removed from nail polish remover pads in the U.K. in 2011, a year after someone got renal failure from it.

Methyl acetate is an acetone alternative of much less concern, though the U.S. EPA still classifies it as a "systemic toxicant." Nevertheless, it's pushed by regulatory officials as a greener alternative to the ethyl acetate (an air-polluting VOC) found in Cutex and some Sally Hansen products. Other pads have the suspected endocrine disruptor triclosan in them (see page 11 for more on triclosan).

HANDS OFF: NAIL BARS

Nothing like the fresh-footed feeling you get from a professional pedicure—as long as the joint doesn't give you a headache. Even if you don't get irritated from an afternoon at a mani-pedi bar, someone else does. Researchers at the Cancer Prevention Institute of California say roughly half of 201 surveyed workers at 74 salons in 2008 reported headaches, skin and eye irritation as well as breathing problems from the high levels of harsh chemicals wafting through poorly ventilated salons. Beyond nail polish fumes, salons that offer acrylic nails have been tied to elevated risks of asthma in their workers.

- No nail polish job can be entirely natural, but for a decidedly more holistic approach, head to the nearest spa that's committed to organics. Beyond offering pedicures with Big 3–free nail polish, they should use soothing all-natural and/or organic scrubs and creams on your feet. But don't take the salon's word for it: ask to see product ingredient lists before they're used on your body.

- Pass on drying sprays, which salons use to speed up the drying process before they send you packing without smearing. These aerosols give off smog-inducing VOCs (volatile organic compounds) and some, such as DeMert Nail Enamel Dryer finishing spray, are made with, gulp, mink oil. Yes, that's dead mink on your toes, ladies.

- Heading to a nail salon–bound bridal shower but don't want to be a bummer and pass on the pedi? Either get clear polish applied (which is way lower on the toxicity scale) or bring your own, more natural polish from home (see Almost-natural Nail Polish, page 117).

Skip the whole shebang and look for health store options instead. You'll need more elbow grease (let the remover soak in for a few seconds before rubbing), but **No-Miss Almost Natural Polish Remover** and **Suncoat Natural Nail Polish Remover** will erase last week's pedicure with earthier ingredients that are fruit and plant based. Though I gotta say, Suncoat's remover with soy/orange oil and corn-fermented ethyl lactate still gives me a whopping headache as soon as I crack open the bottle (an MSDS, or Material Safety Data Sheet, for ethyl lactate reveals the compound can indeed trigger headaches and dizziness when inhaled). FYI, health store brand Honeybee Gardens' Nail Polish Remover used to contain environmentally problematic methanol until it reformulated in early 2010. It now contains methyl acetate, like some conventional brands. Though honestly, water-based polishes such as Honeybee Gardens' can also be removed with vodka, grain alcohol or rubbing alcohol. Keep in mind that water-based finishes get harder and harder to remove the longer you leave them on dry nail beds, which is why you shouldn't leave them more than a week at a time. Darker colours also require more remover and elbow grease. And acetone removers won't work well on water-based nail polish, so don't even bother.

TATTOOS AND PERMANENT MAKEUP

Back in the day, having tats meant you had worn one of two uniforms: a sailor suit or prison stripes. More recently, the *Journal of the American Academy of Dermatology* found that 24% of 18-to-50-year-olds have tattoos. Narrow that down to mid-to-late-20-somethings and 36% have at least one. Besides the eventual regret that comes from engraving your body with the same Chinese character or tribal band as 100,000 other people, is there anything else you should be worried about when considering getting inked? Let's put it this way: in California, since 2005, tattoo parlours and permanent-makeup pros have to post warnings that their products may contain lead, arsenic, mercury, chromium extract, antimony, and more metals known to the state to cause cancer, birth defects or other reproductive harm. Now, those in the biz will tell you that levels of heavy metals in their inks all fall within safety standards, but I'd like to see that warning posted in tattoo shops in Canada so people can make more informed choices.

Even if you're not worried about long-term heavy-metal effects, the metals in tattoo pigments can cause weird allergic reactions in some. By far, red is the dodgiest of all the hues. It's been found to contain mercury in some shades (such as mercury sulphide, cinnabar, vermilion). They're rarer these days, but reactions to red ink continue to be the most common, including among those getting cosmetic tattoos (the perils of permanently red lips). The odd part is that you might not get a reaction for years. By the way, the Mayo Clinic site warns that in rare instances tattoos and permanent makeup can cause swelling and burning during an MRI (especially with inks heavy in iron oxide). Don't avoid an MRI if you need one, but let the radiologist know you have a tattoo.

Tattoo Tips:
- Ask about non-metallic pigments. These are sometimes called "organic" inks. Not that these are totally safe. A 2003 EU report on tattoo safety noted that 16 of 28 organic colorants were azo dyes (a synthetic family of pigments) that your body easily metabolizes into carcinogenic amines, and four had amines directly in them.
- Natural black pigments made from carbon or logwood are considered safer than ones containing iron oxide. Nonetheless, while some tests have found big-brand inks to be lead free, preliminary research at Northern Arizona University found lead in several black ink samples.
- Serious vegans should be aware that tattoos aren't necessarily animal product free. Carbon or "Bone Black" comes from burning animal bones into charcoal, and most carrier solutions used in applying the ink have an animal gelatine base. Ask around for veg-conscious tattoo artists who use vegan inks and carriers. **Stable Color Inks** are 100% vegan.
- Avoid amateur tattoo artists like the plague. They're more likely to use dodgy inks with impurities and toxins.

Temporary Tattoos: Want a little body art without the permanent reminders? Well, surprise, that temporary tattoo might leave you with some nasty blisters and scarring. Any temporary tattoos that are black in colour should be avoided; they could contain skin-irritating PPDs that can lead to open sores (see Hair Colouring, page 136, for more info on PPDs). Pretty gross. True henna body art is made with plant powder and is never black (more brownish or reddish). You might find something labelled "black henna indigo" in Indian stores, but just so there are no surprises, be aware that this one's actually a green plant powder that turns blue when you add water to it. It's PPD free.

FAB GREEN BEAUTY WEBSITES

INFO

cosmeticsdatabase.com

justbeautiful.ca

davidsuzuki.org/issues/health

safecosmetics.org

greenbeautyguide.com

lesstoxicguide.ca

femmetoxic.ca

goodguide.com

lovethelabel.ca

SHOPPING

saffronrouge.ca

pinkgingershop.com

hollyandivy.com

greenbeauty.ca

mintandberry.com

lilou-organics.com

maxandmia.ca

raindancecosmetics.ca

Shampoos and Conditioners	125
Dandruff Shampoos	132
Hairstyling Aids	135
Hair Colouring	136
Hair Removal	140
Hair Salons	144
Black Hair Care Products	148

HAIR CARE

Wash those chems right out of your hair

My childhood memories are clearly

compartmentalized according to hairstyles: there was the
classic bowl-cut era followed by the Flock of Seagulls swoop
(blame my older sister for that one), then the **Cosby Show**–
inspired perm (yes, I was convinced a mousy-haired half-Greek,
half-French-Canadian girl from Quebec could have a good 'fro).
And that was all before I turned 12! Just imagine how much
petroleum-based gel/mousse and nasty perm chemicals my body
was taking in, not to mention the cans of ozone-depleting
hairspray that kept all that in place (or at least tried to).
Through the years, we've all suffered for our hair, and in turn
the planet's suffered too. Can our morals and follicles live in
true harmony?

SHAMPOOS AND CONDITIONERS

You know that famous shower scene in *Psycho?* Well, there's something else hiding behind that shower curtain of yours. It's actually lurking inside the sudsers within your shampoo, to be specific, and though it won't quite kill you (we'll leave that to the movies), it is adding a totally unnecessary carcinogen and suspected kidney toxicant to your daily routine. It's called 1,4-Dioxane, and it shows up in a process called ethoxylation, when harsher chemicals are "softened up" (in bubble-making sodium lauryl sulphate's case, it's ethoxylated to make milder sodium laur*eth* sulphate). The cancer link is an unwanted by-product, and that's why it doesn't have to appear on the label, but that doesn't mean health advocates are cool with it being there. It's considered a probable human carcinogen by the U.S. Environmental Protection Agency. And since 1988, California has forced any product that contains 1,4-Dioxane (either intentionally or unintentionally) to carry a warning label that reads: "This product contains chemicals known to the State of California to cause cancer, birth defects and/or other reproductive harm." Did I mention it's also a significant groundwater contaminant and doesn't break down readily?

The Organic Consumers Association found the highest levels of 1,4-Dioxane in conventional products such as Clairol's Herbal Essences and Olay Complete Body Wash. But much to the dismay of health store shoppers, they also discovered that, in 2008, 46% of "natural-" and "organic-" branded shampoos, body washes and hand soaps also tested positive. The results prompted California's attorney general to file a lawsuit against Avalon Organics, Whole Foods and others in mid-2009 for failing to warn consumers about the presence of 1,4 in their beauty potions. No wonder Avalon, Alba, JASON, Giovanni, Ecco Bella, Nature's Gate, and Kiss My Face had all reformulated their products by the time they were retested in 2009; they now have no detectable levels. Conventional products including Pantene Pro-V shampoo, St. Ives, Dial, Olay, Head & Shoulders, Garnier Fructis and Suave Naturals, on the other hand, still contained the cancer link last checked (Herbal Essences has since reformulated).

Here in Canada, 1,4-Dioxane can't officially be added to beauty products since it's on Health Canada's Cosmetic Ingredient Hotlist (see Cosmetics Regulations, page 5), but no one's saying it can't get there, nudge nudge wink wink, "accidentally." Officials could easily force companies to keep all forms of 1,4 out since plenty of manufacturers like Aveda already vacuum-strip ethoxylated ingredients to remove 1,4-Dioxane before they formulate personal care products (of course, that 1,4-Dioxane has to go somewhere, and mostly it's incinerated). So why not make vacuum stripping mandatory? Ask the feds. And sign the petition on Environmental Defence's website (petition. environmentaldefence.ca/dioxane).

Shampooing Tips:

- Look for shampoos, body washes and bar soaps without -eths or PEGs (polyethylene glycol) in their ingredient list (unless you know for a fact they vacuum the 1, 4 out), on top of all the other Mean 15 ingredients (see page 8) you should be avoiding.
- Products certified by USDA, Natural Products Association, Ecocert, OASIS, BDIH, Cosmos and Soil Association are in the clear since they don't allow the carcinogen-triggering ethoxylation process (see Body Care Labels, page 13).

- Stay away from phony-baloney naturals like Suave Naturals, which has lots of ethoylated ingredients and other Mean 15s (see page 8 as well as page 411 for more on greenwashed labels).
- FYI, lots of shampoos are now advertising they're free of sodium chloride, which is, gasp, table salt. I think they're just trying to come up with random ingredients they can claim they're free from—without doing the hard work of ridding worse offenders.

Conditioner: Hair can take a lot of stripping from shampoos, as long as you give it the right conditioner. That conditioner has one hell of a job trying to give you the right amount of shine and softness without weighing you down with grease. How have conventional conditioners managed to deliver the goods? Silicones, baby. Especially the bioaccumulative, endocrine-disrupting, fish-hurting, environmentally nefarious types called siloxanes, including cyclopentasiloxane, cyclotetrasiloxane and cyclomethicone, which Environment Canada's not happy about (see Mean 15, page 8). Drugstore conditioners tend to combine those with lots of petroleum-based ingredients and heavy formaldehyde-releasing preservatives. And to top it all off, they throw in a dose of estrogen-mimicking, hormone-disrupting sunscreen chemicals such as oxybenzone and octinoxate (a.k.a. ethylhexyl methoxycinnamate) to protect your hair from the sun. You don't need any of that junk. If you want an extra conditioning experience, check out **John Masters Honey & Hibiscus Hair Reconstructor** or cheaper **Prairie Naturals Badlands Hair Reconstructor,** and don't forget to try your own DIY hot oil treatment at home. Even just putting regular olive oil on your hair for 10 minutes before washing will give you some deep conditioning without weighing you down, since you're not leaving it in. Jojoba is the bomb as a leave-in conditioner (doesn't have that olive oil smell or coconut oil crunchiness).

Shampoo and Conditioner Testing: I've heard a ton of complaints from readers who've switched all their body care over to natural products but can't find a shampoo that makes their hair happy. Keep in mind that the purest shampoos with the most natural ingredient lists aren't going to lather and spread the way you're used to, and eco-shampoos that perform well aren't generally as clean, ingredient-wise, though they're certainly much greener than conventional brands. I won't lie to you: some so-called natural brands are just plain garbage at keeping your hair *looking* healthy. FYI, we couldn't squeeze in every brand on shelves since there are dozens out there, and we also didn't include strictly local brands that aren't readily available at health stores across the country, even though they may rock, such as **Lemieux** refillable shampoo in Quebec or **Bish's** glass-bottled shampoos in Halifax or **worldCLEAN Hair and Skin Cleanser** in Toronto. Thanks to expanding interest in natural products, you can find some of the following brands at mainstream grocery stores and drugstores, but you'll have to go to a health store for the rest. By the way, both shampoos and conditioners were tested.

JASON	"Pure, natural & organic"? Puh-leeze. Probably the worst in terms of having way too many questionable synthetics such as cocamide MEA, cyclopentasiloxane and oxybenzone. Yikes.	👎
🍁 DRUIDE BALANCE	This no-sudser is supposed to breathe life into devitalized locks, but even a giant handful of their conditioner leaves my and my testers' hair seriously wanting moisture. This one's 12% organic.	👎
🍁 JEVATEE	This B.C. product is weirdly runny, so half the bottle vanishes in no time. Not impressed.	👎
ALBA	One of the cheapest and largest (volume-wise) shampoo bottles in health stores, with a lot of synthetics but better than JASON. Wide range of products that are generally okay performers.	👍👎
NATURE'S GATE	Some of you love their tea tree shampoo, but of all the more affordable big-name health store brands, this one's tied with Alba for holding on to the most synthetics (including synthetic scents). They also had to strip the misleading word "organic" from their name. Fugetaboutit.	👍👎

AVALON Now 1,4-Dioxane free but, bah, doesn't do much for my locks, and reader reviewers note it makes fine hair look dull, dry hair drier and performs pretty poorly. At least it's higher in organic content than many mainstream "organic" brands, but come on, their conditioner has cyclopentasiloxane, which stays in the environment and hurts fish to boot.

DR. BRONNER'S Fine for normal hair, but don't go there if yours is dry or chemically treated. The conditioner-and-style-crème-in-one works best as a frizz controller on big hair if used sparingly; it's greasy otherwise. The only USDA—certified organic (in other words, 95% organic) product in the bunch.

KISS MY FACE Revamped Big Body and Whenever lines have much cleaner ingredients than other mega health brands such as JASON and Nature's Gate. Just avoid their Miss Treated Shampoo: it has a Mean 15, cyclomethicone. Otherwise, the shampoo is fine for normal hair. Conditioners do better with more hair types.

❀ NATURE-CLEAN The shampoo's an okay basic if you've got "normal" hair but a bit stripping for dry or colour-treated. The conditioner, on the other hand, is quite nourishing for drier hair and heavy for fine or oily hair.

BURT'S BEES

Deliciously scented (too bad it's synthetic), otherwise very high in naturally derived content. But you might need to lather twice for greasy hair. Spreads weirdly but it does suds up quite a bit. Worth a shot if it's the only natural shampoo in sight but there are better performers out there. Let's call this "alright" but not for overly needy hair.

🍁 **GREEN BEAVER**

Reformulated shampoo line works well on oily, fine and normal hair but won't win over dry hair.

GIOVANNI

Whole Foods forced these guys to take the word "organic" out of their brand name since it was misleading, but it's a decent performer at a doable price for all sorts of hair types. Great drugstore/decent health store pick. These are now 1,4-Dioxane free (yay!). My mom's a big fan of 50/50 line for thick, dry, processed hair.

🍁 **PRAIRIE NATURALS**

This one's like the Canadian version of Kiss My Face in terms of mid-grade ingredients. Some products aren't as clean, ingredient-wise, as others, but performs more like a drugstore shampoo. Solid value and a great nourisher for all sorts of hair, especially colour-treated/dry hair.

DESERT ESSENCE	Again, not all natural, but good affordable option that lathers well with little shampoo and does its job. Not every product in the hair line is crowd pleasing but the coconut line is decent for curly/dry/thick hair and the tea tree line scored points with oilier reviewers.	🍁🍁🍁🍁
❧ **LIVE CLEAN**	The greener Pantene. Though it's 96–98% "plant-derived," it still contains lab-altered synthetics (see Decoding Labels, page 13)—but unlike JASON, all the synths score low in toxicity. It performs just as well as your typical drugstore shampoo and conditioner (except the volumizing line), and it smells like one too. Synthetic scent is at least phthalate free. Docking half a point for its use of synthetics. At drugstores and grocers.	🍁🍁🍁🍁
AUBREY	Wide-ranging line that pleases most from the fine-haired (camomile shampoo) to the frizzy (Island Naturals). Pals with oily hair really like the green tea line. Good swimmer's line, too.	🍁🍁🍁🍁
LAVERA	Used to come out in Jell-O globs and didn't spread well, but much improved in recent years. If you've got dry hair, you'll absolutely love their Rose Milk line over the Mango Milk line. Can overcondition though if you've got greasy roots. The Almond Milk wins raves for sensitive scalps; too bad it's discontinued.	🍁🍁🍁🍁🍁

JOHN MASTERS This pricey spa brand lathers well and its various lines should keep all hair types happy. If you've got dry, needy hair, it's worth doling out for their Honey & Hibiscus line, more so than Evening Primrose. Trust me on this one.

Green Thumb Legend: 1 = Better off with vinegar and baking soda 2 = Sorry excuse for shampoo/conditioner 3 = Decent hair cleaner/conditioner 4 = Great, green product 5 = Feels like you just stepped out of the salon

(DIY) SHAMPOO

Heard of the no-'poo movement? This has nothing to do with eating less bran and has everything to do with minimizing your product dependency. A growing legion of people are forgoing shampoo (for real!) and opting for baking soda and vinegar. Try it. You may be pleasantly surprised. Just mix 2 tablespoons (30 mL) of baking soda in 2 cups (500 mL) of warm water and pour it into an old shampoo bottle or glass-free vessel. Pour on hair and rub into scalp and follicles. It won't feel like it's doing much, but it's actually fantastic at gently cleaning. It worked beautifully on my super-greasy hair just this morning! Make your own conditioning rinse by combining 2 tablespoons (30 mL) of apple cider vinegar with 2 cups (500 mL) of water. Pour on head and rinse. And no, you won't smell like a chip truck! Though this isn't for all hair types. Those with really dry or damaged hair may want to use regular natural conditioner, after baking soda washing. Skip this 'poo if you have dyed hair.

DANDRUFF SHAMPOOS

Look, no one likes having a flaky scalp, but that's no excuse for treating your head like a chemical-warfare zone. Just do a little digging on the ingredients in your dandruff shampoo and see for yourself. Selenium disulphide/sulfide, found in Selsun Blue and Head & Shoulders Intensive Treatment, is officially classified as a probable human carcinogen and as very toxic to aquatic organisms. Zinc pyrithione (found in most Head & Shoulders products) is a severe eye irritant that's also highly bad news for aquatic life. And though it's supposed to break down quickly in water, a Swedish study found that 1% to 2% of the zinc could still be detected in water 80 days later. And hell, is anyone else somewhat perturbed that we're using crude coal tar on our scalps and skin (coal tar is found in Neutrogena T/Gel and other shampoos at concentrations of up to 10%), considering the weighty environmental burden of coal mining? Do you really want to be supporting the slicing off of Appalachian mountaintops to get at this stuff? It's also a serious eye and skin irritant that the feds say is only carcinogenic to coal miners, though users won't be thrilled to know that the cancer-linked polycyclic aromatic hydrocarbons in coal tar shampoos have been found in the urine of shampooers. Even the researchers who made that discovery had to ask: should this stuff really be on shelves without a prescription?

Ketoconazole (patented by Nizoral) is a potent antifungal that, when ingested, has been linked to birth defects in animals. It's not recommended for use by pregnant women or nursing mothers. Salicylic acid is actually on Health Canada's Cosmetic Ingredient Hotlist, though up to 2% is okayed for dandruff shampoos (ointments with above 3% have caused nausea, hearing loss, or confusion in some patients with severe psoriasis). The ingredient is commonly found in sewage since the chem is used in dandruff/acne medications and it's also excreted by those taking Aspirin. Its impact in waterways is still being studied.

HOMEMADE DRY SHAMPOO BETWEEN WASHES

You can postpone washings with dry shampoo. Trouble is, it's usually sold as a VOC-spewing aerosol, and even those that are sold as hair powders are loaded with not so natural ingredients (though **Pure + Simple Organic Lavender Hair Powder** rocks). Instead, just dust a little cornstarch into your roots, let it sit for 10 seconds, then brush your hair out well until all traces of the grease absorber have vanished. Best done over a sink or tub. Dark-haired peeps should go easy on the powdering and brush out well.

By the way, plenty of "natural" shampoos use the above ingredients. Prairie Naturals' Avalache dandruff shampoo has selenium (on Canada's Hotlist) and zinc pyrithione. Selsun Blue Naturals has more natural ingredients than Selsun Blue, though nature had little to do with making the whack of synthetics still in there.

Natural Dandruff Solutions: So how do you get rid of pesky dandruff?

- Avoid shampoos with the notorious skin and scalp irritant sodium lauryl/laureth sulphate (SLS). It actually dries out your skin and can lead to flaking.
- Rule out flaky product buildup by giving up hairspray, gel, etc., for a few days.
- Lather up with natural, herb-rich shampoos designed to help dandruff, cradle cap, itching and more, such as Vancouver-made **Botanical Therapeutic** shampoo, conditioner and skin cream (which you can apply directly to your scalp). **Ferlow Botanicals Neem Shampoo** is good for dandruff and dry scalps (ferlowbotanicals.com).
- Most dandruff is caused by a fungus. Try adding a few drops of antifungal neem oil to a palmful of natural shampoo or look for natural shampoos that contain neem oil. Let the lather sit on your scalp for a full minute before rinsing—and don't forget to turn off your shower while you wait! For tougher cases, start with a teaspoon (5 mL) of neem in a teaspoon (10 mL) of olive oil, rub into your scalp and let simmer for 20 minutes before showering/shampooing. Bonus: neem is actually nourishing for your hair too, unlike the antifungal rosemary oil and tea tree oil that are often used in natural dandruff shampoos, which are stripping on dry hair.
- Try combatting the fungal roots of your dandruff with a candida diet. That means, at the very least, swearing off sugars, yeasts and all refined foods. See a naturopath for info.
- Squirt one part apple cider vinegar to three parts warm water on

your scalp, rub it in, and let it sit for 15 to 30 minutes before washing with a mild shampoo. Vinegar has natural antimicrobial properties while restoring your scalp's pH.

- If you only see flakes during the dry winter months, you just need to add more moisture to your head. Rub aloe juice into your scalp and let it sit before washing. Popping omega-3 fatty acids (including algal omegas if you're vegetarian) will really help nourish your skin from the inside out. See Fish Oils, page 245.

HAIRSTYLING AIDS

You might as well style your hair at the gas station when you consider all the petroleum-based ingredients that go into hair gels, waxes, pastes and mousses. Like conditioners, modern style aids tend to be loaded down with lots of silky smooth siloxanes that are persistent in the environment and bad for aquatic life, such as cyclopentasiloxane. That includes über-popular Moroccanoil. These are particularly present in any "glossy" or "shine-enhancing" serums. And when you move into the world of hairsprays, you're mixing in even more air-polluting aerosols and taking in a lungful of hormone-disrupting phthalates, formaldehyde-releasing preservatives (see page 7) and estrogenic sunscreen chemicals (see page 44). Sure, aerosol mousses and sprays got rid of ozone-depleting CFCs eons ago, but they just replaced them with HFCs such as hydrofluorocarbon 152a, which is a greenhouse gas. This is why a genuinely natural product would never come in an aerosol can (I'm talking to you, TRESemmé Naturals mousse). Sprays and mousses should come in a pump, not a can.

Natural Hairstyling: Now, I can't tell you that every natural product on the shelves is going to wow your hairdresser, but one line that has won the hearts of eco-conscious stylists is **John Masters Organics**. The man is actually a hairstylist himself and makes great pomades, hair texturizers and gels, plus volumizers for thinning hair, shine-pumping leave-in treatments and body-boosting sea salt sprays. I use their Shine On product as a decent Moroccanoil replacement.

135

It's better than using straight argon oil, which isn't a great substitute. **Giovanni** covers even more ground, with root-lifting sprays, mousses, frizz busters and finishing mists (though, last time I checked, their smoothing serums contained nasty siloxanes!). For super-firm-hold hairspray, **Aubrey Organics' Natural Missst Herbal Hairspray** holds from day to night, no problemo (though it does get crunchy), without the plastics found in salon and drugstore products. Rocks for faux-hawks too. While we love other Suncoat products (such as their lipstick), their hairstyling aids just don't perform as well.

(DIY) MAMA VASIL'S HOT OIL TREATMENT

Back when I first fried my hair with lemon juice and bad perms, my mom started me on her signature hot oil treatments. So what's the secret? Her basic recipe involved heating up olive oil in a pan or microwave and squeezing in a few capsules of vitamin E. In recent years, though, she's been using room-temperature oil and drizzling in honey (a humectant) as well as a raw egg yolk (your vitamin-rich nourisher). Whisk it up and you've got a homemade hair mayo! Pour it on, sit back, relax, and once you're tired of cooking, shampoo and marvel at your shiny locks.

HAIR COLOURING

Is a real tree hugger supposed to dye her hair? Well, I don't know about the rest of you, but I sure as hell do. I know I'm supposed to love what nature gave me, but I gave up on my mousy shade of ash almost twenty years ago. And according to Clairol, 54% of North American women make similar colour-boosting moves. Over the years, I've tried streaks of blond, red, purple, pink and everything in between. Truth is, even women and men who lather up with natural shampoo and toothpaste often turn a blind eye to the stuff that livens our locks. Except ignorance isn't bliss when you consider that long-term use of hair dyes has been linked, albeit inconclusively, to bladder cancer and non-Hodgkin's lymphoma.

What do I mean by inconclusively? Well, in 2008 a panel of the World Health Organization International Agency for Research on Cancer looked at existing evidence and concluded that hairstylists and barbers were at higher risk for bladder cancer, but the findings were more muddled for personal use. The panel, for instance, took note of a Nebraska study that found "excess risk" for non-Hodgkin's lymphoma as well as another American study that showed no elevated risk for lymphomas. In the end, the panel concluded they couldn't really say one way or the other because the evidence wasn't solid enough, though the media boiled it all down to say that hairdressers should worry but regular hair dye users shouldn't. (To read the report yourself, search for "hair colorants" at monographs.iarc.fr.) Three years earlier, after a review of 79 studies, *The Journal of the American Medical Association* had made another cautious statement: they didn't find "strong evidence of a marked increase in the risk of cancer among personal hair dye users" but said that increased risk of hematopoietic cancer and other cancers "should be investigated further." If any cancer risk, however weak, makes you uncomfortable, it's time to consider your options. You should probably know that women who dye their hair are 37% more likely to get a progressive liver disease called primary biliary cirrhosis. And keep in mind that while the EU opted to ban 22 hair dye chemicals in 2006 thanks to potential bladder cancer links, Health Canada didn't budge.

Some things to keep in mind:

- Brand names such as Natural Instincts or Herbal Essences might make you think you can get the job done without harming the planet, but ammonia-free does not a natural hair dye make (though it is a good irritant and allergen to avoid).
- Ammonia-free permanent colours (from drugstores, salons and health stores) replace ammonia with monoethanolamine, a.k.a. MEA/ethanolamine, which is less smelly and irritating but is still classified as an air pollutant.
- All permanent hair dyes, even the health store brands heavier in botanical ingredients, contain cancer-linked and rash-triggering PPD. The difference is, health store brands have less PPD in 'em,

which, to be honest, leads your hair colour to fade more rapidly, but that's the price you pay for fewer toxins, by and large. Sanotint Light claims to be the only permanent "natural" dye that's PPD free, but it still has other suspect ingredients (see page 139).

Almost-natural Hair Colour: For permanent colours with way fewer synthetics and significantly more natural ingredients, check out brands such as **Tints of Nature**, **Naturcolor** and **Herbatint**. Note: Like Herbal Essences and many other commercial lines, Sanotint contains allergy-causing, suspected hormone-disrupting resorcinol. Herbatint did too, but it has since reformulated, so check your ingredient lists to make sure you don't have old stock.

- The darker your permanent hair colour, the more PPDs it contains. Choose lighter shades or, for deep brunettes, consider going semi-permanent, as I did.
- Semi-permanent hair dyes that are free of ammonia are a healthier choice. **Herbatint Vegetal** and **Tints of Nature Changes** are PPD-free semis.

Natural Hair Colour: The only genuinely all-natural option is henna, though this stuff is nearly impossible to remove if you don't like the hue (which is why hairdressers curse it). Do a strand test first to make sure you like it. Real henna is red. Black henna is neither black nor henna—it's indigo, and if truly natural, it'll smell like peas, run blue and make your hair blue-black. To get a toned brown, black or blond "henna," companies will mix things such as walnut or amla paste into it, though some companies might mix in synthetics and destructive metallic salts, so beware. Any colour with henna in it will fade to expose red undertones. **Aubrey Color Me Natural** offers two shades of henna-based browns. **Light Mountain** offers a dozen all-natural shades, from "neutral" to black, as does **Logona Herbal Hair Colors**, which uses henna, beetroot, coffee and other natural ingredients. **Surya Brasil** also uses strictly natural henna-based formulations in 15 shades.

Hair Dye Testing: You'll notice that none of the following products get stellar reviews. That's because I'm, well, honest. These do fade much more than a drugstore or salon dye, but if you take that as a given, there are some differences in applicability and ingredients.

SANOTINT	Claims to contain the lowest amount of PPD on the market, but their darker colours in particular have too many unnecessary allergenic ingredients, such as resorcinol, as well as toxic hydroquinone and coal tar dye p-Aminophenol.	👎👎
HERBATINT	Easy brush-in formula. Lasts a little longer than Naturcolor, but don't expect colour-fastness. Old bottles contained resorcinol. One bottle lasts two treatments for short hair.	👎👎👎
NATURCOLOR	This was my personal pick when I was dying with permanent colour, but you'll find it still fades faster than drugstore brands and is hard to apply alone (my mama always did it for me!). The bottle isn't squeezable, which is annoying.	👎👎👎
TINTS OF NATURE	Container is hard to squeeze, but it doesn't run, which is nice. Wasteful format if you have really short hair and need only half a container. Otherwise same as Herbatint in terms of colour and longevity.	👎👎👎

👎 Green Thumb Legend: 1 = Might as well put shoe polish on your head 2 = Sorry excuse for hair dye 3 = Decent colour booster 4 = Great, green hair dye 5 = Clairol's green sister

Highlights: You ever try to lighten your locks with a little lemon juice and lots of sun? Natural, yes, but the time I did it I ended up with a crackling-dry brassy yellow 'fro (I was in sixth grade). Most of us learn to give up on DIY dying techniques after our tween years and head to the drugstore or salon for more precise results. Beyond lemon, you can't really lighten your locks without hydrogen peroxide, and while it's caustic at higher concentrations, the 6% used by salons isn't much of an environmental or health worry. It's the ammonia and PPDs that are in permanent dyes that are the real concern. So once your hair's lightened, you'll want to consider all the points I listed under Hair Colouring before you pick your particular shade of blond. If you don't mind the hue that arises after you've been bleached, just don't add a colour to it; that's my trick for my two blond streaks. And I make sure they're lower down on my head so roots won't show since I redo them only once a year.

HAIR REMOVAL

Funny thing about those dense threads that grow out of our skin: we're very specific about where we do and don't want them. On top of our heads, we'll fight to the death for them. But, depending on your sex and your culture, we beat the rest back like bad weeds. Traditional Muslim doctrine calls for beards but no armpit hair. Old European stereotypes insist women let it all grow out. And on Brazilian beaches, bodies are waxed till there ain't a single follicle in sight (even with thongs). I may have started covertly shaving my legs in locked bathrooms when I was in, oh, fourth grade, but by the time I was a hardened feminist hippie chick at 16 I kissed razors goodbye. Of course, the experiment ended the following summer when I started a job that required shorts. Go figure.

Electric Shavers: A typical electric shaver or beard trimmer uses about 15 watts of power, but, like other products with rechargeable batteries, if you leave a regular old electric shaver in its base, it can draw as much as 5 to 20 times more energy than the battery actually holds!

Get yourself an Energy Star–certified electric shaver that uses 35% less energy than the competition. Leave shavers and beard trimmers unplugged until they start fading; just make sure to plug them in the night before a big interview or an important date. My guy only plugs in his beard trimmer once every four to six weeks.

Green energy enthusiasts will totally want to hunt down a **solar**, yes, *solar*-powered shaver. You can actually buy one online (through sites such as outdoorgb.com), and as long as you have a sunny window to keep it in, reviewers give it the thumbs-up. With a little more elbow grease, a **Dynamo** wind-up shaver will do the trick, but keep in mind that you get just over a minute of shaving time for every minute you crank it (e-light.us, stuffjunction.com; modernoutpost. com). I get the feeling most guys will grow impatient with this one and subsequently be stuck with a dusty gadget, so think long and hard before buying it.

Razors: Blame the growing army of stubbly dudes hooked on beard trimmers or the expanding legions of retirees giving up grooming for gardening, but no matter how you slice it, razor sales are on the decline. Still, billions are sold each year, with a growing number of blades per head (for god's sake, Gillette makes a five-bladed, battery-operated vibrating razor; what's next, a 10-headed monster with strobe lights?), and they're generally made with zero recycled content and have zero recyclability. Oh sure, BIC started a razor recycling program and makes a razor out of corn-based plastic, but both are only offered in Europe.

> ## CHANGE BLADE ONCE A YEAR!
>
> How? By drying it between uses. Why? Moisture, not your stubble, dulls blades.

You can score razors made of recycled yogurt cups with replace-able heads by **Recycline** at your local health store, but the blades aren't

wickedly sharp and seem to dull too quickly. You can send your
handles back to them for recycling, but seriously, shouldn't we be
reusing the handles? It's the razor cartridges we need to recycle, and
Recycline doesn't recycle those. Neither do municipalities. Obviously,
it's possible if BIC's doing it in Europe, so keep pushing for it here.

Some bad-ass men and women go silky smooth with simple,
old-fashioned straight razors. I can't say I'm brave enough to have
tried it, but you will find friendly tips online for doing it yourself.
If that seems too intense, check out old-school safety razors with
replaceable heads on sites such as fendrihan.com. Just make sure
that if you invest in either style of razor, you stay away from the
ones with handles made of dodgy exotic woods such as teak or
illegal ivory.

Waxing and Sugaring: Do you really need to be pouring petroleum
substance on your private parts every time you go for a wax job? Skip
the whole environmental catastrophe and try sugaring instead. You
can technically eat the paste (though that would be particularly nasty,
post–hair removal). Plus, this ancient Egyptian technique won't burn
your skin like waxing can and, unlike waxing, the strips are washable. You
can buy sugaring kits from the store (**MOOM** makes them), look for
spas that put sugaring on the menu or make yourself a batch at home.

Shaving Cream: Don't be fooled by the increase in prominently promoted natural ingredients such as aloe/sunflower/
eucalyptus/tea tree/mint oil in drugstore shaving creams. They're still
loaded with Mean 15 ingredients, including formaldehyde-releasing
DMDM hydantoin. You'll find plenty of even more unsettling endocrine disruptors such as BHA in fruity-scented Skintimate Signature
Scents, and soil-, water- and breast milk–contaminating triclosan in a
growing number of shaving creams, including Aveeno's Active Naturals
Therapeutic Shaving Gel and Positively Smooth Shave Gel. (By the
way, the "active naturals" soy in Positively Smooth is creepily touted as
a hair growth inhibitor so you don't have to shave your legs as often.)

Regardless of what's in it, an aerosol cream or gel pumps out smog-inducing VOCs, hence California forcing shaving companies to reduce VOCs from 7% of their product by weight to 4% by 2009. What about Canada?

In my humble opinion, even natural health store–bought shaving creams aren't really necessary. Any natural/organic body wash or conditioner easily does double duty with women's razors, though men (and their skin) will be better off with a simple organic shaving oil (see below). If you're stuck on creams, I can tell you that, again and again, men have told me they don't like Alba's shaving cream but that **Weleda Shaving Cream** is a winner. Beware of pseudo-naturals such as Kiss My Face Moisture Shave, which only reformulated to be paraben free in late 2010; old stock could still be kicking around on shelves. On a packaging reduction diet? Lather up with a simple shaving soap such as palm-free, all-Canadian **Mountain Sky** shaving bar.

Shaving Oil: Boys, forget shaving creams and gels. It's time to open your mind to shaving oil. All you need is a few drops a shave and your skin will thank you. No more razor burn, no more nicks. Just try it. **Cromwell and Cruthers** is an awesome Canadian-made brand with no synthetic fillers. It's full of good oils such as grapeseed, almond, avocado and jojoba, mixed with menthol, aloe and vitamin E. You'll find it at mainstream drugstores as well as Mountain Equipment Co-op for under $5 (cromwell-cruthers.com). Other purportedly natural shaving oils are often cut with synthetics, so look out.

DIY SHAVING OIL

For a two-in-one moisturizer and shaving oil without the need to decode an ingredient list for synthetics, buy yourself a bottle of straight organic jojoba oil from the health store and shave with a few drops. It'll last you years. Straight olive oil or organic grapeseed oil are also good picks.

HAIR SALONS

I remember when my mom started taking me to her women's-only salon in Montreal. At the time, we were living nearly two hours north of the city and it was our ritual to drive in periodically and get dolled up. You knew you were in the right place by the hum of hair dryers and the aroma of chemicals nearly singeing your nose hairs. While hair dye chems aren't nearly as toxic as they were in the '70s or '80s (see Hair Colouring, page 136), salons are still hot boxes of ammonia, formaldehyde and other air-polluting, lung-irritating, headache-triggering chemicals, including a cocktail of aerosols (not to mention the heavy presence of hormone-disrupting phthalate plasticizers in hairsprays and basically all synthetically fragranced products). If a salon does perms or chemical hair straightening, the airborne assault is even more potent.

Ironically, products sold as formaldehyde free, such as Brazilian Blowout treatments, have proven to be some of the worst offenders. This popular brand, much loved in the celeb world, marketed itself as a natural, formaldehyde-free alternative to chemical straightening and soon caught on with mainstream salon goers. It was exploding in popularity when reports of burning eyes, noses and throats, breathing difficulties and even, in rare instances, hair loss started mounting. Finally, the company—which insisted on its packaging and in its marketing that it contained no formaldehyde—said okay, fine, it contains maybe 4% of the carcinogenic air pollutant (way over the permissible limit). Health Canada's own tests proved levels were much higher—more like 12%, a disconcerting 60 times above the allowable cosmetics limit of 0.2%. Not surprisingly, salon workers were plain pissed that their health and the health of their clients was put on the line by a greenwashing fraud, and soon a class action of B.C. salon workers was launched.

By the way, Brazilian Blowout solutions weren't the only high-formaldehyde smoothing products being used by the pros. Health Canada issued warnings about 10 professional hair smoothing treatments, including Brazilian Thermal Reconstruction by Cadiveu, Pro Collagen Rx Keratin Treatment, iStraight Advanced Keratin by ibs Beauty, and

Global Keratin Hair Taming System with Juvexin Strawberry Resistant by Global Keratin. Want a more natural one? Request **Keragreen Keratin Smoothing System** (organiccoloursystems.com).

Healthy Hair Salon Alternatives: Hairstylists are rightly worrying about the effects of their long-term exposure to all sorts of other products in their arsenal, and that's why many have dropped perms and chemical hair straightening from their bag of tricks. Now they offer low-ammonia hair dyes and sulphate-free shampoos (i.e., sodium laureth sulphate–free; see Shampoos and Conditioners, page 125). Some are taking it one step further and opening up full-on green salons, banning ammonia and aerosols altogether and sudsing up with organic products. **World Salon** in Toronto is a perfect example. Owner Brian Philips stopped offering perms in the '90s, washes hair in solar-heated hot water and primps clients using his own World-branded organic product line that can be used interchangeably on hair and skin. (Love World's beeswax hair and body pomade! You can sculpt your do and rub it on cracked hands too! world.ca) **Clover Earthkind Hair Salon** in Vancouver diverts a whopping 85% of its waste (including recycling its foil), offers partly organic and 99.9% plant-based dyes, and does it all in a low-VOC, reclaimed space (cloversalon.com).

Keep in mind that lots of salons will tell you their products are natural or organic when they only contain a few botanical ingredients or there's maybe one green line available for purchase; make sure you scan the labels yourself to get a clearer picture. Alterna Hair Care is a good example of a salon brand that talks up its "natural luxury" slogan, but give me a break: if it were so "conscious of the environment" it wouldn't contain a whack of persistent fish-harming siloxanes being banned by Environment Canada as well as petrochemicals, parabens and other Mean 15 ingredients (see Mean 15, page 8). Even if your salon isn't green, here are a few pointers:

- Pass on aerosol hairsprays and mousses. Just because they're CFC free doesn't mean they don't contain VOCs (volatile

145

organic compounds), which trigger smog and asthma, or HFCs, which are climate-cooking greenhouse gases.

- Make sure the shampoos and other products are at the very least paraben and sulphate free. Kevin Murphy offers one such popular pro line of shampoos, made from "renewable and sustainable resources whenever possible." There are still a good deal of synthetics in the shampoos (the conditioners are much more natural), but it's an improvement, for sure.

- Ask to see the bottles yourself and scan ingredient lists for Mean 15 ingredients (see page 8) such as siloxanes and formaldehyde-releasers like DMDM hydantoin.

- Find out if they offer any all-natural or certified-organic products for sale. Keep in mind that stylists easily assume their products are "all natural" or "organic" even when they're still high in petrochemicals and synthetics, since that's what they've been told by sales distributors. No one's offering close to 100% organic products at the pro level since, to be honest, they just don't provide the same performance.

- Ask about recycling and eco practices.

RECYCLE YOUR PONYTAIL

Planning a big lock chop? Don't let your hairdresser trash those tresses! If your ponytail is at least eight inches long and hasn't been chemically processed, you can send it off to the hair donation program of your choice, for example Wigs for Kids (punch in "hair donation" at cancer.ca for a list of programs from coast to coast).

Professional Colour: Hate to break it to all of you hoping to get your hair dyed naturally, but hair dyes aren't entirely natural unless you're using henna (which hairstylists hate because it's unpredictable, limited in colours and impossible to remove; see Almost-natural Hair Colouring, page 136). And even the greenest salons shy away from using health store–branded hair dyes because they just don't perform as well.

- Ask about ammonia-free or low-ammonia dyes, then press for details. They'll at least minimize irritating fumes (though pretty much all ammonia-free permanent colours use mono-ethanolamine, a.k.a. MEA or ethanolamine, which is less stinky but still an air pollutant). The only company that offers PPD-, ammonia- and MEA-free permanent dyes to stylists is **Teinture by Mastey** (mastey.net/teinture). **Organic Color Systems** uses half the MEA of other brands, only 0.4% PPD, and emphasizes organic, fair-trade and natural ingredients, which makes it unique (carried at Clover Earthkind Hair Salon in Vancouver, Bish Salon in Halifax, Jeanet Spa & Salon in Toronto and Berns & Black Salon and Spa in Winnipeg; contact the company to find a salon near you that offers its dyes; organiccolorsystems.com).

- To avoid cancer-linked PPDs altogether, you'll have to shift to semi-permanent colour (also available free of ammonia). Bonus: you'll kiss drastic root lines goodbye since colour just fades over time. I made the switch years ago and love that my colour "evolves."

- If you want plant-based hair dye, you'll have to do it yourself (see Hair Colouring, page 136) or take two boxes to your hairstylist and very kindly beg him/her to apply it for you. (Note that health store permanent dyes fade more quickly since they contain fewer PPDs, so some stylists will resist using them.)

ARE AVEDA CONCEPT SALONS A GOOD IDEA?

Let me get my scissors out and cut to the chase: compared to 98% of the salons in Canada, an Aveda concept salon (which washes and dyes your hair with nothing but Aveda products) will definitely be a greener choice. Are Aveda shampoos/conditioners/styling products as pure as some health store picks? Definitely not. There are lots of purer brands on shelves if you're looking for high organic or at least all-natural content, but to be honest, those aren't readily available at salons. Aveda beats out Kevin Murphy's sulphate-free, paraben-free pro line for sustainability, considering it continues to green its ingredient lists and is now finally free of parabens, formaldehyde releasers and most silicone-based ingredients, and manufactures its products at a 100% wind power offset facility in the United States, plus its packaging is very high recycled content (unlike Murphy's line, which uses "recyclable" bottles—who doesn't?). Aveda has asked makers of ethoxylated ingredients (which are often contaminated with carcinogenic 1,4-Dioxane) to clean up their processing, and it keeps upping its organic purchases (90% of its essential oils and herbs are organic). Pre-2010, Aveda products still contained way too much crap to get green-lit, but I'll concede that they've definitely improved and keep doing so. They've certainly been ahead of most other salons in terms of the hair colour they offer, too. Their permanent lines still use ammonia, but they claim they're anywhere from 93% to 97% plant derived (of course, as with all "naturally derived" labels, lots of ingredients are so synthesized that they're only distantly related to the coconut or palm they came from; see Body Care Label Decoder, page 13). Their semi-permanent is ammonia free but washes out in four to six weeks and can't be used to lighten hair.

BLACK HAIR CARE PRODUCTS

Can't a person just get ready in the morning and worry about run-of-the-mill beauty problems like "Damn, this shampoo is drying out my hair," not "Holy shit, I'm stewing my scalp in poisons"? Unfortunately, getting the kink out isn't risk free. Truth is, black focused or not, most of the personal care products lining shelves are riddled with questionable chemicals, but 'fro conditioners and relaxers have an even dodgier history. Lye-based relaxers rely on the same lye that cleans pipes and ovens, and even no-lye relaxers are full of dangerously corrosive ingredients such as calcium hydroxide, lithium hydroxide and calcium oxide—all of which can make your hair fall out and blind you if you're not careful (check out the warning on the packaging)!

Beyond the relaxing components, products such as African Pride and John Frieda Frizz-Ease Wind Down Relaxing Creme are loaded with long lists of junky chemicals including cyclomethicone, which accumulates in fatty tissue and is on my Mean 15 ingredient list, as well as other enviro and health suspects. Africa's Best Kids (and adults) Organics Conditioning Relaxer System contains not only totally unnecessary mink oil (yep, scraped from dead mink hides) but also BHA, an endocrine disruptor on California's list of chemicals known to cause cancer. All this to say, don't be fooled by the word "organic" on labels.

Several years ago, a jaw-dropping report came out linking early puberty among African-American girls to what they were smearing on their scalps. Turns out several of the hair treatments were high in the female sex hormone estrogen. For a long time, manufacturers even advertised that their products were rich in hormones, estrogen or placenta (!), as if that were oh so fabulous. Then a pediatric oncologist released a few case studies of girls as young as 14 months old developing breasts and pubic hair after the products were used on their heads. (That's right, I said 14 *months.*) The tiny study didn't really qualify as hardcore proof, but it did get people wondering why half of African-American girls hit puberty by eight years old (this isn't the case with girls raised in Africa), especially in light of the fact that over half of African-American parents, totally unaware of the potential risks, were using the hormone-laced products on themselves and their kids. Once that controversy hit the fan, many brands took the hormone claims off their labels and ingredient lists, though that certainly doesn't mean that every Africentric hair product on shelves is free of unsettling hormone-rich, estrogenic ingredients. Even now, plenty of products pushing cow and human placenta (ick) are readily available online, including Hask Placenta's Henna 'n' Placenta conditioner, and older Warren-Tricomi Pure Strength products are on shelves.

Don't believe the hype: black hair care products often boldly flaunt natural ingredients so the label can scream Olive Oil Creamy Aloe Shampoo or Coconut Hair Conditioner, but they're really just bottles full of cheap petroleum such as mineral oil and dodgy siloxanes.

Safer Options: Look for healthier, more natural options by scrutinizing ingredient lists. Some health stores and even major chains such as Shoppers Drug Mart do carry cleaner options, like **Shea "All Naturals"** hair balm, shampoos and conditioners. Ebenenaturals.com sells wonderful handmade products with really simple all-natural ingredients. Kynk.ca also offers some excellent products.

- For all-natural deep conditioning, use nothing but straight fair-trade organic coconut oil or jojoba oil from the health store on your dry locks. Try once-a-week hot oil treatment with plain olive oil, too (see Mama Vasil's Hot Oil Treatment, page 136).

- Still want that relaxed effect? Reach for relaxers that don't come with blindness warnings. Yes, they exist! Check out **PHYTO Phytodéfrisant Botanical Hair Relaxing Balm**. It's not a permanent relaxer, but it gets great reviews for combating frizz. Just remember, the ingredients are heat activated, so you'll need to blow-dry your hair.

- For serious longer-term relaxing, you can score the **PhytoSpecific** line at Sephora for a pretty penny. I hear Oprah uses this stuff (and it's way less likely to damage your hair). It's marketed as a "non chemical relaxing system" that gets its active ingredients from soy and egg extracts. I'm not going to lie, it has some questionable stuff in there like BHA and BHT, but it's still safer than the competition.

- Looking for a salon that uses gentler relaxers? **PhytoSpecific** is probably, all things considered, your most natural salon line (see above); to track it down near you, hop on phytospecific.com. But for a more decidedly holistic approach, sniff out earthier salons like **Body & Soul Shop** in Toronto, which bypasses chemicals and sticks to vegetable dyes, soap seeds from Africa, shea butter and whole body supplement/dietary advice.

- Dreads wanting to live a strictly ital, or natural, lifestyle should lock down some Canadian-made, hemp oil–based **Knotty Boy** products (knottyboy.com).

- Hair extensions or wigs your thing? Plastic wigs ain't so ecologically fantastic. And since it can be impossible to tell whether imported human/"European" hair was given up voluntarily (just watch Chris Rock's doc *Good Hair*), I'd stick with yak versions, sheered from Asian yaks (not to be confused with "yaki," or wavy textured weaves).

Birth Control   155

Sex Toys   164

Lubricant   166

SEX AND
CONTRACEPTION
Even educated fleas do it

Birds do it, bees do it, and hell yeah,
earth-loving enviros do it too. In truth, there's nothing that
connects us to nature's raw animalism quite like sex. Though
leave it to humans to take a simple instinctual act and complicate it with dodgy plastic dildos, synthetic hormones, ocean-
clogging condoms and lubricants made of fossil fuels. Not that
I want to take your fun away (I'd probably get spanked by the
whole lot of you if I tried), but by now we should be able to
keep playtime healthy and happy without being planetary
masochists. And oh, one more thing: might I recommend
forgetting about the mile-high club? Scoring on a plane is
never green. Try getting your kicks in an eco-sexy location
like, say, a train or a national park.

BIRTH CONTROL

You're here reading this right now because a) you don't want a crying baby in your near future; b) you don't want to be crying about genital herpes or any other sexually transmitted disease; or c) both of the above. Either way, just be thankful that we're no longer using the crocodile-dung spermicide favoured by ancient Egyptians, or the mercury-heavy birth control potions used by the ancient Chinese. Not that all of today's contraceptive options are always so enlightened, ecologically speaking.

Condoms: Linen, intestines, bladders, leather—they've all been used to make condoms in the past (and you thought modern condoms were uncomfortable!). Today's male contraceptive of choice is mostly made with natural latex tapped from rubber trees (with some chemical stabilizers, preservatives and hardeners thrown into the mix). Sounds sort of earthy, but that doesn't mean you should toss your used condoms just anywhere. I mean, look, the United Nations Population Fund says 10.4 billion condoms (not including significantly less popular female condoms) are used worldwide every year, which is a good thing for keeping the population boom in check, but there's some serious potential for trashy sex here (and I don't mean the good kind). Especially when those condoms get flushed down toilets. Once they're in water, condoms never biodegrade.

Flushed rubbers end up clogging pipes and slip out of storm sewers into nearby creeks, rivers, lakes and oceans. That's why marine biologists are finding condoms in seabird stomachs. Ocean Conservancy says it's collected tens of thousands of condoms from dirty beaches. Certainly Milwaukee was shamed into spending $2 million on better sewage screens after condoms started floating in Lake Michigan.

- Bottom line: never, ever, flush a condom. Wrap it in a little recycled toilet paper and toss it in the waste bin.
- Unless you're allergic to latex, stay away from petroleum-based polyurethane condoms (they're super pricey anyway). The plastic is polluting to manufacture and never breaks down.

- Avoid condoms with nonoxynol-9 spermicide like the plague. Turns out it can actually *increase* your risk of HIV, STDs and vaginal infections since it can create skin lesions. Durex discontinued its nonoxynol-9-laced condoms when this data came out, but others, including Trojan and LifeStyles, still make them.
- Vegans will want to look for casein-free options. Glide replaces milk-derived casein with plant extract from thistle. It's the only condom company to offer condoms and dental dams that are approved by the Vegan Society.
- Every condom takes about 102 grams of carbon to make, according to The Original Condom Company, which claims it's gone carbon neutral (theoriginalcondom.com). Still, at $2 a condom for this French import, you might consider planting your own tree to offset your sex life's emissions. Wish I could point you to a local choice, but no one's manufacturing condoms in Canada anymore. Sorry.
- Whatever you do, never reuse or recycle your condoms, kids.

The Pill and the Patch: Free love and the birth control pill went hand in hand in the '60s. It was, undoubtedly, incredibly liberating for women to take control of their fertility, as the pill helped them to do. However, nothing comes without a price, as we learned in the '70s when links to health problems emerged. Of course, back then hormone doses were nauseatingly high. They've come down a lot since, but all the synthetic estrogen (and progestin) 100 million women pee out every year does add up—especially if you're a fish swimming in the stuff. In the fall of 2009, the U.S. Geological Survey revealed that 6% of all fish in American streams are now intersexed (hermaphrodites, with signs of both male and female sex organs). The numbers are alarmingly higher depending on where they looked and what fish they looked at. "The percentage of intersex large-mouth bass per site ranged from 8% to 91% and was most prevalent in the southeastern United States." Canada's data isn't quite as extensive on the topic but a 2011 study out of Ontario found that up to 75% of rainbow darter fish collected downstream from

DO NATURAL SPERMICIDES WORK?

Women are a crafty bunch. They've concocted all kinds of potions over the years to avoid getting pregnant. Over the centuries, women have douched with lemon juice, soaked "contraceptive" sea sponges in it, even used half a lemon as a cervical cap (ouch). Turns out lemon does have spermicidal properties and anti-HIV potential but too much lemon juice can actually irritate vaginal tissues, potentially increasing chances of STDs. Coke isn't exactly natural, but there is some 1950s mythology kicking about that says the sugary soda kills sperm dead. Taiwanese scientists actually tested the theory in the late '80s and found it's ineffective (duh) and can cause infection. A safer, naturally-derived pick is **Contra-Gel**. This is the first Health Canada–approved spermicide made with all-natural ingredients. Plus, it's compatible with natural latex rubber and silicone diaphragms or cervical caps, as well as latex or polyurethane condoms. It's not going to keep you from getting pregnant, but it is useful when used in conjunction with these other forms of contraception.

Guelph's municipal wastewater treatment effluent had eggs in their testes. What the hell is going on? Well, it's hard to say exactly, though scientists point to the flood of multiple estrogenic compounds being excreted into the sewage system (yes, that includes birth control as well as all the estrogenic chemicals in consumer products such as body care). Those poor fishies are still alive and swimming, but they have more trouble reproducing, though scientists insist they're safe to eat. I don't know about you, but the whole scenario kind of makes me lose my appetite.

And while the patch seems so easy-peasy since you don't have to remember to pop it every day (just replace it once a week), it also releases 60% more hormones into the bloodstream than regular pills. In 2006, the manufacturer faced massive lawsuits after it warned users that they're at higher risk of life-threatening blood clots while flying in planes (actually, internal reports leaked to the press in 2010 revealed that the maker of the Ortho Evra patch, Johnson & Johnson, was well aware that their product was 12 times more likely to cause strokes and 18 times more likely to cause clots than regular birth control). The warnings were beefed up in 2008 when new research confirmed the risks. But where are the warnings against flushing or improperly disposing of your hormone-laced patch? Women and Health Protection says a used patch still contains up to 82% of the original hormones that were in there. Folding it in half, as the manufacturers recommend, ain't going to keep this stuff from leaching out in landfill, or into the water supply if flushed. WHP want to see used patches returned to the pharmacy for proper disposal. At least the makers of the NuvaRing, which you have to change only once a month, suggests resealing the ring in its triple-layered foil polyethylene and polyester pouch before you toss it.

And just when you thought progestin-only birth control pills (a.k.a. "minipills") might be an earth-friendlier option, as I originally did, well, a couple of studies found that progestin has a defeminizing effect on female fish and makes it harder for them to have little fishies of their own. You can't win for losin'. At least low-dose pills are just that, low dose, which is way better than the patch on the environment. But if you're not extremely vigilant about taking your minipills as prescribed, your chances of bringing another planet-taxing human into the world are much higher, so set your alarms, girls. You're more likely to have spotting on these pills, too.

IUD: I mentioned IUDs as a great green form of birth control to one sex toy store owner and she immediately recoiled. "Those cause infections," she exclaimed. Untrue, I told her, IUDs don't increase risk of pelvic inflammatory disease, other than a very slight increase during the first month after insertion. A 2010 study out of Stanford University Medical Center published in the *Journal of Pediatric and Adolescent Gynecology* actually recommended them for teenagers, who generally have difficulty taking pills consistently. Still, many women remember the IUD controversy from the '70s when one incredibly poorly designed brand of IUD—Dalkon Shield—was pulled from the market for triggering serious health problems and 300,000 people filed claims against the company. But three decades of evolution have made today's IUDs perfectly safe and hassle free. Intrauterine devices happen to have a top-notch 1% failure rate, are virtually waste free and (depending on the kind you get) are a hormone-free form of birth control (actually, even the hormone-excreting kind does so at significantly lower levels than the pill), making IUDs one of the greenest options in town.

IUDs can be incredibly liberating, because once your doc inserts this T-shaped thingy, you can leave it in for up to 10 years, depending on the kind. Of course, it can, for some, hurt like a son of a b#*@! going in (but much less painful than having a baby!), and for many around the world, it's worth it. IUDs are more commonly recommended for women who've already given birth vaginally (makes it less painful going in), though in 2005 the USFDA reversed its policy of only approving IUDs for women who had given birth, opening the gates for many more women to try this form of birth control. Only 2.9% of Canadian women choose the IUD, compared to nearly 20% in Asia, but the numbers are climbing in North America.

There are two major types of IUD: the copper kind and the progestin-excreting kind. The latter, marketed under the brand name Mirena in Canada, excretes only the tiniest amount of hormones (about one-seventh that of the birth control pill) and is a good option for women who are heavy menstrual bleeders since it actually lightens your flow (reducing your need for pads/tampons). This type prevents fertilization by killing sperm and making the cervix and uterus inhospitable places for the little swimmers/fertilized eggs. If you're not allergic to the metal, copper IUDs are great because the copper acts as a natural spermicide, though they're not recommended for women who have heavy periods since they could make matters worse.

Check with your doctor before you use a menstrual cup while wearing an IUD. The makers of the DivaCup say the IUD can potentially become dislodged or displaced when the menstrual cup is removed if you happen to snag the IUD string.

Sponges, Diaphragms and Cervical Caps: Elaine may have loved her contraceptive sponges enough to hoard them back in

ARE CHEMICALS KEEPING ME FROM CONCEIVING?

There are a million and one frustrating factors that impede our ability to conceive, including basics such as smoking and age. But what's becoming somewhat clearer is that exposure to pollutants in our environment can pose a pretty big threat to reproductive health. Men and women exposed to high lead levels (say, from demolition work, welding/soldering, pottery, ceramics) are more likely to be infertile. The same is said of other heavy metals too. And evidence is starting to mount that endocrine-disrupting chemicals are, duh, disrupting our hormones and contributing to infertility and reproductive problems. Take, for instance, PBDE flame retardants common in household dust: 97% of women have some in their blood, but the higher our PBDE levels, the longer it seems to take women to get pregnant, according to preliminary studies.

By the way, one 2010 study published in Oxford's *Human Reproduction* journal suggested the worse the air pollution levels, the lower your likelihood of conceiving via IVF. Ditto for high blood levels of bisphenol A, according to a 2011 study in fertility and sterility.

Diet may be a factor too. There are a couple of studies, including a 2008 one from Harvard, that suggest the more phytoestrogen-rich soy a man eats, the lower his sperm concentration. One study found that moms who ate over seven portions of red meat a week (in this case between 1949 and 1983) were twice as likely to have sons who consulted doctors about difficulty conceiving, and 18% had low sperm counts (compared to 5% of sons whose moms ate fewer than seven portions of red meat a week). Growth hormones in beef have been fingered as the culprit.

At this point, more research is needed before any strong conclusions can be drawn, but if you're hoping to become pregnant and have been struggling, take the precautionary approach and reduce your environmental pollutant exposure as much as you can. And if you do see a fertility specialist, talk to the clinician about your workplace and environmental chemical exposure history.

Seinfeld's day, but honestly, they're not really as effective in everyday practice as other forms of birth control (failure rate is 9% to 16% in women who've never had children, higher in the rest). Plus, to boost their efficacy, brands are now doused in nonoxynol-9, that spermicide linked to irritation of skin cells and increased HIV risk—seriously (see Condoms, page 155). More disincentives? Women who use sponges (made of totally non-biodegradable polyurethane plastic) suffer from more yeast and urinary tract infections. Yippee.

A diaphragm works in similar ways but is actually a latex or silicone cap. You have to make an appointment with a doctor to get fitted for one and they're pretty uncommon in this country. A somewhat better option is the **FemCap**. This small sailor hat–style cervical cap is made with silicone, lasts a year and can be used in conjunction with the all-natural spermicide ContraGel. The failure rate is about 8% if it's used perfectly. It costs $89 and provides up to 48 hours of continuous protection, which is pretty cool. Plus, you wash it and reuse it. You can get one from a natural health practitioner (femcap.com).

Fertility Awareness Method: Some people swear by this drug-free method of birth control. But I have to be straight about this: the fertility awareness method isn't for the lazy, disorganized or impetuous. If you're cool with keeping a written record of your menstrual cycle for, oh, 8 to 12 months (as recommended) and/or charting your cervical mucus to map out your "wettest" and "driest" days and/or keeping tabs on your internal temperature every morning to see how fertile you are and/or monitoring the hormones in your pee via test strips, this can be a wonderful form of birth control. Women who stick to it swear by it. Since most people slip now and then and have unprotected sex when they're aroused (which conveniently often happens when you're most fertile), my sister, the family doctor, says this technique is ideal for couples who don't mind getting pregnant. Failure rate in typical use is anywhere from 10% to 25%, according to the American Pregnancy Association. Couples can either abstain or use a barrier method such as condoms or cervical caps on fertile days—about a third of her cycle.

Fertility awareness is tricky business, people. You can even buy fertility tracking software or sign up for fertility awareness classes to help you decode it all. If you want to try the pee-on-a-disposable-strip method (which comes with a hell of a lot of packaging—more than a condom, I might add), note that Persona is formatted to help women avoid pregnancy while others, including Clearblue Easy Fertility Monitor, are designed for those looking to get pregnant. (Clearblue, by the way, has been shown to be more effective than other urine monitors, but it costs close to $300.) Some products promise to gauge fertility more easily by monitoring the hormones in your spit, but scientific data says the results are "unreliable."

By the way, the "rhythm method" is basically a super-simplified version of fertility awareness that essentially involves counting back 14 days from the first day of your period to guesstimate ovulation. The problem is that women don't always ovulate at the same time and, well, there's a lot of guessing involved. The **"standard days method"** is purportedly a little more effective, and essentially says days 8 to 19 of your cycle are the peak fertility period.

The Withdrawal Method: Hey, pull-out enthusiasts. You may think the withdrawal method is green since it requires no condoms or synthetic hormones. Alas, with a failure rate of 18% to 19% with "normal use," according to the American Pregnancy Association, this method can have a major impact on the planet if you end up with an unplanned child. While many couples use this method on occasion, under 3% use it full time. To that 3% (including one smart couple who are friends of mine): good luck, you'll need it. On the bright side, pre-jack (a.k.a. pre-ejaculate) does not contain sperm.

IS WEARING A CONDOM THE CHEAPEST WAY TO SAVE THE PLANET?

Back in the '70s, environmentalists were preoccupied with the concept of overpopulation stripping the planet of its natural resources. Some greenies suggested we needed serious population curbs to avoid major catastrophe. Real-world examples of how ugly a one-child policy can get (think forced abortions and sterilization) kiboshed most of that talk. With global numbers expected to hit 9 billion by 2050, though, chatter around saving the world by wearing a condom is back, except this time the focus is on your baby's emissions (and not the bodily kind). In 2009, Oregon State University published a report called "Reproduction and the Carbon Legacy of Individuals." It essentially said you can slash your personal carbon emissions by driving less, switching to greener light bulbs/windows/fridges and recycling your heart out, but having a child will still blow your carbon footprint out of the water.

An earlier British study suggested each U.K. child pollutes the equivalent of 620 return flights between London and New York over their lifetime. Looking at the global picture, the London School of Economics, in conjunction with Brit think tank Optimum Population Trust, released a study which pointed out that condoms might just be the cheapest way to fight climate change around the globe. According to their figures, for every $7 spent on basic family planning, over one ton of CO_2 would be slashed. That's a hell of a lot cheaper than the $32 it costs to cut a ton of carbon through high-tech solutions.

Nobody likes to be told how many kids they should or shouldn't have. But the bottom line is that 200 million women across the world are asking for contraceptives and just can't get their hands on them. And if they don't get the access they need, rapid population growth will only increase their vulnerability to the impacts of climate change (from food and water scarcity to human displacement), says the World Health Organization's Leo Bryant in an editorial in the medical journal the *Lancet*. Do your part by bugging your MP about boosting foreign aid for family planning and medical care for women in developing countries.

As for the rest of you, I won't tell you how many kids to have, but I will bug you to raise your brood as green as you possibly can, because, well, that's what I do best.

SEX TOYS

Looking for a little extra help to spice things up? Sex toys are like the cayenne pepper of adult playtime. Just don't ask me why hormone-disrupting phthalates were finally banned from kids' toys in Canada in 2011 but are still allowed in adult toys. Come on, I know some adults who play with their toys just as much as kids would, and they put them in way more, um, sensitive places for, er, prolonged periods. Not good when one study by the Danish Ministry of the Environment found some plastic sex toys contained up to 70% phthalates by weight, and phthalates are famous for migrating from plastic into our bodies. The Danes also discovered that lube (an essential adjunct to inserting foreign objects in hard-to-reach places) actually increases leaching, though at least water-based lubricants leached 100 times less than oil-based ones. Experts say heat, agitation and age (of the plastic) only increase leaching. Ick. Did I mention that, in 2011, the Danish Ministry of the Environment announced it was banning four phthalates in all consumer products that come in direct contact with either adults or children? So far, Canada's stayed silent on this. Maybe they've got a gag ball in their mouth?

Besides phthalates, harmful volatile organic compounds (including the nerve toxins toluene and carbon disulphide) were discovered off-gassing from vibrators, fetish clothing, gags and—I'll just say it—artificial vaginas.

The good news is that parts of the sex toy industry have woken up to the problem of putting hormone disruptors in their products. Retailers say they're seeing fewer PVC/jelly toys on the market today, adding that it was demands from consumers like you that made it happen. The bad news is that there's also more greenwash out there (yes, even dildo and lube companies pretend to be more eco-friendly than they are). If a company won't tell you specifics on what something's made of, simply stating that it's, say, "body safe," move on to the next sex toy—until you find one that's willing to be honest with you.

Not sure what your wand is made of? If it smells strongly of plastic, you should really landfill it. It's likely vinyl, a.k.a. PVC, a.k.a. jelly. (Sorry, there's no real sex toy recycling at the moment and municipalities don't even recycle vinyl when it comes in non-phallic shapes.) The soft plastic is made with high levels of phthalates and the hard kind is often stabilized with lead. (Remember the whole lead-tainted Mattel toy scandal from 2007? Yep, well, lead's been found in sex toys too.) Price is also an indicator. If it was one of the cheapest vibes in the store, all bets point to jelly again. Committed to your suspect magic wand? Just promise me you'll put a condom over it when you use it.

Ecoholic Sex Toy Tips:

- **Search for safer squishy options:** Your wisest pick with a fleshy feel is silicone. It's a man-made fusion of silicon (basically sand) and oxygen that's moulded into everything from baby bottle nipples and bendy muffin trays (no, that's not a euphemism, I'm talking bakeware, people!) all the way to fabulous sex toys. Silicone products are totally stable and can even be sterilized by boiling. The only real scandal here is that sand mining can be pretty disruptive to ecosystems (as all mining is, including the silica that goes into other basics, such as glass). Too bad that natural latex dildos from rubber tree sap aren't readily available in North America. One mysteriously malleable thermoplastic resin material used in fleshy sex toys is called CyberSkin and has been confirmed by Greenpeace to be phthalate-free, but unlike silicone it's not non-porous, so Toronto sex store Come As You Are recommends you use a condom with it.

- **Try, er, harder alternatives:** They seem cold at first, but glass and stainless steel can leave you positively tingling with pleasure knowing they're totally inert and truly body safe. Good luck finding any with recycled content, but they are durable. You can also score sensually sculpted wooden dildos by **NobEssence**. Their wood comes either from their own tree plantation in Costa Rica or from Forest Stewardship–certified farms (with new-growth not old-growth trees, phew). Don't worry, you won't get splinters from these, and they're a perfect erotic gift for the, ahem, tree huggers in your life (nobessence.com).

- **Get off on rechargeables:** Wanna talk buzz kill? Most cheap vibrators run on disposable batteries that end up leaking in landfill. Avoid the whole mess by investing in a quality rechargeable vibrator that gives you 60 to 90 minutes of fun.
- **Ignore claims of recyclability:** Sorry, no municipal recycler I've spoken to even accepts glass toys in its bins. But you can mail old toys across the border to Oregon's scarletgirl.com.
- **Love the local:** Surprise: 70% of sex toys come from China. Time for a "buy Canadian" policy. Try the handcrafted Ontario-made silicone toys from happyvalleysilicone.com, super-durable locavore fetish gear from aslanleather.com and leatherbeaten.com. We-Vibe isn't made here (just headquartered), but they do have good sustainability policies and are "carbon neutral" (we-vibecanada.com).

LUBRICANT

Need a little extra ocean in your motion? Typical drugstore and sex store lubes like K-Y and Astroglide are loaded with questionable and unnecessary ingredients including parabens and petrochemicals such as propylene glycol. Vagisil and You'll Never Know It Isn't Boy Butter both have formaldehyde-releasing diazolidinyl urea (Boy Butter also contains environmental mood-killer cyclopentasiloxane; see Mean 15, page 8). Maximum has, count 'em, four parabens, including two being banned from kids' products in Denmark. But at least it doesn't claim it's natural. I almost had to laugh when I flipped a bottle of Astroglide Natural over and found methylparaben on the ingredient list. What a joke. (Astroglide does offer a paraben-free product though.) By the way, a vegetable glycerine base is fine as long as you don't already have a yeast infection; the sugars in it may feed the yeast. Finally, stay away from silicone-based lubes whenever you can since they're made with environmental villains like siloxanes (see Mean 15, page 8).

Natural Lubricants: Lookin' for lovin' from organic lubes? It's hard to find a 100% organic lube but the closest you'll find more commonly

SURFING FOR PLANET-LOVING SEX STUFF?

Looking for eco-friendly lube, sex toys or contraceptives but don't have a progressive sex toy shop near you? Have no fear, online shopping is here. Just hop on **ecosex.ca**, which is, as the name suggests, exclusively earth-conscious. Or check out the web boutiques of enlightened sex stores: **comeasyouare.com**, **goodforher.com**, **artofloving.ca**, **venusenvy.ca**, **joytoyz.com**.

across the country is **Sliquid Organics Natural**. It's glycerine free, contains certified-organic aloe, hibiscus, flax and green tea, and gets its slippery side from plant cellulose (sliquidorganics.com). It's greener than their Sliquid Naturals line. Their Silk lubes use dimethicone, which contains residual siloxanes. The U.K. company **Yes** makes both water-based and oil-based certified-organic lube (yesyesyes.org). Bonus: it's been Vegetarian Society approved.

Can't find organic? Natural brands such as aloe-based **Good Clean Love** and Vancouver-made **Hathor Aphrodisia** lubricant have green-lit ingredients, though Good Clean Love's aren't totally unscented. Even the basic option contains vanilla bean (goodcleanlove.com, hathorbody.com). By the way, the horny goat weed in Hathor's lube is all cultivated, not wild-sourced, which is great. O'My Natural Lubricant does contain glycerine as well as some threatened herbs of concern like yohimbe extract and a few synthetics, so I'm not a big fan (omyinternational.com).

Fertility-aiding Lubricant: Hoping to be, shall I say, with child? Note that most lubes, even those that aren't marketed as spermicides, such as Astroglide and K-Y, admit to having sperm-inhibiting properties thanks to their effect on PH levels. Just don't ask me why a fertility lubricant, Pre-Seed, designed expressly for couples trying to conceive doesn't have a purer, paraben-free ingredient list.

(DIY) LUBE

A safe kitchen-cupboard alternative? Depends if you want to get pregnant or not. Not really? Go for 100% pure certified-organic aloe gel (it's also beautifully healing and latex compatible). If your answer is yes: egg whites. Yep, egg whites. Clinical research has found they actually boost sperm motility. Egg white is also condom compatible, unlike butter, nasty hydrogenated Crisco and oils.

Massage Oil and Candles: Trying to set the mood with a little candlelit massage? What's romantic about the artificial dyes, petroleum-based chemicals and sickly scents you get with typical sex store massage oil? Honestly, just hit a health store and stock up on an all-natural massage oil, or simply leave a jar of jojoba, almond or even coconut oil by the bed. Massage bars are in the clear as long as all the ingredients are ones you'd want to eat (or at least lick): cocoa butter, edible oils, essential oils.

Massage candles provide nice mood lighting and just so happen to turn into hot massage oil. Just make sure you're not using conventional petroleum-based paraffin wax candles, which can emit many of the same nasty vapours your car's tailpipe does. Once lit, **O'My Enjoy Soy Massage Candle**, for instance, basically gives you hot massage oil on demand. Pour the melted oil on your partner and snuff out the candle when you're done; it'll reharden. Be sure to pick the unscented type to avoid the headache that comes with synthetic scents (see page 83; omyinternational.com). You can actually make your own soy massage candles with the **Sensual Soy Massage Candle Kit** with optional essential oil scent from B.C.-based voyageursoapandcandle.com. Whatever you do, don't pour hot beeswax on your lover: it melts at a higher temp and so could very easily scald the pleasure right out of your lovemaking sessions.

WHAT'S UP WITH AROUSAL GEL?

Curious about those warming/arousal gels popping up next to the regular lube on shelves? Well, let's just say it ain't a natural way to get off. They're pretty much all cooked up in a base of petroleum-based antifreeze ingredient, propylene glycol (it's actually one of the warming ingredients), and then Kama Sutra Intensifying Gel (Warming) adds not-so-sexy parabens and the toxicant cinnamal. Durex Play Utopia Female Arousal Gel has the same suspect parabens. If you want a little zip in your zipper, better to look for something totally natural like **Zestra Feminine Arousal Fluid**, made with borage seed oil and evening primrose oil, as well as herbal angelica and coleus forskohlii extract (grown on an "eco-friendly" farm in India, according to the company). **Sliquid Organics Stimulating O Gel** is all vegan with L-Arginine, peppermint oil and menthol to "take your arousal level to new heights." **DermaMed Yes** is another all-natural pick, with aloe and apricot kernel oil mixed with extracts of damiana, wild yam, L-Arginine and more. Wild yam always makes me nervous because of concerns about the overtaxing of wild sources, though.

Pharmaceutical Pollution   173

Antibiotics   177

Alternatives to Antibiotics   179

Pain Relievers   195

Mental Health   209

Heart Health   216

Estrogen-Related Health   220

HEALTH

Might as well face it, we're addicted to drugs

No matter what they may think of the recreational kind, most Canadians say yes to drugs. In fact, over the last decade or so, sales of prescription and over-the-counter varieties have exploded, well, like tie-dye at a hippie fest. The number of prescriptions filled jumped 80% between 1999 and 2009, to the point where our tiny population of under 34 million had an astonishing 484 million—that's nearly half a billion— prescriptions filled in 2009 alone. And as quickly as we can sing "a spoonful of sugar," that stream of painkillers, antibiotics, antidepressants and cholesterol meds is turning up downstream. With this recent swell in the number of pills popped, someone's got to ask: do we need them all, and what exactly are all those drugs doing to the planet? The good news is that most Canadians have figured out by now that there's more to staying healthy than we can glean from a prescription pad. We're craving deeper, whole-body solutions. Enter **Ecoholic Body**, with a look at some of the most popular pharmaceuticals turning up downstream, as well as some more sustainable options offered up by the original Dr. Mom—Mother Nature herself.

PHARMACEUTICAL POLLUTION

Drugs are, no doubt about it, the most expedient way to treat a health problem in a system that offers doctors only a few minutes, max, per patient. And yes, medicines have been a huge benefit to so many lives. Still, in a country where we spent $22 billion on prescriptions in 2010, the government-sanctioned Health Council of Canada has slammed costly status quo decision making for encouraging too many Canadians to take drugs they don't need. Actually, if the World Health Organization is right in their estimate that half of all medicines are prescribed, sold or dispensed "inappropriately," that means we're, in their words, "wasting," oh, $11 billion every year on drugs. So what are the hidden planetary costs of all that excess drug downing? Just like milling pulp and paper or manufacturing a shiny flat screen TV, making prescription pills has an irrefutable environmental impact. To get one kilo of an active drug, pharma companies typically use an astonishing 46 kilograms of raw materials—over half of which are air- and water-polluting solvents. While big-name drug companies say they've cleaned up their act and reduced their emissions over the last decade, Canada's pharmaceutical manufacturers were still pumping out over 2 million tons each of smog-inducing volatile organic compounds and nitrous oxides in 2009, as well as over 10 million tons of lung-irritating particulate matter. "Green pharmacy" is clearly still a sideshow for the sector. Hell, that same year an investigation by the Associated Press south of the border found traces of all sorts of drugs downstream from big pharma factories, from the blood thinner warfarin (which you'll also find in the rat poison aisle of your local hardware store) to codeine. But that ain't nothin' compared to the noxious chems emitted from Chinese pharmaceutical plants. The nation's second-largest drug maker, which also exports to North America, was outted in 2011 for spewing 1,000 times the legal limit of poisonous hydrogen sulphide for years, plus its penicillin waste was turning a nearby creek an uninviting shade of yellow.

Down our drains: We're also—how to put this delicately—*excreting* more drugs than ever before into the ecosystem with every flush and shower (yep, our sweat releases compounds like antibiotics and steroids, too). There are traces of everything from Prozac to painkillers (150 pharmaceuticals and counting) in our sewers, streams, groundwater and even our tap water. And their potential impact in the wild is starting to come into focus. Antibiotic-resistant *E. coli* has turned up in our recreational lakes from coast to coast. Synthetic estrogens are creating hermaphrodite fish and frogs (see Estrogen, page 220). Antidepressants create reckless shrimp (I'm not kidding you, see page 210 for more info).

What's becoming clearer is that lots of drugs may not have an impact on their own, but combine them with other chems lingering in the environment and a more alarming picture emerges. In one study, seemingly harmless traces of Prozac mixed with equally benign traces of a synthetic herbicide suddenly spiked the death toll of water fleas (water fleas being one of the basic species on which the government tests chemicals such as herbicides since they're sort of signposts for things going wrong in the broader ecosystem). When the fleas were exposed to trace levels of two types of antibiotics as well as antibacterial triclosan, another widespread waterway contaminant, 20% fewer males were born. As author Sonia Shah noted in a 2010 Yale report: "The witch's brew of drugs, pesticides, and other trace chemicals in the environment could be acting synergistically to ratchet up the adverse effects on wildlife." Too bad Health Canada isn't asking that the potential environmental ramifications of new drugs be looked at synergistically, in combination with other drugs. Would make sense, wouldn't it? That's how we take 'em and that's how they end up in the wild. Sure, Health Canada can technically request chronic eco-toxicity testing of new pharmaceuticals, but Health Canada says they've never actually made such a request. Considering how things are run, it kind of starts to make sense that the feds have never actually prohibited or even restricted a drug for environmental reasons. If only everyone in charge thought more like the executive director of the European Environment Agency who, in 2010, publicly warned that the inherent benefits of modern medicines "could be offset if we ignore pharmaceuticals' environmental impacts."

It certainly doesn't help that Canada dumps a head-spinning 150 billion litres of raw sewage into our waterways every year, making municipal sewage the single largest source of water pollution in this country. Things were supposed to get better with new federal waste water standards created in 2010, but as municipalities upgrade their treatment systems, the only thing they're being told to minimize is bacteria and pathogens such as *E. coli*, not man-made chemicals like antibiotics and cholesterol medication. Furthermore, some municipalities have been given a knee-slapper of a 30-year deadline to get their upgrades done. And where laws already exist to protect our water supply, we're plain ignoring them. Take B.C., for instance, where half of residents admitted to flushing or tossing their unused meds, even though there's a ban on doing so in Metro Vancouver. Combine our cross-country lavatory shame with the aquatic pollution that streams into the water system from heavily medicated farm animals as well as our favourite furry friends (who often get the same drugs as humans) and, Houston, we've got a problem.

Out our taps: Now, for those of you whose minds are two steps ahead and who are planning to run screaming from tap water right into the hands of the bottled water companies, stop right there and put the bottle down. Bottled water is not, I repeat *not*, a solution. Testing by Environmental Working Group, Natural Resources Defense Council and others has found several contaminants in bottled water samples, including traces of Tylenol, degreasing chemicals, fertilizer and ammonia pollution (runoff from farms), as well as carcinogenic by-products of chlorination, not to mention plastic leachers including antimony (a heavy metal), acetaldehyde and toluene. And don't forget that 1.5 million barrels of planet-wrecking oil go into making plastic water bottles every year. So, if you're concerned about pollutants in your water, filter your tap to improve its purity. Government testing at the municipal level is finding that basic activated-carbon filters are surprisingly good at removing most drugs as well as other contaminants. By extension, even a simple activated-carbon pitcher or sink-mounted filter can be a decent, accessible choice. Brita's own internal tests show a

96.5% reduction in five key drugs, including pain relievers, hormones and seizure meds, though at this point there is no formal third-party certification available for these drug reduction claims. (FYI, Brita filters are now recyclable again in Canada: see filterforgood.ca.) Reverse osmosis systems are famous for filtering out the most pollutants, but these are *mucho dolares* and most are super wasteful, trashing several litres of water for every litre you swallow. Though Watts Zero Waste Reverse Osmosis System does claim to be the first 100% efficient system on the market today (last checked, Costco carried these; wattspremier.com).

But a filter ain't going to solve the bigger problem. As individuals, we have to start questioning whether we really need to jump full speed ahead with a prescription that will end up polluting the environment around us.

Minimize Pharmaceutical Pollution: How do we do that?
- Never flush expired or unwanted medication down the toilet or chuck it in the trash (it might leach into groundwater from landfill). Look for a drop box at your local pharmacy, or snoop around on medicationsreturn.ca for info on what to do with them in your province, or ask your pharmacist.
- Harass your provincial politicians to bring in mandatory medication recycling, and talk to your MP about putting the green squeeze on Big Pharma: we need Health Canada and Environment Canada to assess the full life cycle impact of both old and new drugs. Doing more chronic toxicity testing would be a start. We also need to copy European legislation that limits antibiotic use in farm animals to those that are sick. Right now, Canadian animals can be fed a steady stream of low levels of antibiotics to boost their size and speed up their growth. That's got to change.
- Encourage farmers to reduce their antibiotics use by requesting and buying meat that's antibiotic free and hormone free.
- Use natural supplements and alternatives whenever possible — making sure they're sustainable too, of course! And wouldn't you know it, that's what the next few chapters are all about.

The following section covers the most widely used pharmaceuticals
that have been found contaminating Canada's waterways, as well as
some natural, sustainable alternatives that are gentler on the earth.
For specifics on natural health remedies, see chapter 8.

ANTIBIOTICS

It all started with a little stray mould. When a Scottish researcher
observed that bacteria wasn't growing near certain spores, he was well
on his way to discovering the powers of penicillin and kicking off an
era of antibiotics in medicine. Along the way, a litany of infections
have been cured and countless lives have been saved. But have we
taken our love of antibiotics too far?

Overuse of Antibiotics: Despite all its miracle working, this is one
family of drugs that we take way, way too much of, and to be honest with
you, our fixation with antibiotics is putting all of us in peril. I hate to be
all dramatic about this, but I'm not the one issuing the warning call: the
World Health Organization says antibiotic misuse "represents a crisis
which threatens to rob the world of opportunities to treat or cure many
infectious diseases." Here in Canada, 24 million prescriptions were filled
for anti-infectives in 2009, and antibiotic misuse and antibiotic-resistant
bacteria have reached such alarming levels that the Canadian Medical
Association and the College of Family Physicians of Canada have
publicly pleaded with the feds to get a grip. How does all this damage
arise from one little bottle of infection fighters? Well, if you don't finish
your prescribed course of antibiotics (and fully kill the bugs that made
you ill to begin with), if you've taken repeated courses of the stuff, or if a
wrong diagnosis gets you swallowing antibiotics unnecessarily, bacteria
can mutate and become antibiotic resistant. (Eating doped-up meat
tainted with antibiotic-resistant bacteria or picking up antibiotic-resistant
bacteria from a hospital are other ways of becoming closely acquainted
with superbugs.)

Meanwhile, back in the wild, the U.S. Geological Survey found
antibiotic-resistant bacteria in every river they tested in 1999, and in

2010 researchers found superbugs, a.k.a. antibiotic-resistant bacteria, in seven species of shark and redfish swimming off American waters, as well as in wild Arctic birds, rats and others. Combine all the antibiotics we eliminate with all the antibiotics excreted by factory-farmed animals and maybe it's no surprise that a University of Michigan scientist found antibiotic-resistant bacteria in Toronto's tap water. Yep, you heard me. Sure, the researcher added that the water is still safe to drink, but is anyone else starting to sweat?

Now, as I said, there are plenty of cases where antibiotics are necessary, but doctors are now admitting there are far too many times when they're not. If you've got a virus—like, say, a chest cold or flu—don't go begging your overworked health care provider for antibiotics; they won't help you. Antibiotics are antibacterial, not antiviral. Research has found that two rounds of antibiotics six months apart results in a depletion of healthy, immune-buttressing bacteria that's been shown to linger for months. The potential long-term impact of stripping our healthy balance of flora (good bacteria) is only starting to come into focus. A 2009 UBC study of 12,000 children found that the more antibiotics were taken by infants under the age of one, the higher were their rates of asthma later in life.

These days, many physicians will recommend letting certain infections run their course if you're a young and healthy adult. So what

DON'T ASK, DON'T GET

You or your little one are feeling just awful, so you run to your doctor for help. Logical move. Whatever you do, don't be pushy and ask for antibiotics; let your doc decide on whether or not they're necessary. One study published in *Pediatrics* showed that pediatricians prescribed antibiotics 62% of the time if they thought parents expected them, but only 7% of the time if they didn't feel pressured. Similar results were found for adult patients who really didn't need the drugs to begin with the vast majority of the time. Give the pros some breathing room to judge for themselves.

can you take if you've got an ailment that really doesn't need behind-the-counter meds? Here are a few more sustainable options for giving your body a natural antibacterial boost when prescriptions aren't called for.

ALTERNATIVES TO ANTIBIOTICS

If your practitioner suggests you try to fight off a nasty bug without antibiotics, what natural, sustainable arsenal should you keep in your holster? It depends on what's ailing you, of course. This section gives a list of some common general natural antibacterials available and then outlines a few suggestions for specific ailments. Keep in mind that antibiotics are prescribed for a number of reasons, many of them essential to personal and public health, others not so much. **Be sure to consult a health practitioner about a recommended course of action before you start self-medicating.**

General Natural Antibiotics: Did you know you've got natural antibiotics hiding in your pantry? Yep, basic **garlic** doesn't just kill your breath, it also has excellent natural antibacterial powers, thanks in large part to the active ingredient allicin that is released when you crush it. Countless studies, including one published by the biochem department of the Weizmann Institute of Science in *Microbes and Infection*, attest not only to garlic's antibacterial properties against all sorts of bacteria, including drug-resistant strains of *E. coli*, but also to its surprising antiviral, antiparasitic and antifungal powers. But sautéing it with your dinner won't cut it (though it is tasty); to get the full power of garlic, you need to crush or chop it, and then let it sit for five minutes before eating it raw (the natural enzymes present in garlic need time after crushing to convert the alliin to allicin). If you opt for garlic pills, keep in mind that when vitamin watchdog ConsumerLab.com did testing, a full 7 of 14 products failed for having less allicin than claimed. On average, most allicin-claiming garlic pills contained about the same amount you'd find in one small clove of garlic (4,000 to 12,000 mcg of allicin, according to ConsumerLab). If you can eat garlic raw, you'll often get more for your money and save on packaging. Look for the organic kind while you're at it (conventional imports are often irradiated to prevent sprouting, bleached and commonly sprayed with ozone-depleting methyl bromide if it's imported from some developing countries). By the way, aged garlic extract doesn't contain allicin but does have beneficial S-allyl-L-cysteine, which the allicin in raw garlic would naturally create in your gut. S-allyl-L-cysteine is considered another bioactive antibacterial component of garlic that helps make it so beneficial.

Goldenseal is a top-gun antibiotic commonly prescribed by herbalists and naturopaths thanks to the active ingredient berberine. Make sure to only get the certified-organic kind, though, since wild goldenseal is on the Species at Risk list (see page 233). As with all herbs, before taking it, you should talk to your health provider if you have any pre-existing conditions or are on any medication. Otherwise, it's considered safe for short-term use only and naturopaths advise you not to take it for more than 10 days before taking a break for five days. **Olive leaf** is also a great natural antibacterial with bonus antifungal and antiviral properties. This one comes with no green clauses, so you don't have to worry about its environmental sustainability while you're on the mend. **Bee propolis** (or beehive glue) is another of nature's great antibacterials that happens to be antifungal as well. Certain strains are also antiviral, but vegans aren't going to like the idea of exploiting bee labour (the bees aren't harmed, but the propolis is extracted from grilles placed in hives). **Oregano oil** is an up-and-coming antimicrobial (meaning it's anti-bacterial, antiviral, antifungal and antiparasitic). For more details on picking the right oregano oil for potency and sustainability, see page 232.

Here are some common infections that are often over-treated with antibiotics, as well as some routine treatment alternatives.

Respiratory Infections: First of all, can I just say that North Americans spend over $1.1 billion annually on "unnecessary" adult upper-respiratory antibiotic prescriptions alone, according to the Archives of Internal Medicine. Why "unnecessary"? Well, for one, upper respiratory tract infections (URIs) are largely viral and there-fore don't respond to antibiotics (case in point: over 90% of acute bronchitis cases are viral, not bacterial), and yet the U.S. Centers for Disease Control says over half of all antibiotics doled out by office-based doctors go to treat URIs. These days, most doctors are supposed to encourage you to wait it out a bit unless you've got other chronic medical conditions (such as an underlying lung disease or diabetes), sharp chest pain, a high or prolonged fever or if you're coughing blood—that kind of thing (then contact your health practitioner pronto). If you've just got a rattling, wheezy, phlegm-heavy cough combined with mild aches and/or a low-grade fever, you've probably got acute bronchitis (less dramatically known as a chest cold), so it's time to bring in some big-time natural support. Consult a holistic practitioner for advice on getting your immune system humming again, but in the meantime, here's a taste of some naturopath-favoured, eco-friendly suggestions:

- **Pump up on probiotics.** Several studies, including one published in *Pediatrics*, the official journal of the American Academy of Pediatrics, have found that probiotics reduce the incidence and duration of respiratory tract infections. Probiotics are best used preventatively throughout the cold and flu season to be effective. If you do end up on antibiotics don't forget your probiotics to help prevent their complications, such as antibiotic-related diarrhea and yeast infections. See page 253 for more on picking probiotiocs that aren't a waste of packaging and money.

- **Dose up on vitamin D.** Studies have shown that a deficiency in this vitamin is linked to upper respiratory tract infections.

- **Get a humidifier and do some DIY steam therapy** (with a few eucalyptus drops thrown in). It'll help loosen and expel that junk in your chest.

- **Sip on lots of tea.** The kind made of marshmallow root and/or certified-organic slippery elm, such as **Organic Traditions** powder or **Traditional Medicinals Organic Throat Coat** tea, which contains both. (Note: wild sources of slippery elm are

threatened and should be avoided at all costs; see page 233.)
Both are extremely soothing on the throat and can help bring
up mucus. Marshmallow root is also anti-inflammatory and
antimicrobial.

- If you suffer from chronic bronchitis, look into **N-acetylcysteine**
(**NAC**). It's a potent antioxidant and expectorant that thins
mucus. Studies found it beneficial for chronic bronchitis
patients who took it daily over the course of the winter, and
doing so should also reduce your chances of getting a bad flu.

Sinus Infections: My good friend was slogging through sinus
infection after sinus infection, year after year, until she started flushing
saline water up her nose. Yep, a **neti pot** was the answer, and since a
one-person study isn't much proof, let me assure you that ear, nose and
throat surgeons and specialists are recommending neti pots to their
patients too, since studies are finding they help wash away congestion,
pressure and pain while flushing out bacteria and allergens. This little
Aladdin-shaped pot should really be your main tool for keeping
sinusitis in check. Mix a quarter teaspoon of quality sea salt in warm
water and take the plunge. If you're prone to sinus infections, docs
will tell you this is best started at the first sign of every cold. You'll be
asking yourself why you didn't try it earlier. Steam is also your friend.

Natural Cold and Flu Remedies: Supplements taken within
48 hours of your symptoms first appearing will have the greatest
impact on shortening your cold or flu. So what are some effective,
as well as sustainable, natural options? Not all do the job promised.

- **Get the right echinacea?** Admittedly, super-popular echinacea
has had pretty mixed results in hundreds of studies and also
comes with a mixed environmental record. Many studies,
including a big headline-making one published in 2010, have
shown that echinacea has little to no effect. Still, the *Lancet*, one
of the world's best-known medical journals, did a meta-analysis of
14 studies and found that echinacea decreased your odds of getting

WHAT'S IN YOUR COLD AND FLU REMEMDIES?

Uh-oh. That sneezy, achy feeling is creeping up on you. No matter how tired you feel, this is the precise moment you need to throw the blanket aside, get up off that couch and run to the health store to stock up on remedies. Whatever you do, don't send your mate off for typical drugstore junk. Cold and flu syrups don't cure anything; they just sugar-coat your symptoms with buzzy, side effect–heavy drugs (which is precisely why Health Canada says children under six shouldn't be taking them and also why the American College of Chest Physicians has advised the public against wasting their money on cough medicines). Besides the usual drowsiness they induce, cold and flu meds can trigger nervousness, insomnia, dizziness, even tremors. As if you need any of that when you're already rundown. Plus, you're loading up on some pretty unnecessary chemical fillers. Do you want to be swallowing petrochemical antifreeze ingredient propylene glycol (see Mean 15, page 8, and Oil Spill in the Bathroom, page 24, for more on petrochemicals) and a whack of artificial dyes like the D&C Yellow no. 10 aluminum lake in Benylin? Sure, Buckley's nasty cough suppressant gets some of its power from natural ingredients such as oil of pine needles, camphor and Canadian balsam, but what the hell are butylparabens doing in there? They're banned from children's products in Denmark, and the presence of that particular paraben in the urine of men tested at fertility clinics has been linked to DNA damage in sperm cells. *So* not worth that godawful taste. Forget the whole scene and do a herbal-supplement run ASAP.

a common cold by 58% and ended colds 1.4 days earlier. So what's the deal? It all depends on what type of echinacea you use. Never get dried echinacea in capsules, especially the leaf; it's totally useless. Herbalists will tell you to make sure you get a tincture of organic echinacea root and down a teaspoon every hour if you want to see results. By the way, buying organic echinacea guarantees it wasn't taken from the wild, where the herb is threatened. (See page 233 for more info on picking sustainable herbal medicines.)

- **Start taking zinc, ASAP:** A 2011 meta-analysis of 15 zinc trials concluded that sucking on zinc lozenges or swallowing zinc syrup within 24 hours of the onset of your cold symptoms will reduce the duration and severity of the common cold in otherwise healthy people. Taken for at least five months, "it reduces cold incidence, school absenteeism and prescription of antibiotics in children." For short-term relief, pop a lozenge every two hours, but after a week, cap daily doses at 40 mg in adults, 7 mg for children ages 1 to 3, 12 mg for those 4 to 8, and 23 mg for those 9 to 13, says ConsumerLab.com. Avoid zinc nasal gels, which can lead to loss of smelling abilities. Bizarre, I know.
- **Swallow a spoonful of elderberry:** This awesome cold and flu remedy has gotten popular ever since TV physician Dr. Oz plugged its antiviral and immune-boosting properties. Double-blind, placebo-controlled studies found that flu sufferers who swallowed a tablespoon (15 mL) of elderberry extract four times a day (twice a day for kids) for five days saw symptom relief after three or four days, a whole four days earlier than placebo takers. FYI, this one's pricey since it takes 1,000 elderberries to make 120 mL (1/2 cup). You can score adults' and kids' versions of **Dr. Dunner's Sambu/SambuGuard** as well as **Sambucol**. Note: long-time Nestlé boycotters (see infactcanada.ca/Nestle_Boycott.htm) aren't going to like that Dr. Dunner has been owned by Nestlé since the '60s.
- **Pop probiotics all season:** Kids who take a good combo of **probiotics** twice daily for six months experience 50% fewer cold and flu symptoms (73% fewer fevers, 59% fewer runny noses and a 62% drop in coughing), according to a study published in *Pediatrics*. Similar results have been shown for adults, so make sure your whole household is taking these. FYI, probiotics have no sustainability issues for you to worry about, but there are some quality concerns. See page 253 for info.
- **Flush your sinuses:** The Mayo Clinic recommends irrigating with a neti pot as a safe, inexpensive way to relieve congestion—and all you need is a pot and salt water. One study found that cold

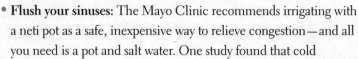

sufferers who do it are more likely to go back to work sooner and less likely to reach for antibiotics or drugstore meds since it flushes away infectious gunk. Works on kids too (and with luck, they'll get a kick out of pouring water up their nose). For the solution, skip store-bought, packaged saline solutions and just dissolve a pinch of non-iodized sea salt into 1 cup (250 mL) of warm water.

- **Take some C:** Taking a little **vitamin C** hasn't proven to do much, though 2,000 mg a day has been shown to shorten a cold by 24 to 36 hours. One study published in the *Journal of Manipulative and Physiological Therapeutics*, where participants popped 1,000 mg every hour for the first six hours of coming down with symptoms and then 1,000 mg three times daily until symptoms were gone, showed promising results for slashing cold and flu symptoms by 85% compared to those on pain relievers and decongestants. Orthomolecular medicine (a form of complementary medicine sometimes referred to as megavitamin therapy) recommends you take several thousand milligrams of time-released vitamin C, but talk to a practitioner first. For more on synthetic versus natural sources of vitamin C, see page 236.
- **Pop an allicin-rich garlic pill daily all winter long;** it's been proven to reduce your chances of catching a cold in the first place. Don't be shy about cooking with lots of garlic, too—but eat it raw! See General Natural Antibacterials on page 179 for more info.
- **Soothe with honey:** Several studies on kids have found that honey before bed has a curing impact on cough frequency, cough severity and sleep quality of everyone in the house—surprisingly, more than cough-repressing drugs such as dextromethorphan (DM) and diphenhydramine. Well, maybe it's not so surprising after all, considering the American College of Chest Physicians now officially advises against over-the-counter cough medicines, saying they haven't been proven to work. By the way, all honey will help, but **dark honey** is most beneficial. Unpasteurized honey should only be given to kids older than one year.

SAFE TRAVELS: STAYING HEALTHY WHILE ON THE ROAD

by Nick Vasil, Herbalist and Holistic Nutritionist

Are you planning on travelling to the tropics? You can pack in peace knowing that there are plenty of alternative, effective and safe ways to protect yourself from travel diseases.

Pre-trip preparation is key. How well you resist disease during your travels depends a lot on how healthy your immune system is before you leave. You'll need to start preparing early with a healthy diet, exercise, nutritional supplements, herbs and a good detox. A naturopath can help you assess your status and tailor a program to meet your specific needs for travel. Part of your prepping should include a good daily multivitamin and mineral supplement with antioxidants. Start using it two months before leaving and continue taking it while away, especially when your diet is unbalanced or deficient in any way. Also, two to three months before you leave, start taking a herbal immune tonic. This could include a combination of herbs such as **astragalus**, **reishi** and North American ginseng or Siberian **ginseng** (see page 233 for more on avoiding wild American ginseng), all of which are immune-balancing adaptogens (relatively slow acting but deeply tonifying, strengthening your body's resistance to disease). Then, throughout the trip, either continue the tonic or use an immune stimulant such as a tincture of **echinacea root**, ten days on, ten days off (see page 182 for more on picking the right echinacea). Immune stimulants produce a rapid but short-term boost in immune function.

Once on the road, the first rule of prevention is precaution: as much as possible, avoid coming into contact with the causes of disease. Contaminated water and food are the source of many travel woes. Typhoid, cholera, hepatitis A, giardia, dysentery and simple diarrhea (as well as *E. coli* and salmonella) are all transmitted through food and water. The risk of infection and the need for caution are greatest where sanitation is primitive, be it at a roadside food stand or in a rural village. But in all cases, avoid undercooked meat and seafood (or go vegetarian on the road) as well as raw, unwashed fruits and vegetables and tap water. And wash those hands, especially before eating or preparing food.

No one's perfect—especially when travelling in the developing world. Whether you're eating on the run, trying out a new restaurant (when will you not be?) or dying for a drink of water, there will be times when, despite your best intentions, some bacteria or amoebic parasites will get into your gut. You can increase your resistance to these by strengthening your friendly intestinal bacteria before you leave home and taking antimicrobials daily while travelling. So, a month before leaving, repopulate those hard-working protective bacteria by taking a good **probiotic** daily. Then, while you are travelling, take a broad-spectrum antimicrobial (something that kills micro-organisms such as bacteria and viruses) twice daily to eliminate any bad guys that are left before they grow out of control. **Oregano oil** is a proven killer of *E. coli,* salmonella and many other food-borne micro-organisms, as well as some amoebic parasites (see page 232 for info on making sure you're picking the right oil). Oregano oil also excels against fungi that thrive in the hot and humid tropics. For athlete's foot and other fungal infections, it can be diluted and applied topically. As effective as it is, however, using oregano oil does not give you carte blanche to drink out of puddles.

A word of caution: if diarrhea is accompanied by blood and mucus or by a fever, or if it is severe and persists for more than a few days and does not respond to treatment, seek medical care.

Although rarely included in travel health guides, holistic or allopathic, the last preventative is no less important: a positive attitude. Your mind, emotions and body are one multi-dimensional system, and any one can affect the others. Negative emotions such as anger and worry, research has shown, can depress the immune system, while positive states such as love, compassion and gratitude can enhance it. It's all in your perspective: remember, this is a vacation, not a race. The best place to be is where you are. Travel sometimes means expecting the unexpected: delays, detours, unfamiliar surroundings, strange languages and customs. But it's all part of the journey. Who knows what wonderful place the unexpected might lead you if you let it? As Carolyn Myss, author of *Anatomy of the Spirit*, says, "Interpret unscheduled events as divine guidance."

Bon voyage!

IS COLD-FX IN THE CLEAR?

COLD-FX has been shown to reduce the frequency, severity and duration of colds, and is made with poly-furanosyl-pyranosyl-saccharides (say that three times quickly), which, though it sounds terrible, is extracted from Canadian-cultivated Panax ginseng (thankfully, since the wild stuff is endangered). It's just a shame the ginseng isn't organic, and vegetarians won't be thrilled that the gelcaps are beef and pork gelatin based.

Ear Infections: Nothing quite like the feeling of a drill in your eardrum. Ear infections are particularly violating at any age, but kids aren't shy about screaming their heads off if they get one. Considering that many ear infections are viral, not bacterial, taking rounds of antibiotics when they've been proven to increase the risk of childhood asthma should really be avoided. Truth is, doctors will tell you that ear infections should really go away on their own after two to three days, but docs will often suggest ear drops to help with the pain (that being said, if your child is under two years old or the pain is severe you should see your doctor right away). Turns out a 2003 study published in *Pediatrics* found that patients who were given a natural herbal ear oil alone made with garlic, calendula, mullein and St. John's wort in an olive oil base faired relatively better than patients who were given ear drops combined with amoxicillin, though really all patients got better around the same time.

- As luck would have it, Quebec-based **St. Francis Herb Farm's Ear Oil** happens to contain a certified-organic blend of all those ingredients (especially fantastic because you wouldn't want wild St. John's wort for sustainability reasons; see page 233).
- Even plain warm oil will offer some symptomatic relief. Naturopaths recommend a couple of drops of warm garlic oil in the ear canal every four waking hours. (Slowly warm one large bulb of garlic, minced, with a little olive oil for an hour on the stovetop, ensuring it's cool enough that it won't scald the ear canal.

Use a dropper, and plug up the ear opening with a cotton ball for half an hour afterwards.) Keep oil in a sterilized bottle in the fridge when not in use but best to make a fresh batch daily.

- If your little one is getting a lot of ear infections, holistic practitioners and physicians specializing in integrative medicine will often advise you to try taking your child off cow-based dairy products.
- Second-hand smoke is a major trigger of ear infections in little ones. One more reason why adults shouldn't smoke inside the house or with their kids in the car.

Eye Infections: Not to brag, but I'm sort of the queen of pink eye. Yep, it's a title I earned back when I had a three-month-long recurring bout of the eye infection while I was backbacking across Europe in college. I didn't take my eye drops properly and the little buggers became resistant to antibiotic drops. I was, literally, crying a river of puss in Spain. Don't do what I did. Take your drops consistently, as recommended. And you don't need to resort to antibiotic drops, either.

Herbalists and naturopaths will advise you to try a herbal eye bath instead of drops. You can find **goldenseal** eye baths prepackaged at health stores, though in order to ensure the goldenseal's not taken from the wild where it's threatened, look for certified-organic sources (see page 180 for more on goldenseal). **Ophthacare** drops, made with a variety of antimicrobial and anti-inflammatory herbs, performed well in several studies, including one published in the journal *Phytotherapy Research*. Oh, and ladies, toss your mascara and concealer pronto and disinfect eyeliner, makeup brushes, etc., with rubbing alcohol. Avoid using eye makeup entirely until the infection clears up. That's how I kept getting re-infected—I was too cheap to buy new makeup. By the way, if you're looking for recommendations on new natural makeup, see pages 97–100.

Urinary Tract Infections: UTIs are a total PIA (that's pain in the ass). The burning, the incessant peeing, never getting relief—it's

189

enough to drive you batty. I know from experience that docs are quick to throw anyone with a UTI on antibiotics, which aren't doing your body or anyone downstream any good. From my legion of friends who suffer chronic UTIs I can tell you that drinking cranberry will only work if you have a mild case, and while sugary cranberry cocktails still worked well enough in studies, it's best if the juice is totally sugar free (not those cran cocktails you see in regular grocery stores) and you drink gallons of it. Easier just to get yourself some high-quality **cranberry extract pills** (unsweetened cranberry juice is seriously sour). But after years of experimentation, both my posse and trusted naturopaths will tell you that **D-Mannose** is the single most effective treatment you can buy (you'll find it at health stores). It's a naturally occurring simple sugar that prevents bacteria from binding to your bladder wall better than anything and is worth the high price tag. If you get kidney pains or see blood in your urine, though, run, don't walk, to your doctor. You're dealing with serious shit.

If you have ongoing and persistent symptoms of a bladder infection and your doc keeps giving you antibiotics but never finds any sign of infection when he/she tests your urine, you could possibly have a condition called interstitial cystitis. It's basically a chronic inflammation of the bladder lining. I endured round after frustrating round of ineffective, body-depleting antibiotics in 2001 for seemingly incurable bladder infections before I was finally diagnosed with the condition. IC is tough and invasive to test for, but can often be controlled with diet. When mine flares up, I avoid spicy and acidic foods as well as alcohol (bummer, I know) and I pop anti-inflammatory quercetin, which helps manage it, as does the amino acid L-Arginine and methylsulfonyl-methane (MSM). IC-aiding Cysto Protek contains shark oil so build your own replica combo by taking glucosamine, chondroitin, quercetin, sodium hyalouromate and rutin. It's a complicated condition, so look for support from a pro practitioner and info at ic-network.com.

Yeast Infection: This is one infection we tend not to chit-chat about around the water cooler. So when TV ads reach out to us

WHAT DRUGS AND SUPPLEMENTS GO BACK TO THE PHARMACIES?

I'm just going to assume that I don't have to remind you it's a terrible idea to dump old prescriptions down the toilet or into your garbage. Drugs can leach out from landfills, contaminating groundwater, and if you flush drugs they'll go straight to the fishies and back up our taps (see page 173). Still, old habits die hard, and even in a province like B.C., where pharmacies have been taking back unused and expired meds since 1997 and where Vancouver has an outright ban on dumping or flushing your meds, 50% of residents are still flushing and dumping. And the other 50% are likely still trashing stuff like cough remedies, antifungal creams and vitamins when they're expired. I myself had no idea I was supposed to take expired supplements back, but it turns out even those are supposed to go. All prescription and over-the-counter conventional and natural health meds are on the take-back list at **medicationsreturn.ca**. What exactly does that include?

- Orally ingested meds such as cough and cold remedies and stomach remedies.
- Topical antifungal and antibiotic creams.
- Natural health products, including vitamins and minerals.
- Anything obtained by prescription and all non-prescription meds.

about vaginal itching, burning and discharge, we're more susceptible to taking their advice without question. Let me tell you, ladies, your woes won't go away with yet another trip to the drugstore. All you're doing is masking your problems with a squeeze of petroleum-based fillers (mineral oil, white petrolatum) and antifungal chemicals (plus, creams with propylene glycol in them can actually trigger intense burning in some women). If Monistat moments are frequent in your life, it's time to overhaul your diet, sister.

First and foremost, stop feeding the yeasts: cut out sugar, including hidden sugars in things such as ketchup, flavoured soy milk and cereal. Dump yeasty baked goods and refined starches as well as booze; they all break down into sugars in your body. And do it all for at least three months. I'm not kidding. If you're serious about getting rid of this curse, you'll have to do the time. Stock up on quality probiotics (see page 253 for recommendations) to reboot your good bacteria. It works well when used internally, too, as a suppository with products like **Purfem** (purfem.com). Also pump up on antifungal herbs such as **olive leaf extract** and **oregano oil** (see page 232 for sustainable picks) three times a day (just don't take them at the same time as your probiotics, since these antimicrobial herbs could kill them). By the way, holistic practitioners will often suggest pau d'arco to treat candida infections, but you should know that pau d'arco is taken from the inner bark of now-endangered *Tabebuia* trees in South America (see page 232 for more info). It's hard to guarantee a sustainable source, so it's probably safest to just avoid pau d'arco altogether. If **goldenseal** is prescribed, make sure to only source it organically, for similar reasons (see page 232). **Barberry** (as long it's not endangered American barberry and, like goldenseal, you don't take it for longer than your naturopath suggests) should be a safe choice for combating yeast (and as a bonus, studies have found it may also help lower blood pressure in those with high blood pressure). If you're ready for a more thorough detoxing, talk to a naturopath about going on the candida diet—which basically means avoiding everything you usually eat except vegetables, protein and specific grains such as brown rice, millet, quinoa and buckwheat. Or pick up *Complete Candida Yeast Guidebook: Everything You Need to Know About Prevention, Treatment and Diet*. It's important to remember that if your infection keeps coming back or there's a funky odour and/or grey/green discharge, you may have bacterial vaginitis that basic yeast treatments just won't cure. See your practitioner. Note that **boric acid suppositories** work well on both yeast and bacterial vaginitis (you can score these from independent compounding pharmacists like smithspharmacy.com).

Acne: I was barely a teen when a dermatologist took one look at my face and put me on antibiotics. I had the honour of being his

youngest acne patient on the antibiotic tetracycline (fabulous). Not

IS THAT PETROL IN YOUR LAXATIVE?

Having trouble with the, um, back end of the human digestive cycle, are you? If you (or your child) regularly gets plugged up you might have already tried a popular constipation remedy made from an offshoot of motor fuel. Yep, mineral oil is a by-product of manufacturing gasoline for your car or bus ride. I could make all kinds of crass jokes about engine oils keeping your system running smoothly, but I'll refrain. I'm classy that way. Let me just tell you that not only is mineral oil environmentally questionable, but long-term use also causes a deficiency of vitamins A, D, E and K since it gets in the way of your body's absorption of nutrients. Not good if you're pregnant. Even old-fashioned castor oil isn't a good idea long term because it can cause chronic constipation.

Instead, down loads and loads of organic **prune or fig juice** as well as good **probiotics** (see page 253 for more on probiotics). If you don't get enough fruits, veggies and whole grains, adding fibre like, say, psyllium husks is helpful, but the plant found in many over-the-counter laxatives such as Metamucil is often mixed with a lot of artificial sweeteners, colours, flavours and other junk. Organic **triphala** is a great Indian herbal alternative. Herbal laxatives such as cascara and senna will get you moving, but these can be habit forming so you don't want to use them all the time. An essential mineral to get your colon running is **magnesium**, which most of us are seriously deficient in. Taking a daily dose of this stuff should help you avoid having to use laxatives at all. For a quick laxative fix, magnesium oxide will do, but to improve bowel function take chelated or amino acid–bound magnesium on a daily basis. You'll sleep better and get rid of painful leg cramps, too. Get a good fix by loading up on magnesium-rich foods like pumpkin seeds, almonds, oat bran, spinach and chocolate (make sure it's fair-trade organic, of course). Avoid starchy magnesium binders like bread products. As a general mantra, eat more fibre-rich foods and drink lots more water. If you're chronically constipated, you should rethink your dairy intake, too, since it bungs you up.

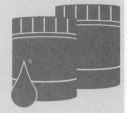

good for the long-term health of the body, let me tell you. Studies have found that taking the stuff leads to drug-resistant zits, which develop in up to 50% of those taking antibiotics, as well as chronic yeast infections, candidal superinfections, *C. difficile* diarrhea and worse. Side effects get riskier the more potent the treatment. In the United States, women deciding to take isotretinoin, also known by its

IS GRAPEFRUIT SEED EXTRACT A SCAM?

As a wide-eyed 17-year-old backpacking through South America, the only thing I was sure of was my little squeeze bottle of grapefruit seed extract. The miracle-working antibacterial and antifungal was supposed to kill everything from athlete's foot to stomach bugs, and I believed it saved me from serious intestinal upset. When rumours later swirled about GSE being a fake, I looked the other way; surely regulators would stop allowing it if it were made with antibacterial chemicals that weren't declared on the label, as was suggested.

Well, I finally did my own digging to find out if GSE really has triclosan or some other synthetic antimicrobial. And yep, two studies in the '90s confirmed the presence of the eco-pollutant triclosan in some brands, but NutriBiotic, the biggest GSE brand on the market, says it tests each batch to confirm it's triclosan free. Good news, except for the fact that it says nothing about testing to ensure it's free of benzethonium chloride, a synthetic disinfectant that the USDA says is what gives GSE products their real antimicrobial power. NutriBiotic argues it's all a big mix-up, the result of "false positives." So I tracked down Gary Takeoka, the lead USDA scientist who did the testing in 2001 and again in 2005. He confirms that they did indeed test NutriBiotic and other GSEs, and says the mix-up claims are totally false. "They're putting a synthetic antimicrobial in the product." He and his team found, as other researchers have, that citrus seeds have no inherent antimicrobial power. Will benzethonium chloride hurt you? Not likely in the quantities taken, says Takeoka, but it's still upsetting to long-time users like me who thought they were relying on nature to fight their battles. Will you buy GSE again? I know I won't.

former brand name Accutane, have to sign a waiver acknowledging they understand all the risks, and women have to pledge to not get pregnant since birth defect risks are so high. Several Accutane users who developed bowel diseases such as Crohn's and colitis after taking the drug have sued for millions and won.

Want to try a more harmonious approach to acne? For one, cut down on your dairy intake, particularly cow's milk. Several studies (including one with 47,000 participants) found that the natural growth hormones in milk actually stimulate acne. Skim milk was, for some reason, the worst. A 2010 study published in the journal *Clinics in Dermatology* added that foods high in sugar, including carbs high on the glycemic index, boost production of the androgen hormones responsible for acne, so cut those out too. By the way, one tiny study pitted patients with nodulocystic acne who were on tetracycline against others on the Indian herb guggul twice daily and found the guggul worked as well or slightly better, knocking back lesions by 68%. This herb comes with a lot of contraindications, so talk to a health practitioner before taking it. As well, it's been pushed to the brink of extinction in the wild, so make sure you get a certified-organic source (see page 235). A naturopath will have you megadosing on vitamin A then tapering off after a few months, but again, you want to do this right, so consult a pro (though don't be shy about ODing on vitamin A–rich produce such as carrots, leafy greens, dried apricots and squash). If your acne is severe, you should most definitely book a visit to a holistic dermatologist, naturopath, herbalist or traditional Chinese medicine practitioner for more advice. For info on junk-free topical treatments, see Acne Washes and Gels on page 33.

PAIN RELIEVERS

I'm saddled with a major pain in the neck. Not a lazy husband or cranky boss, but literally a recurring pinched nerve in my neck that shoots blinding pain into my skull and down my back. I'll admit that when a flare-up gets particularly debilitating, I'll sometimes pop a handful of over-the-counter analgesics as a last resort. Then, once the pain subsides,

I put in a call for more meaningful help—especially since pretty much every over-the-counter painkiller, from acetaminophen to Aspirin, is floating in our waterways. And that's just the over-the-counter stuff. Then there are the residues of the over 25 million prescriptions for pain relievers filled in 2009 in this country (up 14% from the year before).

Over the years, I've done everything to get my chronic neck and back pain under control, and honestly, the biggest pain reliever I've tried comes in a needle, dozens of them actually, inserted by a skilled acupuncturist. Of course, every body hurts in different ways, so here's a bevy of treatment options for pain, from supplements and ointments to bodywork and deep breathing. Experiment and find the right combination for you. By the way, while Japan's Public Works Research Institute found that 95% of Aspirin and ibuprofen breaks down in most waste water treatment plants, the Ontario Ministry of Environment detected traces of, say, ibuprofen in waterways (21%) and drinking water (15%) at levels higher than other over-the-counter painkillers.

Supplements for General Pain Relief: Want to pop something for your pain but would rather avoid the litany of drugstore painkillers polluting waterways and our bodies?

- **White willow bark** is known as herbal aspirin and is commonly taken for headaches, muscle aches and cramps (as well as lowering fever). This stuff contains salicin, which was originally used to make aspirin (today's Aspirin is totally synthesized, surprise, surprise). I use it for my neck pain.
- Pineapple enzyme **bromelain** is good at tackling both acute and chronic pain, inflammation and swelling, and can even be taken pre-emptively before surgery or an athletic competition. But you have to take it on an empty stomach or else it functions more as a digestive aid and won't do much for your aches (those with ulcers will want to avoid it altogether).
- Put a teaspoon of **turmeric** in all your cooking. Suffice it to say, this wonder herb is way more than just a flavour enhancer and clothes stainer. The anticarcinogenic root can do fabulous work

CUTS LIKE A KNIFE: NATURAL FIRST AID

Got an owee? For basic cuts, scrapes or minor open wounds, you definitely do not need petroleum-filled drugstore antibiotic ointments such as Polysporin (even if they do have a couple of natural ingredients, including cocoa butter and olive oil) or smog-inducing first aid aerosols such as Lanacane (with nominal vitamin E and aloe). Skip the tissue-harming alcohol and largely ineffective hydrogen peroxide too. That's right, peroxide has been found not to decrease bacteria counts (too bad, I always liked the fizzing action). According to the National Institutes of Health, the best way to clean a wound is first to wash your hands and then to wash the wound itself with mild soap (all natural, of course) and water. Keep an ointment on hand made from herbs and extracts with proven antimicrobial powers, such as **calendula ointment** (a marigold extract that has no major environmental concerns; **Clef Des Champs** and **St. Francis Herb Farm** both have organic calendula salves), **bee propolis** (a.k.a. bee hive glue; see Natural Antibiotics, page 179) or certified-organic **goldenseal extract** to speed minor wound healing (see Herbs, page 229). One great remedy found to boost healing times is plain honey. All honey is antibacterial, though **manuka honey** has the most research behind it. You can apply naturally antiseptic manuka honey directly on wounds. Apply a natural latex bandage (the plastic ones are often made of dodgy PVC that's softened with hormone-disrupting phthalates). By the way, propolis is also excellent on herpes cold sores.

reducing inflammation throughout your body; it's also a mild blood thinner (as is bromelain) and is being tested for its impact on everything from Alzheimer's to HIV. Add black pepper to your turmeric in cooking and it'll bump up its bioavailability thanks to the piperine in there. To get more of turmeric's active ingredient, you can buy straight curcumin pills, though you'll need other ingredients in there to help with absorption like bromelain, piperine and lecithin or a natural turmeric extract called BCM-95. Combo-ing curcumin and **glucosamine sulphate** also ups the efficacy of both anti-inflammatory compounds.

- Feeling blue about your never-ending physical discomfort? The amino acid **SAM-e** (pronounced "sammy") is really useful for reducing both chronic back pain and depression (see page 207), offering a good one-two punch, but talk to a naturopath before you take it.

- If you complain of frequent muscle pain, chances are high you're deficient in magnesium. Ditto for omega-3 fatty acids and vitamin D. Talk to your doc or naturopath about dosages for your particular predicament. I had my mag levels tested for free by my doc and for a few bucks, you can get your vitamin D levels tested too. See page 246 for picking a sustainable fish oil.

- There are a ton of anti-inflammatory combos on the market. Each will be effective for various people. Many report relief with **Purica Recovery** formula (I've tried it myself and found it helped). Though you may want to skip it if you're prone to yeast infections since it does contain a type of sugar (fructooligosaccharides). Another well-revered anti-inflammatory is **New Chapter's Zyflamend**, which contains a whack of great inflammation-busting herbs including turmeric, Holy Basil, ginger, green tea polyphenols, barberry, oregano and more. For more options, see Arthritis, page 205.

Ointments for General Pain Relief: There's something gratifying about rubbing warming muscle-relaxing ointments on sore spots (especially if someone else is doing the rubbing). They won't cure your pain, but they do offer some relief on contact. Of course, for the most part you're rubbing petroleum refinery by-products into your skin, though the soothing benefits of many herbs are so obvious that even mainstream pain-relieving creams have sourced their active ingredients from nature, from the menthol in classic rubs to **arnica**, **capsaicin** and **calendula** in more recently developed drugstore creams. Cut the crap and get yourself an all-natural version from the health store. By the way, the go-to cream for aches and pains in my family has long been the combo cream **Traumeel** (traumeel.com).

This homeopathic cream/gel with calendula/arnica/**belladonna** is great at reducing bruising and swelling. A 2011 study published in the *International Journal of General Medicine* concluded: "Traumeel has shown comparable effectiveness to NSAIDs [non-steroidal anti-inflammatory drugs] in terms of reducing symptoms of inflammation, accelerating recovery, and improving mobility, with a favorable safety profile." I was, however, disappointed to realize that Traumeel's base is all petroleum (namely, paraffin and petrolatum). Come on, isn't it time for a little updating? I now buy other brands of arnica cream (see below).

- **Capsaicin** (cayenne pepper) cream desensitizes pain receptors called C-fibres and really helps to reduce nerve and muscle pain on contact. I warn you, though, to keep this cream away from your eyes and mucous membranes: it'll burn like hell.
- **Arnica** cream is a staple in many cupboards for slathering on bumps, bruises or pulls. This European herb has great anti-inflammatory properties and helps speed up healing. Remember to avoid wild arnica. Best to get a certified-organic arnica product by Canadians **St. Francis Herb Farm Oil** (stfrancisherbfarm.com) or **Clef des Champs** (clefdeschamps. net). For sustainability issues, see page 231.
- Look for combination creams. A good all-natural rub with a combo of beneficial herbs is **St. Francis Herb Farm's Free to Move** joint soothing cream. The MSM, white willow, boswellia, mullein and calendula in there should ease all kinds of aches and pains (stfrancisherbfarm.com). Too bad Bell's Joint Pain Pepper Cream contains formaldehyde-releasing preservative diazolidinyl urea since the combo of capsaicin, arnica, ginger, MSM and more works like a charm.
- If you're dealing with muscle cramps or restless leg syndrome, **magnesium gels** are fantastic.
- Go high-tech natural. How do high tech and natural go hand in hand? Well, **LivRelief Pain Relief Cream** does just that by offering the anti-inflammatory citris-derived flavinoid rutin via a

petrochemical-free base designed to speed up delivery of the anti-inflammatory (livrelief.com).

Bodywork for General Pain Relief: Downing a handful of pain-reducing supplements might get you moving without wincing, but for persistent or chronic problems you'll want to consider some deeper bodywork. Depending on your particular aches, you might find comfort with a chiropractor, physiotherapist, shiatsu therapist, osteopath or acupuncturist and beyond. I've tried all of the above and found relief with each of them, but in my specific case I get the most immediate and longest-lasting relief from acute pain flare-ups by combining acupuncture with ultrasound treatments. No, I'm not sending you to view a baby in utero. Ultrasound machines give off super-high-frequency sound waves, essentially vibrating the tissue beneath the skin's surface to help break up scar tissue, and this has been shown to speed up healing of cartilage and injured bones. You can ask either your physio, chiropractor or naturopath to use it on you, if they have an ultrasound machine on hand. I'd advise against getting an ultrasound machine for the home, though (too junky and not powerful enough).

Four million Canadians a year visit a chiropractor for all kinds of aches and pains, and chiropractic care has been shown to help with back and neck pain, migraines, knee/shoulder/elbow problems, whiplash and more. Keep in mind that the chiropractic approach sees the body as needing intermittent tune-ups ("adjustments") over the course of your life, so your chiro will likely put you on a "maintenance" schedule. What else can you try? Sign up for **restorative yoga**, which is more injury and limitation conscious than your standard yoga class (in which plenty of people push themselves too far and end up at a physio, chiro or massage therapist for help).

Up for something completely different? There's a whole world of realigning out there involving various schools of bodywork that teach you how to improve the way you use your body so you can shift away from habitual ways of walking, moving and sitting that are doing you no good. The **Alexander Technique** and the **Feldenkrais Method** are very

OUCH, PASS ME THE GINGER

So you're achy and thinking of popping a painkiller, are you? You may just want to reach for a slice of ginger instead. The gangly root has been wowing researchers in all sorts of pain studies in recent years, tackling everything from migraines (see page 202) to run-of-the-mill exercise pain (2010 *Journal of Pain*). Those workout fiends who popped two grams of ginger daily saw a 25% reduction in exercise-induced aches, and arthritic patients saw significant reductions in pain, swelling and morning stiffness. Just don't look for the wildcrafted kind in stores; wild ginger's classified as a Species at Risk in this country (see page 233).

similar in that they both work to undo pain-inciting body habits through movement retraining, but Alexander is more often one-on-one and focuses heavily on the alignment of the head, neck and spine. Feldenkrais is less about ideal form and more about ease of motion and minimizing the effort your body puts into motion. The **Mitzvah Technique** evolved from the Alexander Technique but focuses on the interplay between the pelvis and the spine as an upward-rippling wave (you gotta try it to get it). It's a pretty cool, easy-to-learn rehab and self-care discipline that's more fluid than Alexander. **Rolfing** is a form of rehabilitative bodywork that's more hands-on. It's been said that rolfing is sort of like having someone else do yoga for you. There's usually a lot of deep-tissue manipulation involved. Keep in mind that all of the above usually require a good 10 or more sessions to really sink in (up to a couple of dozen sessions, depending on the modality and your teacher's assessment of your problems), and then you're supposed to continue the discipline on your own clock to maintain your progress. All this to say, it can get pricey—but many find it worth the time and cost.

Meditation for General Pain Relief: If only Calgon really could take you away. If you suffer from intense chronic pain, figuring out ways to psychologically cope with flare-ups (whether they're hourly, daily or weekly) is essential, and meditation might be the very thing you need.

A study published in the journal *Pain* in 2010 revealed what people who meditate have known all along, that mindful meditation practitioners experience less pain by essentially shutting off areas of their brain through focus on the breath and beyond. Basically, the researchers concluded that since meditation trains the mind to be more present focused, meditators spend less time anticipating negative events, including pain. This helps explain why meditators with chronic pain are much less likely to suffer from the depression that often accompanies it (not to mention the spiritual interconnectedness–heightening aspect of meditation that can help ease depression and pain as well). Anyway, I think this finally answers the riddle, if a meditator gets a headache in the forest, will anyone feel it? Just keep in mind that depression is a common problem for people with chronic pain, so if you're suffering from more than just a bit of the blues, talk to your health care provider or seek help from a licensed mental health provider (see page 209 for more on depression).

Natural Alternatives for Headaches: You can ignore a lot of pain in life, but it's damn hard to look the other way when your skull is throbbing. Try swallowing some **white willow bark** to kill an existing headache. Migraine sufferers will want to stock up on preventative **feverfew** if they haven't tried it already, and it should be taken daily. Actually, combined with **ginger** sublingually (under the tongue), feverfew is effective as a first-line treatment in migraineurs who often get a mild headache prior to the onset of a bigger one, according to a 2011 study published in the journal *Headache* (**GelStat** makes a ginger/feverfew combo). Feverfew's actually become an invasive weed in many parts of the world, so you don't have to worry about it being overharvested from the wild. If feverfew doesn't work for you, check out herbal **butterbur**, which also gets the enviro green light. A study published in *Neurology* found that patients on 75 mg of the extract daily had 48% fewer migraines. Weekly **acupuncture** for three months also had a long-term impact on headache rates. Spinal manipulation by a chiropractor can be really helpful for those with chronic tension and

DOC, WILL THIS BRACELET TAKE MY PAIN AWAY?

There are a hell of a lot of gadgets out there that promise to bring you pain relief. I wish I could tell you they work. Magnetic and copper bracelets are a multi-billion-dollar industry heavily marketed to those with arthritis, fibromyalgia or other types of chronic pain. Both magnets and copper bracelets have a lot of theories behind them positing how they impart relief, but the Mayo Clinic found that $200 Q-Ray bracelets (made of "bio-metal") were just as effective as placebos. The U.S. Federal Trade Commission sued the bracelet maker in 2003, and the company has since removed pain-relief claims from its website. CBC's *Marketplace* had the Q-Ray tested at an electron microscopy lab and found the thing wasn't even ionized, as claimed. A more recent 2009 study in *Complementary Therapies in Medicine* confirmed the dud findings. Regardless, don't knock the power of the placebo effect. Lots of people stand by their bracelets, and at least there's no physical harm in wearing one.

cervicogenic (a.k.a. pain in the neck) headaches. In my case, both acupuncture and chiropractic support seriously alleviate my chronic upper neck–originating headaches that take over my whole skull. If you're wary of having your neck cracked, talk to your practitioner about doing more gentle neck adjustments.

By the way, if you're a migraine sufferer, pay attention to what foods put your head in a Vise-Grip. It could be anything from artificial colours and sweeteners to chocolate, cheese, wine, weather, even citrus. Keep a headache/diet log until you figure it out. If you're having migraines for the first time or are experiencing a change in migraine patterns, have it investigated by a pro.

Natural Alternatives for Menstrual Pain: If you believed everything you saw on television about women's health, you'd assume that yeast infections can paralyze a woman, that girls on birth control are, like, super cool, and that an annoying woman in tweed brings your

203

"monthly gift." Watch too much of it and you might also assume we couldn't survive in this world without the help of lots of pharmaceuticals, petrochemicals and plastic dry-weave. Time to reclaim our bodies from the grip of Big Pharma and trust in the tools Mother Nature's laid out for us. So how to deal with the monthly party that is PMS, complete with an ill-received guest list including bloating, backaches, headaches, diarrhea, irritability, depression and an inability to concentrate?

Now, as much as you may want to self-medicate with sugar, alcohol and/or coffee, depending on your preferred poison, these will only make things worse. Sorry. You may be confused about what you *should* take since there are, like, 60 vitamins, minerals and herbs that claim to help with PMS. Your best bet is to pop some **calcium**, since it's been shown to really improve PMS symptoms, from cramping, swelling and cravings to mood swings (see page 250 for more on calcium). **Magnesium** can help too, but you have to take the right kind (oxide definitely doesn't help, but mag glycinate or chelate are well absorbed). A good cal/mag combo could be the right thing for you. Also, toss some natural **vitamin E** in the mix to help with your long list of symptoms. St. John's wort may aid some PMSers with anxiety. Evening primrose oil hasn't fared as well under medical studies, which have also been wishy-washy about chasteberry and B6. Oh, and ignore the small studies that say krill oil helps. Krill is a controversial fish with sustainability issues that pushed Whole Foods to ban it from shelves. Best to stay away. (For more on fish oils, see page 245.) If your pain is so bad you're considering going on the birth control pill, talk to your practitioner about the Mirena IUD, which helps reduce menstrual pain and flow (see IUD, page 158 for more info).

Natural Alternatives for Fibromyalgia Pain: You think you know pain? Try living with fibromyalgia. Your muscles ache everywhere; you're exhausted all the time but you can't sleep; your brain fog is so thick it can feel like you're walking through the misty streets of London town. Plus, you probably have irritable bowel syndrome and multiple chemical sensitivities to round out the festival of symptoms. All in all, a grand old time. Your doc may try to prescribe pharmaceuticals, but fibromyalgia is notoriously resistant to treatment so most doctors will tell you to work on sleep, stress and exercise in order to improve pain. Time to experiment with supplements and alternative treatments to help keep your symptoms in check. But with a condition this complex, it's particularly important to see a health practitioner such as a naturopath who can come up with a tailored treatment plan for you. Here's a sampling of some of what they may suggest:

- Mood-lifting and inflammation-reducing amino acid **SAM-e** has been found to be helpful for many but not all fibromyalgia patients. It's definitely worth a try.
- After a month of taking the amino acid **5-HTP (5-Hydroxytryptophan)**, studies have found fibromyalgia sufferers showed significant improvement in pain, stiffness, fatigue and sleep.
- You'll likely need extra **vitamin D** (the drop form is the easiest way to get a higher dose) as well as **magnesium** and **malic acid**. Talk to your doc about dosing and getting your D and mag levels tested.
- Several studies have shown success with **electro-acupuncture** (where needles are pulsed with an electric current), but there's not been so much success documented with traditional acupuncture, so spend your money at the right practitioner who has experience in the electro kind.
- **Tai chi** can also do you some good, according to small studies. Actually, 30 minutes a day of any exercise, particularly the low-impact kind, such as **swimming** and hatha or **restorative yoga**, can be particularly beneficial for fibro sufferers, even if you seem too tired or achy to start.

Natural Alternatives for Arthritis: Once childproof lids become a full-blown impossibility and your knees start seizing up with every sunrise, it's easy to let arthritis slow you down. The Public Health Agency of Canada says 85% of Canadians will have osteoarthritis by the time they're 70 years old. About a third of seniors take daily painkillers for their arthritis, but they aren't without serious risk. The *New England Journal of Medicine* has noted that at least 16,500 rheumatoid arthritis and osteoarthritis patients die from NSAID (non-steroidal anti-inflammatory drug)–related gastrointestinal complications every year in the United States. By the way, a third of those deaths weren't from high-priced prescriptions but from low-dose Aspirin, according to a report published in the *American Journal of Gastroenterology*.

Looking for relief from osteoarthritis without the worrying risks? There are a lot of promising natural options. Just keep in mind that those with rheumatoid arthritis, the often debilitating auto-immune condition, as well as those with moderate to severe osteoarthritis should see a natural health provider to have a complete course of action prescribed. Also, if you're taking other prescription meds, such as blood thinners, be sure to run your supplements by your pharmacist.

Arthritic vegans may not be fans of them, but **glucosamine** (often taken from shellfish shells) and **chondroitin** (derived from cow or pork cartilage) are hands-down the most popular alternative treatments for osteoarthritis. However, the reports on them are definitely conflicting. Some studies and study reviews have found that long-term treatment with glucosamine slows the progression of knee osteoarthritis and reduces pain (see *Journal of Internal Medicine*). But the highly anticipated U.S. government–funded GAIT study (Glucosamine/ Chondroitin Arthritis Intervention Trial) found that the supplements, both alone and together, didn't do much for most of the participants. What you didn't hear so much of was that the combination did help those with moderate to severe pain: 79% of people in that smaller subgroup who took glucosamine and chondroitin together experienced significant relief. Another criticism is that the study largely looked at glucosamine hydrochloride (HCI), whereas most successful trials have used glucosamine sulphate. Now there's speculation that a certain percentage of people can't readily absorb the sulphate kind and benefit more from HCI. You might want to do your own trials, first with sulphate and then with HCI varieties, but stop after three months if there's no sign of improvement. A couple of studies have found a combo of glucosamine HCI, sodium chondroitin sulfphate and manganese ascorbate was effective for the treatment of mild to moderate osteo in the knees. Others found glucosamine helpful when taken with MSM.

If you're in search of something that's backed up by more solid clinical evidence, look into **SAM-e** (S-Adenosyl methionine). A meta-analysis of 11 studies published in the *Journal of Family Practice* concluded that SAM-e (pronounced "sammy") is as effective as non-steroidal anti-inflammatory pain relievers in reducing pain and alleviating the functional limitations that can accompany OA, without the nasty side effects. Bonus: it's a great depression fighter, too. Integrative docs say to take it with a good multivitamin and folic acid.

There's an avalanche of joint-health combo products out there that can do you more good than taking a single supplement on its own. Some quality suggestions? **New Chapter's Zyflamend** is loaded with turmeric, ginger and other anti-inflammatory herbs and is a Dr. Weil pick. **Platinum Naturals' Relev-X** also has turmeric's active ingredient, curcumin, as well as glucosamine, omega-3s, cat's claw, the classic arthritis-buster devil's claw, and white willow bark for more immediate pain relief. **Platinum Naturals' Nutri-Joint Complet-X** has glucosamine, chondroitin and popular joint and skin lubricant hyaluronic acid, as well as important omega-3s. **Nature's Way Hydraplenish** contains hyaluronic acid, MSM, Type II collagen and chondroitin, and is particularly designed to help with joint pain/inflammation and nourish your skin at the same time (you can see why this one's a hit). **SierraSil Joint Formula 14** is a mineral combo that claims to prevent degradation of joint cartilage as well as inflammation and pain.

What else do natural health practitioners say you should be taking for arthritis?

- Well, 2.5 grams of **fish oils** a day has been found to reduce arthritis pain in knees by 30%. Make sure you're popping the most sustainable kind (see page 246) and eat sustainably chosen fish (the small ones such as mackerel and sardines, or inland-farmed varieties such as tilapia); check out seachoice.org.

- Munch on a lot of **vitamin C–rich foods** (too many isolated vitamin C supplements might make osteoarthritis worse), including red peppers, citrus, kiwis, as well as dark leafy greens (kale and broccoli are also high in anti-inflammatory quercetin).
- Keep beneficial **selenium** levels high with a daily handful of Brazil nuts.
- Get cooking with lots of anti-inflammatory **turmeric** powder. The abundantly cultivated root from the ginger family has shown significant promise in easing arthritis.
- Stay active to keep those joints limber. Walking, swimming, elliptical machines and particularly tai chi have been proven

DIABETIC DIET: GO VEGAN?

With our national blood sugar levels skyrocketing alongside diabetes rates (two million Canadians now have type 2 diabetes), the message is out that type 2 diabetes can be managed and even avoided with lots of physical activity and the right diet. Of course, what constitutes the right diet depends on whom you ask. Conventional sources such as the Canadian Diabetes Association basically just say to follow the Canada Food Guide: lots of produce, a little protein and plenty of starchy whole grains, rice and potatoes with every meal (since starches are broken down into the glucose your body needs). Though it wasn't widely advertised, the American Diabetes Association found that those who followed a strict low-fat vegan diet improved blood glucose levels, lost weight and lowered their cholesterol levels more than people eating the standard diabetes diet. It also happens to be one of the most planet-friendly diets around, since animal products are the most carbon-heavy things on your plate, so if you're up for the challenge—give veganism a go. Just steer clear of sugary/refined/processed white carbs and eat more unrefined carbs such as beans, legumes, whole grains, fruits and vegetables (preferably organic). Talk to your doc first, though.

effective for arthritis pain management. As my physio would say, making time for movement is probably more important than anything you could do.

- Probably the number one move that helped my mom and many others with inflammation was the elimination of wheat (a big-time allergen). You should try an elimination diet, getting rid of big inflammatory foods such as sugar, wheat, corn and dairy one at a time for a few weeks to see if any are irritating your joints.

MENTAL HEALTH

Notice how whenever anyone asks us how we're doing, at worst we say "okay"? Maybe a "could be better." I've always wondered how the check-out clerk or even your workplace associate from two departments over would react if you replied with a "feeling kind of depressed actually." Truth is, we might complain to our friends and colleagues about our sinus infection or bum knee, but too few of us are sharing status updates about our mental health. Almost 3.4 million Canadians are currently coping with depression and anxiety, and yet the Canadian Mental Health Association says that more than two-thirds of them don't seek help. If you're feeling anxious or depressed and are pharmaceutical averse, nature may just have some help for you tucked into alternative supplements. See a health practitioner for advice on which treatment avenue to take, and keep in mind that there are also holistic psychotherapists out there who focus on the mind, body and spirit.

Antidepressants: In around the time it took skinny jeans to make a comeback, prescriptions for antidepressants in Canada jumped a mind-blowing 353%, from 3.2 million in 1981 to 14.5 million in 2000. By 2009, nearly 32 million prescriptions for antidepressants were filled in this country (up 1000%). On the upside, people are less closeted about their emotional state than they were decades ago, and are more open to revealing their depression to family, friends and physicians. But as we've morphed from a Prozac Nation into a Zoloft Nation, what's also become clear is that our emotions have been medicalized and boiled down to a simple biological problem of chemical imbalance, one that can be "fixed" with a pill.

While antidepressants do help countless Canadians get through dark times, prescription depression fighters can also make you feel anxious, agitated and weirdly detached from your own life, sensations that can all add to a sense of hopelessness and despair, according to the Centre for Addiction and Mental Health. More worrisome still, 4% of people on antidepressants can become violent or suicidal.

Considering how many of us are taking antidepressants, it's hardly surprising that Prozac and other chemical SSRIs are turning up in our waterways. In 2011, researchers out of the Université de Montréal and Environment Canada found that brook trout exposed to Montreal's sewage discharge (the very stuff dumped into the St. Lawrence on a daily basis) had significant quantities of antidepressants in their livers and brain tissue. The reseachers could detect changes to their brain chemistry but weren't yet able to figure out what impact it would have. Interestingly enough, when U.K. scientists exposed prawns to the same trace levels of Prozac found in waste water, those shrimp became significantly more reckless than usual, swimming into bright, sunny spots where they were more exposed to deadly predators and parasites.

Natural Supplements for Depression: Thoughts of drugged-up fish, tainted water and general climate change anxiety getting you down? See what's on offer at Mother Nature's dispensary that may be able to help shift your mood.

- The most popular herbal depression combatant is **St. John's wort.** This is one you definitely don't want to get wild-sourced, since it's threatened (see page 233). But otherwise, is it worth taking? It basically gets its power from being, in part, a weak SSRI (selective serotonin reuptake inhibitor), and though it hasn't been found to work on severe depression, studies have found it helps many with mild to moderate depression. Note that it can take a couple of months to become fully effective.

IS THE FATE OF THE WORLD GETTING YOU DOWN?

The fact that human beings can read about melting ice caps, vanishing wildlife and mounting global catastrophes and still get up, head to work, line up for some Tim's and forget about it all is pretty amazing, really. We're either really resilient or totally clued out. Or both. But what if you can't disengage from the heavy news of the world and the fate of the planet is bringing you down? Well, you're not alone. More and more people are blaming climate change and environmental woes for their depression and anxiety. A 2011 report out of Australia entitled *A Climate of Suffering: The Real Cost of Living with Inaction on Climate Change* noted that our mental health really suffers in the face of extreme weather events and that rates of depression and post-traumatic stress will increase under a shifting climate. Now what are you supposed to do about it? It's time to channel those deep emotions into action. Get involved in positive forces for change, however small, by volunteering with a local environmental organization, or lending a hand in your local community garden or nature preserve. Connecting with nature may be just what you need. Green therapy and horticulture therapy—going for walks in your local park or digging in the dirt in your backyard or neighbourhood garden—are incredibly restorative and psychologists are coming to realize what deep down we've known all along, that connecting with nature can do wonders for our mental and physical health. Actually, if we all spent more time truly listening to, taking in and connecting with nature, we'd be on the right path to curing the planet's fever, too. Call it the Ecoholic prescription for healing.

Keep in mind, too, that St. John's wort comes with a lot of contraindications, so cross-check it against any other meds you may be taking.

• One of the best-researched alternative treatments for depression, with no environmental ramifications, is the amino acid **SAM-e (S-Adenosyl methionine)**, a naturally occurring compound found in all living cells. It kicks in faster than St. John's wort, and patients on this supplement have shown a 50% decrease in depression symptoms without the troubling side effects of pharmaceuticals. It's popular in Europe and also happens to perform double duty as an anti-inflammatory and liver-function booster, and docs recommend it as a booster for the 29% to 46% of patients with major depression who aren't really responding to basic antidepressants. Integrative medicine practitioners will tell you it should be taken with a high-potency multivitamin and folic acid.

- One supplement that can have a surprisingly strong impact on major depression is **omega-3 fatty acids**. (Of course, you want to make sure you're not picking the wrong fish, sustainably speaking, so see page 246 for recommendations.) A 2010 multi-university Canadian study found that participants with straight-up unipolar depression (with no anxiety) who took three capsules of an omega-3 supplement containing fish oil with 1,050 mg of EPA/day felt as much improvement in their mood as with conventional antidepressant drugs. Consult your health practitioner for more info.

- Another helpful supplement that naturopaths will point you to is **5-HTP**. This amino acid is a serotonin neurotransmitter precursor that's been found to help with mild to moderate depression. Just don't combine it with prescription antidepressants; it can be dangerous. The Indian herb **Holy Basil** is a gentle though less researched spirit-lifter that seems to work for some. Make sure it's certified organic if you try it.

As with anxiety, it's important to delve into the deeper issues that are weighing on you. A good therapist can help. If you've had bouts of depression before, you may want to pick up *The Mindful Way Through Depression: Freeing Yourself from Chronic Unhappiness*. Mindfulness-based therapy loosely borrows from Buddhist concepts, and clinical studies have found it helps prevent relapse in patients who have endured multiple bouts of depression. Incorporating supportive practices into your everyday life—including daily exercise (five days a week has been shown to help ease depression symptoms), yoga, energy healing, as well as cutting out drinking and other depressive vices—is also essential to pulling yourself out of the depths of depression. Easier said than done, of course, so if you're having trouble getting motivated, talking to a counsellor can help you get started.

Note: Thoughts of suicide are a serious symptom of depression. If you're having thoughts of harming yourself, reach out to your health care provider or call 1-800-SUICIDE.

Anxiety: Modern life pulls us in so many different directions, it's like we're surrounded by high-speed escalators and moving sidewalks. It can be tough to figure out how to slow it all down. We're disconnected, discontented and forever worrying about what's around the corner (including environmental disasters). In fact, stats show Western cultures, from the U.S. to the U.K., getting more fearful with each passing year. Sure, we all feel overwhelmed at times, but what happens when that nervous feeling that kicks in before a big test, a speech or, say, a Revenue Canada audit starts to hang around like a dark cloud and everyday activities and decisions fill you with dread? Well, you take a deep breath and join the club. One in four of us has had an anxiety problem at some point in our life. It can get in the way of sleep, work, studying, relationships, you name it. No wonder anti-anxiety meds such as Xanax and Ativan are so popular. In fact, anti-anxiety and antidepressant drugs are the second most prescribed group of meds, after heart medication. So I guess we shouldn't be surprised that traces of anti-anxiety medication have turned up in sewage effluent as well as drinking water in cities across the continent (not that you really need one more thing on your plate to worry about).

Although taking meds or herbs may help your symptoms in the short run, they won't necessarily resolve your anxiety over the long term. And the pros will tell you that avoiding or suppressing your fears can only make the situation worse. If you're feeling unable to control your anxiety, it's important to get help. For many people, counselling is an integral component of managing and even overcoming their anxiety. Perhaps one of the most widely accepted and research-supported treatments is cognitive behavioural therapy (CBT), which can be done with a CBT-trained therapist or on your own. It's designed to teach you how to break anxious thought patterns, to shift your perspective and actions so that you're way less likely to relapse.

If you want to try the self-help route, pick up either *Cognitive Behavioral Workbook for Anxiety: A Step-by-Step Program* or *The Mindfulness and Acceptance Workbook for Anxiety: A Guide to Breaking Free from Anxiety, Phobias, and Worry Using Acceptance and Commitment Therapy*. Borrowed from the concept of mindfulness in Buddhist meditation, mindfulness-based therapy fosters a be-in-the-present awareness and acceptance of feelings and thoughts. A meta-analysis of 39 studies on the impact of mindfulness therapy revealed its value in treating anxiety and mood problems.

Now, if your anxiety feels manageable but you need a little extra support, don't be shy about trying what nature has to offer. A naturopath or holistic practitioner can help you design a whole health strategy for combating your anxiety.

Natural Supplements for Anxiety: What are some helpful natural supplements that won't stress out the planet? The herb with the most substantive research backing its positive effect on mild to moderate anxiety, according to the American Association of Family Doctors, comes from the root of a tall tropical shrub called **kava**. Unfortunately, kava's been barred from sale in Canada since 2002, though it's available in the United States and the EU lifted its ban a few years ago. Why the drama? It's essentially equivalent to acetaminophen in terms of liver concerns, and so shouldn't be taken regularly by heavy drinkers or those with existing liver problems, but if you can buy Tylenol over the counter, many suggest you should be able to access kava just as readily. (Health Canada permits Canadians to order kava direct from manufacturers abroad, such as konakavafarm.com, which sells farmed kava rather than the threatened wild Hawaiian variety.) If you're looking for kava across the border, always avoid wild sources, which are threatened with overharvesting.

- **Soothing supplements:** So, what are the best easily accessible options for anxious Canadians? **Niacinamide** (nicotinamide), or B3, is a good research-supported supplement often recommended by naturopaths—including Jonathan Prousky, author of *Anxiety: Orthomolecular Diagnosis and Treatment*—for those suffering from anxiety disorders. Just so you know, it can cause flushing (temporary skin reddening) in some, so don't freak out if that happens to you. Look for flush-free versions.
- **Panic support:** If you're more prone to panic attacks, naturopaths may advise you to put a teaspoon or two of the neurotransmitting amino acid **glycine** (powdered crystalline) under your tongue at the onset of an attack. Also, ask your practitioner about **inositol,** which is a simple sugar classified as part of the B vitamin family. Some studies found it to be as successful as prescription SSRIs at reducing the intensity and frequency of panic attacks. As well, inositol has had a positive impact on obsessive-compulsive disorders and post-traumatic stress disorder.
- **B good:** Holistic practitioners will tell you that a good **B vitamin complex** is considered an essential foundation supplement for combating stress.
- **Herbal harmony:** Several studies have shown positive results for passion flower extract, so it's worth a shot. Valerian and rhodiola are also commonly recommended (see page 232 for more on rhodiola). **Ashwagandha** is a traditional Ayurvedic adaptogen that helps the body resist environmental and internal stress and is more of a slow-build supporter for chronic stress. It's one of the rare Indian herbs that isn't on India's threatened/endangered species list, because it's cultivated in large quantities. To avoid pesticide residues, make sure yours is certified organic. **Relora** (a proprietary blend of magnolia bark extract and phelloden-dron, or cork tree, bark) has been found to help those with mild, passing anxiety. Now, the *Magnolia officinalis* it uses is classified as "near threatened" in the wild, but the makers of Relora say it uses cultivated sources.

Techniques for Managing Anxiety: Ultimately, you've got to do the practical work of learning how to manage your anxiety or panic attacks with concrete techniques.

- Daily meditation is high on the list of practices found to help you get a grip on serious stresses.
- Research has found qigong (an ancient Chinese internal art of moving meditation) useful as well. Tai chi (slow-mo martial arts), yoga and specialized techniques such as EFT, or Emotional Freedom Technique (sort of like self-applied acupressure for stress), are all great stress reducers that'll help you ground yourself and develop a calm inner core. (I've done EFT right before stepping onstage for a big talk.) See the EFT tutorial at eft.mercola.com.
- Just getting up and moving by exercising three to five times a week or going to dance therapy has been found to really help mild to moderate anxiety as well as panic disorders.

HEART HEALTH

If my family were a hockey team, we'd have a giant heart emblazoned on our jerseys. We are, after all, seasoned heart disease experts. All four of my grandparents passed away from heart attacks or heart disease, three of them well before I was born. After heavy finger wagging from his doctor, my father turned his fate around by overhauling our family diet to the Mediterranean style back in, oh, 1985 (as a 10-year-old, I wasn't exactly thrilled about shifting from buckets of fried chicken to baked fish, let me tell you). Nonetheless, he's still had to climb his way back from a heart valve transplant, a double bypass and a stroke. No wonder they started testing me for cholesterol when I was just 11 years old.

My family's not alone: Canadians take more heart drugs than we do any other single category of pills. A whopping 74 million prescriptions for them were doled out in 2009 (mostly the high blood pressure and cholesterol kind), up from 53 million just four short years earlier, according to the Health Council of Canada. That partly explains why cholesterol-lowering gemfibrozils (fibrates that also go by Jezil and

Gen-Fibro) are some of the most frequently detected compounds in both untreated and finished drinking water, according to Ontario's Ministry of the Environment. (Bezafibrate, another cholesterol-lowering fibrate drug, turned up in 10% of lake and river samples but broke down before reaching taps.) Environment Canada's also found heart-boosting statins and hypertension medications in sewage and surface water samples. Ironic, really, considering that some have actually called for statins to be added to tap water as a heart-health booster alongside fluoride. But since statins have been found to mess with the natural cholesterol levels of rainbow trout, we might want to give that one a good think.

To be frank, if these drugs are messing with the environment, they bloody well better be doing their heart-saving job. So are they? Well, just a few years ago, the medical community was stunned when studies revealed that the cholesterol drug Ezetrol may lower bad cholesterol but did nothing to prevent plaque buildup in the arteries. Although there's certainly a lot of evidence that other heart drugs (namely older generation statins) do help a lot of people with heart disease, Big Pharma's push to rope the broader healthy population into popping their pills as preventatives relies on pretty dubious and contested evidence. Even if you've been diagnosed with heart disease and are taking medication, this is no time to slack off; you've got to keep making healthy choices on a daily basis.

Lifestyle Changes for Heart Health: Sorry, people, there are no short cuts to heart health. Quitting smoking, losing some weight (any weight), exercising, de-stressing (with meditation, yoga, tai chi, you name it) and eating well are the top things you can do to keep your heart happy. That last part means staying away from partially hydrogenated oil and refined carbs (the first raises LDL and the second can raise triglycerides) and shifting to a Mediterranean-style diet high in fruits, green veggies, beans, nuts, olive oil, garlic, herbs, the right fish (no unsustainable picks for Ecoholic eaters! Go to seachoice.org to make sure your fish dinner gets the environmental green light), even a glass of (ideally local and/or organic) wine with dinner. By the way, a dozen studies involving a total of 1.5 million people found that those who stuck with the Mediterranean way of eating saw a 9% decrease in mortality, a 9% drop in fatal heart attacks, 13% less Parkinson's and Alzheimer's and 6% less cancer. Plus, it's delicious, so it makes getting healthy tantalizing.

Natural Supplements for Heart Health: If you do want to try to be good to your heart via more environmentally sustainable supplements, there are a few things you can experiment with, but see your health practitioner for advice. And by the way, many of these supplements perform double duty, tackling high blood pressure and preventing various forms of heart disease.

- **Load up on garlic:** Raw, very lightly cooked or in pill form (make sure it's high in allicin; see page 179). Several studies have found that garlic helps lower blood pressure and prevent heart disease and protects against diabetic cardiomyopathy, the leading cause of heart attacks in diabetics. But it is a blood thinner, so consult your doc if you're taking blood-thinning medication.
- **Go for Q: Coenzyme Q10** (CoQ_{10}) has been shown, in a dozen trials, to be another good blood pressure reducer (you need to take it for a month or three before seeing results). It also has the potential to treat high cholesterol and triglycerides, coronary artery disease and congestive heart failure, and considering its exemplary safety record, it certainly won't do you any harm. Holistic practitioners will tell you it's especially important to pop this stuff when you're on statin drugs because they're known to deplete your natural CoQ_{10} levels, which drop as we age.

PETROL IN YOUR VITAMIN E?

Synthetic vitamin E isn't just less bio-available than the natural kind, it's also made from petrochemicals. Fakes have "dl" or "all rac" in fine print.

HONK IF YOUR HEART HURTS

We all know that sitting in traffic is enough to give you a coronary, but what about inhaling all those pollutants churned out by a city full of cars? Recent studies have found that people living near heavily trafficked roads were 20% more likely to die of heart disease. Yep, scientists out of the University of Michigan looked at patterns in Michigan and Toronto and discovered that all that bad air can make your blood pressure jump and vessels constrict. Not good for anyone with heart disease or at risk of stroke, let me tell you. It seems the culprit isn't so much smog-inducing ozone but the particulate matter that lodges in your lungs. Once it's in there, it can start tightening your blood vessels, creating longer-term damage. Oh, and if your appendix starts acting up on smog-alert day, you'll know whom to blame: a University of Calgary study found that those exposed to high levels of air pollution were twice as likely to suffer from appendicitis (four times as likely if they were over 64). Particulate matter has also recently been linked to diabetes and obesity. The lesson here? Don't add to the pollution by driving to work. Hop on the bus/subway/streetcar/train instead and lobby your politicians for tougher pollution controls.

- **Dose up on D:** Several studies have tied low vitamin D levels to higher risk of heart attacks. Get your levels checked!
- **Reach for red yeast?** If you're looking for a drug-free cholesterol-lowering agent, holistic practitioners will often point you to **red yeast rice extract**, a source of naturally occurring statins (lovastatins). Since lovastatin is also the active ingredient in prescription Mevacor, a statin drug, the U.S. and Canada, not so surprisingly, cracked down on it. To avoid getting in trouble, red yeast rice products don't tell you how much lovastatin may be in there (testing by ConsumerLab.com found that lovastatin contents ranged by a hundredfold, though at most, they're about half that of prescription doses). Some products were also, in 2008, found to be contaminated with a toxic rice fungus (Solaray, Natural Balance and VegLife claim to have since

switched manufacturers). Of note, when red yeast rice extract
was combined with triglyceride-busting fish oils (see page 245
for sustainable picks), a Mediterranean diet and daily exercise,
one study found a 42% reduction in LDL levels, versus 39% in
prescription drug takers. Pretty amazing.

- **Snack on plant sterols and stanols**: There's healthy evidence
  backing their LDL-lowering claims. You can get some from your
  pantry (via nuts like pistachios, and barley, psyllium, flaxseed,
  olive oil, oat bran, green tea and beans—the kids are right, beans
  are good for the heart).

ESTROGEN-RELATED HEALTH

One of the highest-profile and most disruptive compounds to pollute
our waterways to date has been the synthetic hormone estrogen.
Researchers across the planet have documented synthetic estrogenic
compounds that are gender-bending fish by saddling males with
ovaries, feminized testes and fewer offspring. To date, women have
been considered pretty much exclusively responsible for this situation,
through excretions of birth control and hormone replacement therapy
drugs. The good news (if you can call it that) is that further analysis
shows we get to share the blame (yippee!). In truth, our pill popping is
only part of a broader picture where livestock also excrete vast quantities
of both natural and artificial hormones into rivers and streams, and
estrogen-mimicking chemicals in everything from plastics and pesticides
to body care products make their way down drains and runoff from
fields. Still, 26 million prescriptions for hormones were doled out in
Canada in 2009 alone. And a study out of New England found higher
rates of hermaphrodite frogs around urban and suburban waterways
than in agricultural and rural areas. While most waste water treatment
plants around today don't effectively remove most chemical compounds
from the water, the technology is there to break down anywhere from
80% to 99% of synthetic estrogen emissions. Researchers have been
calling for policy-makers to make such a move mandatory by regulating
those emissions, but so far it's a no go. While we're pushing for

regulatory changes, we also need to ban estrogenic bisphenol A from cash register receipts so it doesn't end up recycled into toilet paper and in our sewage, as it does today. Creepy, I know.

By the way, while research on the impact of estrogen pollution on females is ridiculously rare, some early research has found that female fish exposed to synthetic estrogen were more likely to thwart advances from male suitors. Kind of interesting, when low sex drive is a side effect of being on the pill itself—except in this case, the fish didn't swim by a doctor's office to sign up willingly.

Birth Control: For more information on birth control and the alternatives, see page 155. Some women have such bad menstrual cramps that they turn to birth control for help. For more on dealing with menstrual pain naturally, see page 203.

Hormone Replacement Therapy: What, hot flashes, mood swings and night sweats don't sound like a good time to you? Lots of women have been tempted to take hormone replacement therapy (HRT) to alleviate the symptoms of the "change of life," but in 2002 docs started warning about the potential health risks of menopausal women taking HRT. Combined estrogen and progestin replacement treatment has raised big red flags thanks to its strong link to elevated rates of breast cancer, heart attack and strokes. Some estrogen-only hormone replacement therapies were actually yanked from the market in 2004 after they were linked to an increase in strokes, but the Society of Obstetricians and Gynecologists of Canada still advises the use of HRT under certain conditions.

Through all this, few people have been looking into the environmental ramifications of millions of menopausal women collectively excreting large doses of horse hormones into the environment. Equine, a.k.a. horse, estrogen is the most common component of HRT released from patches, tablets, creams and vaginal rings, which makes it easy enough to track in sewage discharges. And surprise, a study published in *Environmental Health & Science* in

2009 found horse estrogen in every sewage treatment plant tested (and it ain't because urban horse riding is making a comeback). They concluded there's a "strong likelihood that these compounds contribute to feminization in exposed wildlife." The happy news is that since the health risks became apparent around 2002, HRT use has dropped off dramatically. From 2001 to 2007, 60% fewer senior Canadian women were using HRT, according to the Canadian Institute for Health Information.

Bio-identical Hormone Replacement Therapy: Soon after all the bad press around conventional HRT, natural, a.k.a. bio-identical, versions started touting their safety and miraculous benefits, with Suzanne Somers as their poster child. (Yes, she found something new to sell after the ThighMaster.) By 2008, however, the U.S. Food and Drug Administration was sending out letters to pharmacies telling them that bio-identical HRT is no safer than regular HRT. Wyeth, the maker of two conventional HRT hormones, petitioned the FDA to restrict the availability of bio-identical hormones, but so far the FDA hasn't. Just like risk-addled conventional HRT, bio-identical hormones are still available by prescription on both sides of the border. By the way, just because they're marketed as bio-identical doesn't mean their non-medicinal ingredients are in any way natural. These pharmaceuticals still tend to be full of petrochemicals, artificial colours and Mean 15 ingredients. Just read the non-medicinal ingredients on products like Estradot and EstroGel. For progesterone, bio-identical Prometrium pills and vaginal gel come in a more natural base. Your practitioner may recommend you get custom-compounded bio-identicals (that's when trained pharmacists custom-tailor hormones for you), but authorities aren't fans of it since active ingredient levels aren't standardized.

Question is, should you be taking any of them? There's a lot of controversy and conflicting messages clouding this topic, so I looked to a reputable source: MD and endocrinology prof at UBC, Jerilynn Prior, who founded the Centre for Menstrual Cycle and Ovulation Research. Prior says, "Any hormones, bio-identical or not, should be used with care. They are not like skin lotion or Aspirin. Bio-identical hormones are powerful substances with effects throughout our bodies." She adds that menopause, and the low estrogen and progesterone levels that come with it, is not a disease. It's normal life-cycle stuff, and most women really don't need any hormone treatment, including the bio-identical kind. Adds Prior, "Don't be swayed by the folks who want you to buy products and take preparations when you don't need them." However, if you have severe symptoms (that is, you have premature menopause or surgical menopause, i.e., you had your ovaries removed), dig around on the Centre's website for info on her program for ovarian hormone therapy (cemcor.ubc.ca).

WILD YAM A SHAM (AND THREATENED TOO)

Have you been smearing yourself with wild yam creams hoping they'll stop the clock or keep hot flashes in check? I hate to burst any bubbles, but while wild yam contains a precursor of steroid hormones called diosgenin, your body has no way to turn it into progesterone. Sure, the progesterone prescription Prometrium gets its hormones from yams, but they tinker with the diosgenin in the lab to help the process along. So put the tube down, especially since wildcrafted wild yam (*Dioscorea villosa*) is a threatened species on the United Plant Savers list (see page 233). Only products that are certified organic can guarantee they're sustainable.

Relief from Menopausal Symptoms: So what should you take instead for menopausal discomforts?

- Black cohosh may or may not help with your hot flashes. One 2009 meta-analysis of 16 studies was inconclusive, while another 2010 meta-analysis of nine studies found it reduced menopausal symptoms by 26%. In any case, it's a threatened species, so only buy it if it's certified organic (cultivated, not wildcrafted; see Herbs, page 229). It also comes with side effects, so check with your practitioner.

- **Rhapontic rhubarb root** is widely used for menopause in Germany, and is backed by several clinical studies (including two published in the journal *Menopause*) demonstrating it's excellent at reducing hot flashes, sleep problems, anxiety, and a broad range of menopausal and perimenopausal symptoms. Metagenics sells some called **Estrovera**.
- **Chasteberry** helps boost natural progesterone levels and may aid with poor sleep and irritability. Studies have been inconclusive, so experiment with it. Take it with calming GABA, too, to help counter anxiety.
- **5-HTP** may help with hot flashes and mood swings (see 5-HTP, page 212).
- Fend off bone loss and osteoporosis by pumping up on **vitamin D** (talk to your health practitioner about dosage). High doses of calcium have fallen out of favour in recent research, including a large study of 61,000 women published in the *British Medical Journal*. Talk to your doctor about appropriate dosage, reflective of your personal health history. (For more on calcium, see page 250.)
- Keep heart disease at bay with regular exercise and a healthy diet, and by giving up smoking (see Heart Health, page 216).
- If you're looking for phytoestrogens from soy, get them from whole soy such as certified-organic tofu, tempeh or edamame, not processed veggie dogs and isolated supplements.

WHOLE HEALTH ADVICE ONLINE

Looking for online health advice from alternative sources? Here are a few you should bookmark.

wholehealthmd.com: Punch in your ailment in their virtual Healing Centre and get a list of the "most effective" as well as "beneficial" supplements and herbs, with dosage recommendations. Healing recipes, a reference library, expert Q&A and a whole-body news section round off this highly useful site.

alive.com: The online version of this Canadian alt health mag has a ton of easy-to-access archived stories on holistic healing, food and nutrition, and beauty, as well as event listings and a handy Health Retailer Search to help you find a health store near you.

drweil.com: For a physician's perspective on holistic health, this is a great site to visit. Dr. Weil approaches wellness from an integrative health angle, combining conventional and complementary medicines with lots of excellent whole health suggestions. The site's live vitamin advisers are useful, but don't feel pressured to buy the specific brand of supplements they're peddling. You can find the same supplements in Canadian health stores.

consumerlab.com: This watchdog does independent testing of vitamins, minerals, herbs, energy products, functional foods and much more for potency, purity and overall honesty. Sign up for their free newsletter. For detailed reports on over 900 supplement scores, you'll need to cough up just over $2 a month—totally worth it.

Hans.org: The Health Action Network Society site is a non-profit natural health resource venue based in B.C.

healthycanadians.gc.ca: This Health Canada–run website is a quick 'n' easy place to find details on product recalls, including drugs and natural health products. You can subscribe to have consumer alerts sent to your email, too.

nccam.nih.gov: The website of the U.S. government–run National Institutes of Health's National Center for Complementary Medicine. This one offers a cautious assessment of what the research says (both for and against a particular herb or supplement), and tells you the side effects and cautions around particular natural health products, from acai to zinc. The Center also conducts its own clinical research trials on things such as acupuncture, breast cancer and green tea.

altmedrev.com: Want to dig deeper for medical studies on supplements and alternative medicine? This is a good place to start. *Alternative Medicine Review* is a peer-reviewed journal.

Herbs   229

Vitamins   236

Superfoods   239

Fish Oils   245

Minerals   249

Weight Loss Remedies   254

Endangered Animals   257

NATURAL
HEALTH PRODUCTS

An acai berry a day
keeps the doctor away

If I get a clingy cough or a weird pain,

I've never had to stumble very far for advice. I grew up in a family of alternative-health junkies, each with his or her own crowded cupboard of natural supplements, and everyone always had a prescription pad of suggestions for me. My pioneering older brother was a herbalist and holistic nutritionist (and the first to feed me alfalfa sprouts and botanical remedies); my sister is a family physician out west with a special interest in vitamin therapy and integrative medicine; and my younger brother is a natural health educator planning his own healing centre. But we're not the only health nuts on the block: nearly 75% of Canadians have tried alternative therapies, and we're forking out $7.8 billion a year and climbing on complementary practitioners, vitamins, herbs, fish oils and beyond. Now, keep in mind that popping natural supplements doesn't automatically vault you into eco-sainthood. We need to make sure that the natural remedies we swallow are sustainable, too. You didn't think your antioxidant/vitamin/superfood could escape Ecoholic scrutiny just because it makes you feel good, did you?

Sustainable Supplements: Oh sure, Health Canada's Natural Health Product Directorate asks supplement manufacturers to attest to their products' safety, efficacy, potency, purity and stability, as well as listing any contraindications or possible side effects. Any claims made have to be approved by the feds, too. If you see a DIN number on your supplement, that means it's got the green light (many without are still waiting in the queue). But what about a supplement's sustainability and long-term ecological viability? I stumped you there, didn't I? Unfortunately, Health Canada isn't asking supplement makers to demonstrate their environmental friendliness before allowing them on shelves. Truth is, most of us don't stop to consider whether our source of calcium or the latest superfood is being consciously plucked or carelessly yanked from nature. Don't forget, there's a multi-billion-dollar industry behind these products. You don't want to boost your health on the back of the planet's, do you? But don't panic (have a whiff of lavender or something), *Ecoholic Body*'s here to tell you what's green and what's mean—and make some brand recommendations along the way, too.

HERBS

You want to talk about the marrow of medicine? Forget dime-a-dozen drugstore vitamins and tap into the most deeply rooted of health disciplines, which finds its healing powers in the bellies of the planet's forests. Yes sir, millennia before there were pharmacists, there were herbalists. Native American healers were astutely prescribing arnica to treat back pain, and American ginseng as a tonic for digestive disorders or sexual dysfunction, carefully utilizing hundreds of healing plants on ailing patients. Actually, practitioners in all ancient medicinal systems have relied on the healing properties of the flora sprouting up around them, from traditional Chinese medicine (which is 80% plant based) to 5,000-year-old Ayurvedic medicine (with 2,000 healing plants in its arsenal). Hell, according to primate researchers, great apes and chimpanzees have been found to self-medicate with parasite-killing and bowel-soothing barks and bitter piths—proof that nature gives us the tools and the instincts to heal. And yes, today, in the concrete jungles of

North America, you'll find even the squarest Canadians have caught on to the powers of ginseng/ginger/garlic/ginkgo (and those are just the gs), making herbs a multi-billion-dollar business on this continent alone.

Endangered Herbs: As the Western world awakens to the fact that at least 25% of lab-born prescription drugs have active ingredients that originally came from or emulate compounds in flowering plants (for example, foxglove-derived digitalis prescribed for heart-rhythm problems), it would be a crying shame to lose any of the world's 50,000 to 70,000 medicinal plants to the history books. But lo and behold, it's happening. According to the International Union for the Conservation of Nature, 15,000 of those plants are under serious threat from habitat loss and overharvesting. It's too bad threatened herbs just don't galvanize the same public attention as other endangered species (it's hard to compete with fuzzy pandas and majestic tigers, and even they have a tough time maintaining our attention). It can also take time to shift practitioners towards the belief that cultivated herbs can be as medicinally virile as wild (a.k.a. wildcrafted) varieties, but that's happening too (just don't offer them pesticide-laden monocrop alternatives). Of course, it's illegal to sell officially endangered herbs such as wild American ginseng or wild white ladyslipper, but you can still find wild goldenseal on health store shelves even though it's listed on Canada's At Risk list as "threatened."

- We don't want the herbs on today's safe list to show up on tomorrow's threatened list, so avoid wild or wildcrafted herbs. Unless you know for a fact that the herb is being sustainably harvested and doesn't come from threatened populations, it's best to be safe and steer clear.
- Look for certified-organic and biodynamic herbs whenever possible. That tells you that a herb was planted and grown without synthetic or chemical inputs in carefully nurtured soil. Formulas sold by **Clefs des Champs, St. Francis Herb Farm** and **Naturally Nova Scotia** are primarily organic (though St. Francis carries a couple of wild herbs on the United Plant Savers Threatened list,

such as osha and false unicorn; their wild mullein, on the other hand, isn't a concern since it can actually become quite invasive). **Organic Connections** and **Frontier Natural Products** also sell organic herbs in bulk.

- In some cases, a third-party certifier such as Ecocert regulates wildcrafting to ensure it's done sustainably (i.e., no overharvesting, roots left in place when possible), but organic certification of wild herbs is a grey-zone topic that raises a lot of questions (like can anyone ever have full control over the growing conditions of a wild herb?).
- Because so many herbs are true medicines, always talk to your health practitioner about contraindications.

Arnica: This bruise-healing wonder plant has been used for centuries, especially in Europe, where it grows wild in mountain meadows. Wild populations have unfortunately been over-exploited in central Europe in particular because of "unsustainable levels of collection for use in medicine," according to the IUCN (International Union for Conservation of Nature) Red List of Threatened Species. The good news is it's now technically protected. Luckily, this plant is also widely cultivated (even though it's supposedly a pain in the butt to farm), but to be sure, look for certified-organic sources. **St. Francis Arnica Oil** (stfrancisherbfarm.com) is a good green pick as is **Clef Des Champs Organic Arnica salve** (clefdeschamps.net).

Ginkgo Biloba: If you've got a faulty memory, you've probably been told to get your hands on some ginkgo biloba. I actually took some when I was an undergrad, hoping it would boost my retention skills during exams and all I got was a lousy headache. But I digress. This ancient tree (historical evidence dates it back over 150 million years) is now endangered in the wild, however, it's widely cultivated, so just be sure you're not buying the kind labelled "wild." Organic's always best. Also, don't be shy about planting this hardy, disease-resistant specimen in your front or back yard—it's a great urban tree.

Rhodiola: This adaptogen may be used for combating stress, but you want to make sure you get the right kind. After decades of uncontrolled harvesting and habitat destruction, rhodiola is considered highly threatened in Russia (the International Union for the Conservation of Nature says collection is now strongly controlled there) as well as eastern Europe. They're still largely in the clear in Scandinavian countries. Good luck finding the certified-organic kind in capsule form. **Starwest Botanicals** sells some USDA organic rhodiola root in bulk. I'm super excited about Alberta-grown rhodiola (nantonnutraceuticals.ca).

Pau d'arco: An ancient Amazonian remedy that comes from the bark of several species of the *Tabebuia*, a.k.a. ipe tree, in Latin America. The ipe tree is also very commonly logged for deck wood and patio furniture. Several species of *Tabebuia* are currently vulnerable, threatened or endangered, and it can be difficult for customers to discern whether or not pau d'arco is sustainably sourced. Best to avoid.

Oregano Oil: If my Greek grandmother were alive to see oregano flying off the shelves as a popular cure-all, she'd be one proud *yiayia* (that's "nana" to you non-Hellenics). Over the last 5 to 10 years, oregano oil has become one of the hottest cold and flu remedies and biggest-selling herbs in the country. I've personally forced droppers of the potent stuff down the throats of many a sniffly colleague and friend. Still, one thing that's always bugged me about the concentrated antiviral/antibacterial/antifungal/antiparasitic wonder is that pretty much every producer claims to use wild versions of the Mediterranean herb. Sure, there's a hell of a lot of oregano growing wild in that region, but what happens when the Western world decides it wants a lot of it? Especially since it takes 3,000 pounds of the tiny leaves to make 2 pounds of oil.

The vast majority of oregano oil manufacturers source from the mountains of Turkey, and it doesn't take much sniffing around to discover that Turkey does have a bit of an overharvesting problem. One 2009 report by the United Nations University on medicinal plant harvesting in a Turkish national park concluded, "There is an

DON'T BUY THESE NORTH AMERICAN HERBS WILD, GROW THEM INSTEAD!

The following North American herbs are listed as "at risk," which means they're fine to buy cultivated but never to buy wild—unless the herb is certified organic. For a list of seed companies that sell rare or endangered herbs so you can grow your own and boost populations, go to Seeds of Diversity at **seeds.ca**, which has a directory of heritage seed companies (many of which sell medicinal plant seeds). And talk to a herbalist about using a different herb in place of a threatened one. For instance, marshmallow root can be used instead of slippery elm, and raspberry leaf instead of false unicorn root. United Plant Savers' book *Planting the Future* lists sustainable substitutes for all the following at-risk herbs (**unitedplantsavers.org**).

- **American Ginseng** *Panax quinquefolius*
- Black Cohosh *Actaea racemosa (Cimicifuga)*
- Bloodroot *Sanguinaria canadensis*
- Blue Cohosh *Caulophyllum thalictroides*
- **Echinacea** *Echinacea spp.*
- Eyebright *Euphrasia spp.*
- False Unicorn Root *Chamaelirium luteum*
- **Goldenseal** *Hydrastis canadensis*
- Lady's Slipper Orchid *Cypripedium spp.*
- Lomatium *Lomatium dissectum*
- Osha *Ligusticum porteri, L. spp.*
- Slippery Elm *Ulmus rubra*
- Trillium, Beth Root *Trillium spp.*
- True Unicorn *Aletris farinosa*
- **Wild Yam** *Dioscorea villosa, D. spp.*

(Source: United Plant Savers; the ones in **bold** are the most popular in health stores)

urgent need for regulating and/or controlling the wild-collection of the [oregano] species traded at international level." It noted that one popular species, *Origanum minutiflorum,* is one of the top 50 most-threatened medicinal and aromatic plants in Turkey thanks to the intensity of collection. Another report, this time from Anadolu University in Turkey, noted that poorly educated collectors looking to earn some extra cash were ravaging wild stocks by harvesting them by hand (rather than with sharp tools), damaging or yanking out the roots unnecessarily. An even bigger problem are those collectors harvesting wild oregano when it's too young.

Not that all harvesting is problematic. There is sustainable wildcrafting going on too, and some mountain villages have been policing their own practices by starting oregano co-ops. The question is: does your brand of choice have any sustainability policies in place to safeguard wild groves? After speaking to several companies, it's clear that many are fuzzy on how the herbs are harvested in Turkey and can offer few details as green assurances.

Oregano oil's pioneering brand, **North American Herb and Spice** (marketed as **Oreganol P73**), says it actually owns land in Turkey and has conservation programs in place mandating how much villagers can pick. "We pay them more to pick less," say company reps. This is also among the top-reputed brands in the biz when it comes to quality. One Canadian company, **Pure-Li,** chooses not to get its oregano from the wild and instead cultivates it in fields without pesticides or herbicides. **Hedd Wyn** and **Joy of the Mountains** both use certified-organic wild oregano and organic olive oil. Now, "wild" and "certified organic" don't often go hand in hand, but Ecocert, the certifier in Turkey, checks that all wildcrafting practices are sustainable and that the herb isn't being overharvested, and collection sites are inspected once a year.

But how do you know how strong a product is? You've perhaps noticed carvacrol percentages listed on many brands (carvacrol being one of the important medicinal components in oregano oil). Some put this front and centre—i.e., "75% carvacrol"—but that doesn't mean your bottle contains 75% of the stuff. In Joy of the Mountains' case, the bottle is actually 75% organic olive oil, the other 25% being wild oregano with a minimum potency of 75% carvacrol. Many labels will tell you the ratio of oregano oil to olive oil (for example, 1:3 olive oil, or as high as 1:1 on some St. Francis bottles), but they don't always tell you how high the carvacrol content is. Holy confusing! Pure-Li is a little more direct on their front labels. Their bottles contain a grand total of 20% (or in the case of their super strength, 40%) of the active ingredient. Top dog Oreganol P73 says its oregano's carvacrol content (62% to 83%) is only part of a blend of natural phenols that makes its oil effective. It points to research showing that its blend beats pure carvacrol for efficacy (to be honest, Oreganol is the only oregano oil that has clinical research behind it). Many herbalists agree that maxed-out carvacrol content isn't necessarily a measure of a good oil. In fact, a good number will tell you that carvacrol content above 85% is somehow spiked. All that said, it's best to use carvacrol content as a rough potency gauge.

Endangered Ayurvedic Herbs: Traditional Indian Ayurvedic medicine has been healing with plant power for thousands of years. The only problem is that of the 359 medicinal herbs assessed by the government's botanical survey, 335 have been categorized as anywhere from near threatened to critically endangered. Pretty grim scene. India's Ministry of Environment and Forests concluded that, oh, 95% of Ayurvedic medicinal plants are snagged from the wild, and the vast majority of these are taken in such a way that the plant is killed. The Indian government is trying to figure out how to grow these plants on farms instead, but there's still a long way to go.

Take guggul, for instance. The tapped resin of this shrubby tree has been important in Ayurvedic medicine since as far back as records go (3,000 years, actually). But because it's been improperly tapped to such an extent (the damaging copper sulphate paste used on the trees to triple the resin yield ends up killing them), and because the plant is so slow growing and not really cultivated, guggul is now an endangered "Red Listed" species with the IUCN. As with all Ayurvedic herbs, don't buy it unless it explicitly says "certified organic" to ensure it's been cultivated, not wildcrafted, and harvested sustainably.

Some good brands that offer certified-organic Ayurvedic herbs include **Himalaya Pure Herbs, Organic Traditions** and **Tattva's Herbs** (himalayahealthcare.com, advantagehealthmatters.com, tattvasherbs.com). Not all of Himalaya's herbs are certified organic, but the company says they're all cultivated pesticide free, supporting largely female farmers paid fairly for their herbs (none of Himalaya's products are sourced from the wild except its honey). Quebec's **Clefs des Champs** and **St. Francis Herb Farm** carry a couple of certified-organic Indian herbs, including ashwagandha. To see whether an Indian plant you're using is on the threatened list, search the online database at the Government of India's Ministry of Environment and Forests Botanical Survey of India (though it doesn't cover all Ayurvedic herbs) (bsi.gov.in).

VITAMINS

I remember when Centrum was pretty much the only vitamin in most people's cupboard (that and maybe a bottle of Bayer Flintstones for the kids). And not too long ago, vitamin C was vitamin C was vitamin C; the only difference between two bottles was the brand name and the potency. Now you can get your C from whole foods supplements made of freeze-dried camu camu berries (see page 241) with organic amla fruit bioflavonoids. It's all part of the growing recognition that food is our best source for nutrients and that vitamins can't save you from a junky diet. Hallelujah, praise the lettuce!

Synthetic Vitamins: As more and more naturally sourced food-based vitamins appear in stores (demand for natural vitamins is expected to reach $7 billion by 2013), it's becoming clearer to consumers that most of the vitamins on shelves are synthetically sourced. Is that a problem? Well, it depends on who makes them, what they're made with and which precise vitamin we're talking about. Synthetic vitamin E (made of petrochemicals) is a notorious waste of money compared with the naturally sourced kind. On the other hand, synthetic melatonin is better absorbed than the natural variety. And Aileen Burford-Mason, president of the Holistic Health Research Foundation of Canada, says only 70% of us can get the folate out of food-sourced folic acid, whereas 100% of pregnant moms can absorb one synthetic type of folic acid called L-5 methyl-tetrahydrofolate (L-5-MTHF)—an important difference when trying to prevent birth defects. (Interestingly enough, pharma giant Merck patented the compound, trademarked it Metafolin, and only certain alt brands such as Metagenics, Thorne and Solgar are permitted to sell it.)

Who can keep track of which is the right one to swallow? You can eliminate the guesswork by buying from quality vitamin companies that prioritize the most highly absorbable forms of a supplement, be it natural or synthesized. Compared with cheap and even mid-grade brands, supplement insiders will tell you the top brands are differentiated by the form of vitamins they use. For instance, brands such as **AOR**, **Metagenics** and **Genestra,** which use both synthetic and natural sources, are famous for prioritizing nutrient forms and combinations that are high-absorption and are known for their research-based formulas. On the other hand, cheap brands you find at drugstores tend to use isolated vitamins/minerals that have poorer absorption rates (for example, calcium carbonate, synthetic vit E) as well as junky binders and fillers (such as maltodextrin, dicalcium phosphates, soybean oil, and aspartame in chewables) that lead to a crappy end product.

Let the Merck story about trademarked folic acid remind you that vitamins are big business, and ingredients are often supplied by major multinationals. The largest isolated-vitamin suppliers in the world include BASF (a chemical company), Pfizer (a pharmaceutical company) and DSM, which has its fingers in drugs, chemicals, plastics and more. Actually, DSM is the only supplier of synthetic vitamin C manufactured in the Western world; an astounding 80% of the world's vitamin C comes from China. When the government of China suddenly started enforcing pollution laws in 2007, their output of vitamin C crashed, making it clear just how polluting vitamin factories can be. According to the *Christian Science Monitor*, several vitamin C producers had to stop production altogether just to limit their waste water emissions.

Put all this together and you can kind of see why the U.S.-based Organic Consumers Association launched a campaign called Nutri-Con a few years back, arguing that the public is being misled about what they're consuming. The OCA suspects over 90% of vitamins contain some synthetics, ingredients that the OCA feels should be labelled to boost transparency.

- Look for supplements that don't load up your vitamins and minerals with junky fillers like maltodextrin, soybean oil, aspartame.
- Avoid tablets when you can; they're full of unnecessary fillers.
- Veggie-caps and gel capsules are much easier to break down in your body and have fewer fillers. Look for hexane-free gel caps whenever possible.

 NOT MUCH ORGANIC ABOUT ORGANIKA SUPPLEMENTS

You've heard my warnings about pseudo-organic personal care products with the words "organic" or "natural" built into their brand names to give them an aura of purity (see page 13), but who knew this practice extended to the vitamin aisle too? Case in point: Organika supplements from Richmond, B.C. Their slogan may be "Truth in a bottle," but their brand name is totally misleading since, in 2011, only five, count 'em *five*, of over 100 products in their line were actually certified organic (namely, their coconut oil, flaxseed oil, spirulina, coconut palm sugar and green barley). Let this be a lesson to you: don't judge a supplement by its cover! Always read the full ingredients to see whether the contents are actually certified organic.

Food-sourced Vitamins: These days, food-based supplement lines such as **New Chapter**, **Garden of Life** and **MegaFood** are made from a grocery basket of often organic dehydrated fruits and veggies, plant-based powders like **Greens+** are all the rage, and nearly every supplement maker is throwing grasses and berries into the mix. Keep in mind these are not necessarily 100% food based. Well-respected brands marketed as food sourced, such as MegaFood, may use an isolated synthesized vitamin as a base, culture it with probiotics to make it easily absorbed, then add certified-organic fruits, veggies and herbs. Ditto for New Chapter.

Food-sourced supplements aren't necessarily a clear-cut solution in part because they aren't in everyone's price range. High-end whole-food multis can cost up to $60 for a one-month supply, so conscious consumers on a budget are more likely to sprinkle food-based supplements in with synthetics. Also, food-sourced vits aren't available in the higher doses needed to treat particular diseases or ailments, so if your integrative physician suggests you take, say, 10,000 mg of vitamin C, you're going to have to get it the conventional way (but make sure there are natural bioflavonoids in there to help with digestion). FYI, Garden of Life had some trouble with the law in 2006 when the Federal Trade Commission in the United States charged the company with making false claims that clinical studies had proven their supplements treated cancer, leukemia, rheumatoid arthritis and more. Garden of Life settled for $225,000. They're barred from making any further such claims unless they have reliable proof.

- Don't let any supplements, no matter how revered, replace a healthy diet. Megadosing on fruits and vegetables and consuming healthy portions of true whole grains, organic dairy and carefully chosen proteins should really give you most of the nutrients your body needs.

SUPERFOODS

Superfoods are so hot right now, even good old blueberries have attained rock star status. It seems half the produce in our fridge has now got some sort of superpower, and companies are perpetually talking up the next exotic "superfood" from farther and farther afield. The whole thing was going a little too far for the EU, which decided in 2007 to bring in a ban on using the term unless a food item (such as, say, soy or spinach or Salba seeds) comes with an authorized health claim on what makes it so nutritious. Some hysteria ensued when rumours flew that goji berries would soon be removed from shelves, but that was never a possibility. What is true is that we all need to take a step back from the marketing hype and realize that the British Dietetic Association makes a good point: all fruits and vegetables should be labelled superfoods. Yes, some have more, say, vitamin C than others, but we need a healthy mix of all sorts of produce in our diets. Okay, so white potatoes and celery may have only so much value, but nutritional biochemists will tell you a portion of broccoli or spinach will give you more vitamins and minerals than a pricey shot of wheat grass, and you'll get more fill for your buck, too. Bottom line: I'd rather see you load up on local, organic produce in season whenever you can, rather than sink your budget on exotic imports such as noni juice or goji berries that have to be flown/ shipped/trucked in. And let's not forget, some of these superfoods do come packed with environmental implications. As a rule of thumb, fruit in general won't face threats of extinction, but exotic imports can and often are sprayed with dodgier pesticides than you'd find in North America. That means get your noni, mangosteen or raw cacao certified organic (and preferably fair trade).

Acai Berry: Everyone knows about the "Oprah Effect"—the Empress of TV's ability to turn most every product profiled on her now-defunct show into gold. It seems her favourite physician, Dr. Mehmet Oz, has a similar Midas touch when it comes to supplement recommendations. So when Dr. Oz was on the *Oprah* show in 2008 and placed a little-known South American wonder berry called acai (pronounced AH-sigh-EEE) on his anti-aging checklist, you can just imagine how many supplement makers made a beeline for the rainforest to track some down. Between 2007 and 2009, sales of products containing the antioxidant-rich berry exploded by 1400%, according to SPINS market research. So how is all this impacting the rainforest where it's being plucked? Greenpeace, in 2005, noted picking berries from the highly valued trees in living forests can be a great alternative to clear-cutting. But by 2008 the *L.A. Times* reported sprawling acai monoculture farms were actually responsible for knocking down diverse rainforest. The hands-down leader in sustainable acai is **Sambuzon**. Sambuzon offers certified fair-trade organic wild-picked acai berry products (sambuzon.com). Whatever you do, don't sign up for a free introductory acai offer on dodgy acai websites; they'll only end up scamming you and your credit card (as *Acai Berry Detox* and *Acai Berry Edge* have been found to). And beware of anyone making exaggerated health claims like, "Eat this and you'll lose 25 pounds and look 10 years younger." The U.S. Federal Trade Comission cracked down on "news" websites that were purporting to investigate the benefits of acai as a weight loss miracle food but were really just sham marketing sites. FYI, Oz ended up suing 40 Internet marketers and supplement makers for falsely claiming that he and the Big O endorsed their products and their wild claims.

Camu camu berries: If you're getting your vitamic C from food-sourced supplements, chances are high you're getting it from this tiny C-packed fruit. Fantastic, except that its popularity has been seriously stressing wild populations of the *myrciaria dubia*, a.k.a. camu camu tree, in the Peruvian Amazon. The good news is it's a relatively easy tree to grow and the Peruvian government has been promoting the cultivation of the camu camu tree to help boost rural incomes and kick-start a new export economy. And so far Amazonian farmers have largely been growing camu camu trees on small, diverse plots of previously cleared land, according to the president of the Rainforest Conservation Fund, Jim Penn, rather than clear-cutting rainforest to make way for this valuable crop. Still, even today, Penn says most camu camu is wild sourced. Definitley avoid any products that advertise they're wild. The best way to know yours isn't unsustainably

241

SEVEN SUPERFOODS TO ALWAYS BUY ORGANIC

Just because your favourite superfood is super healthy doesn't mean it comes without headaches. In fact, some of the biggest health boosters in your fridge may be laced with unwanted residues.

Blueberries: These antioxidant-dense berries are full of vitamins C and E as well as magnesium, selenium and fibre. Oh, and some of the highest pesticide residues—even after you wash them thoroughly. Up to 13 pesticides have been found on a single berry.

Cherries: The antioxidant anthocyanin in cherries is great for joints, and cherry juice is actually a surprising painkiller. These red wonders are also on the dirty-dozen list of produce high in pesticides, with 90% of cherry samples revealing chemical residues.

Green Tea: Green tea leaves are chock full of flavonoids and other cancer-fighting polyphenols that are definitely sip-worthy. The only problem is that pesticide residues have frequently been found on imported tea. Moreover, a 2005 study found that 32% of Chinese tea samples exceeded national standards for lead thanks to leaded gas air pollution. Until 2013, when leaded gas is phased out globally, look for green tea from Japan or Morocco (where gas is already unleaded) as well as certified-organic sources to be sure it's free of pesticide residues. (The Canadian Food Inspection Agency says all Japanese imports, including green tea, are screened to ensure they don't exceed radiation safety limits.)

Salmon: Gotta love salmon's omega-3 fatty acid–rich flesh. It just bites that the farmed stuff has 16 times more PCBs, dioxins and chemical pesticides than the wild kind. Spend the extra money and buy wild Pacific salmon. And remember, mackerel and herring actually have more omega-3s (sardines are tied with salmon) and fewer contaminants. Canned salmon is always wild, by the way.

Kale: Richer in antioxidants than almost any other vegetable. On top of vitamins C, K, A and beta carotene, it's got calcium, magnesium and much more. You can just taste the health. Too bad it's also the tenth most tainted piece of produce (75% of 20,000 samples had detectable pesticide residues).

Chocolate: Yes, dark chocolate is definitely the sexiest superfood, with many touted health benefits, but you want to make sure you avoid the usual pesticide-sprayed, labour-rights fiasco that is conventional west African–grown chocolate and get your fix from certified-organic/fair-trade sources instead. European studies found pesticide residues on 10% of chocolate.

Strawberries: Yet another über-beneficial berry loaded with antioxidants that's great for your heart, eyes, skin—pretty much every part of your body. It's also got the highest pesticide residues of any fruit besides peaches, and commonly carries about three types of pesticide on its skin. Get it organic instead!

wildcrafted is to look for certified-organic camu camu. You can get some in powdered form from Navitasnaturals.com (this one's USDA certified organic), **Organic Traditions** (advantagehealthmatters.com) and **Ojio** (myojio.squarespace.com).

Goji (wolfberry): Either dried or as juice, this red berry is one of the big stars of the superfoods world. There's no denying it's packed with beneficial vitamins, minerals, amino acids, phenols and much more. So what's the problem? Well, these berries are by and large grown in China, where pesticide use can be pretty ugly (the FDA has stopped several shipments of goji/wolfberry at the border because of illegal-pesticide concerns). Funny how no goji in town fesses up to coming from China. Actually, many goji juices don't tell you where their goji is grown, while others say it's wild-picked in Tibet. To avoid organic fakers, only get your certified-organic goji in health stores (not online), and look for brands such as **Organic Traditions** certified-organic goji and **Extreme Health USA** certified-organic and wild-crafted goji. By the way, another myth perpetuated by some goji companies is that Chinese peasants can't afford pesticides so the goji is naturally green. Don't buy it. What you should buy is certified-organic goji. Period.

Seaweed/Kelp: Whether wrapped around rice or dumped on fields as fertilizer, that slimy macroalgae known as seaweed has been put to creative use by coastal communities globe-wide for thousands of years. While most Westerners couldn't imagine ingesting the green goop that thrives on boat hulls and rocky shores until sushi came along, our spas have been tapping into the health properties of sea vegetables in wraps and treatments for years now. Although governments no longer publicly advocate kelp as a protective treatment against radioactive fallout, as they did in the '50s, several seaweeds are still recommended for radioactive and heavy-metal detoxification (no wonder seaweed supplements vanished from shelves in B.C. after the Japanese nuclear disaster).

But just as they're useful for absorbing toxins from your system, the spongy weeds are also able to suck up pollutants from the sea. Some regions have used various species to help clean up polluted waters and DDT-contaminated soil. One type of invasive, genetically altered algae, *Caulerpa*, so thrives on agricultural runoff and sewage that it smothers other organisms in dirty waters. Actually seaweed feasts on the nitrogen-rich fertilizer running off farms into rivers and into the sea to the point that those seaweed blooms creative massive "dead zones" inhospitable to all other underwater life. It's all quite horrifying and you have to wonder if what's on your plate and in your supplements is also loaded with toxins from the deep.

Many seaweed suppliers tell you their goods come from clean waters, but what constitutes clean? Seven of the kelp supplements tested by the University of California, Davis in 2007 failed to meet U.S. Food and Drug Administration standards for arsenic in food. The journal *Environmental Health Perspectives* published a case report of one woman

244

whose kelp-rich diet gave her high levels of arsenic, which created mental confusion and dizziness and accelerated her hair loss. A year later, Health Canada was warning consumers not to use the natural health product Trophic Kelp & Glutamic Acid HCI due to the health risks posed by exposure to high levels of iodine (that was in '08).

Blue-green Algae: Things get a little more muddled when you're talking about blue-green algae other than spirulina. Basically the stuff you'll find in health stores comes from natural blooms in Klamath Lake, Oregon, and it's got a totally unsexy name: Aphanizomenon flos-aquae, or AFA. It's often called "the most ancient food on earth." The big problemo is that Health Canada's 1999 report noted: "Testing indicates that for many non-spirulina blue-green algal products, harvested from natural lakes, natural consumption according to manufacturer's directions results in a daily intake of microcystins above that considered acceptable by Health Canada and the World Health Organization." A 2005 study found all 12 blue-green algae supplement samples tested contained toxigenic cyanobacteria. Now, products such as **E3Live** say they test each batch to make sure contamination falls below regulatory levels for drinking water. **Chlorella** doesn't have this problem because it's mostly grown in man-made ponds. Ditto for spirulina.

FISH OILS

Forget Filet-O-Fish; we North Americans love our fish in capsules. Depending on who's doing the ranking, fish oil is always one of the top three most popular supplements (one 2011 survey found it's knocked multivitamins out of first place!). Either way, we swallow a billion dollars' worth of this omega-3-rich oil a year. Now, eco-conscious fish fans know that our seafood is swimming in a sea of industrial chemicals and that those fish kindly return those pollutants to their makers (yes, us) whenever they enter our bellies via a fork or chopsticks. At the same time, we know that fish oils nourish our hearts/minds/eyes/moods/skin/joints. So more and more of us buy from supplement makers who source their oils from smaller fish and screen for impurities. Overall, smaller fish such as sardines and anchovies have fewer contaminants in the vast majority of cases (menhaden fished near the industry-heavy shores of American Atlantic states are an exception). Health Canada, for instance, found the highest contaminant levels in shark oil, and FishOilSafety.com found the highest levels in two brands of salmon and cod liver oil. But even smaller fish that have impurities which are screened using state-of-the-art distillers—including those coming from deep Nordic waters and small sardine fish—can contain traces of the nasty compounds. It's impossible to avoid toxins entirely, just as you'll find trace pollutants in organic food and in mother's milk. They're everywhere. Is it worth giving up the many body-enlivening benefits of fish oils to avoid those traces?

Health outcome studies say fish oils are worth it. Keep in mind that eating a portion of fish every day would deliver more pollutants to your system than swallowing a couple doses of fish oil a day (and eating nine portions a week of high-mercury fish meals would offset a lot of fish oil's benefits, according to a 2010 study). Still, can we get tougher on oils to bring contaminants down further? Absolutely. Health Canada does have federal limits for the intake of PCBs, dioxins and certain pesticides in fish oil, but the standard is many times weaker than California's and really only demands that a company test its fish once. Seriously? Health Canada's own testing has found that one batch of shark oil from one species might have relatively high, but still acceptable, levels, while the next batch from another species from a different part of the world can have more worrisome levels. As a general rule, stick to oils made from small fish (herring, sardines, anchovies, mackerel), and search for indications that the oils have been purified in some way. U.S.-based Environmental Defense Fund's Fish Oil Supplement Guide only grades supplements on whether they say they purify their fish oils; EDF hasn't done its own testing or rated for sustainability (edf.org).

Sustainability of Fish Oil: Beyond our own navel-gazing health concerns, how sustainable is our fish oil habit for the health of the global fisheries? The smaller sort (sardines, mackerel, anchovies) are generally considered the most ecological. When the U.S. Environmental Defense Fund surveyed fish supplements a few years ago, it noted that while small fish reproduce quickly, making them resilient to fishing pressures, the fisheries themselves don't necessarily get the ecological green light. Basically, the EDF said marine predators such as seabirds and whales all rely on small fish for their survival, yet "these factors are rarely considered in setting catch limits for reduction fisheries." Interestingly enough, the eco-supermarket Whole Foods banned krill fish oils from its stores in 2010 for that very reason (Antarctic sea animals dependent on krill are in decline) after a coalition of 30 enviro organizations complained about how krill was getting certified as sustainable. Even with small fish, sustainability depends on where it's caught. European anchovies, for instance, have been critically overfished, but Peruvian anchovies have made a comeback, and that country has sought certification by the Marine Stewardship Council (some MSC-certified fisheries have been heavily critiqued by environmentalists as being less than sustainable, but the Peruvian anchovy fishery is off the hook, so to speak). Enviros agree that some of the worst eco-offenders are supplements made from overharvested menhaden from the United States, like that found in OmegaPure. Be sure to press your fish oil company of choice for details on its sourcing. Too few tell customers exactly where their fish comes from. Not great considering 20% of fish supplements sold in North America come from China, where environmental standards are notoriously lax. Sourcing isn't necessarily listed on labels, so check a company's website before you buy.

Best Choices for Fish Oil: My very favourite fish oil brand is **Ascenta NutraSea**, which gets its sardines and anchovies (and a little mackerel) off the coldwater coast of Peru, certified by the Marine Stewardship Council. Ascenta has a strict policy against using unsustainable fish such as krill, shark, cod and tuna. Bonus: 1% of their profits go to the David Suzuki Foundation and Environmental Defence (ascentahealth.com). Ascenta gets every batch third-party-tested for purity by Pure Check. Among the 24 products that ConsumerLab.com selected for review, only 17 passed quality testing (meaning they were as fresh, pure and high potency as promised). Some of the ones that passed are **Garden of Life's Oceans 3** (anchovies and sardines), **New Chapter's Wholemega** (100% wild Alaskan salmon, which gets the environmental thumbs-up), **Nordic Naturals' DHA** (anchovies and sardines, mostly from Peru where the fishery is certified), and **Quest** (anchovies, salmon and sardines, though some come with environmentally suspect tuna). All fell below detectable mercury levels in this testing.

Fish-free Oils: Strict vegetarians already know you can get omega-3 from flax and hemp, but they don't contain the same beneficial EPA and DHA. Flax and hemp oils have another omega-3 called ALA, which can be converted into DHA and EPA in healthy individuals, but fish oils still score better in heart- and brain-boosting studies. Luckily for those looking to get the best omegas from fish-free sources, there are algae-based supplements. You can track down some algal supplements that have DHA and EPA on the Net (for example, v-pure.com from the U.K.), but if you ask at Canadian health stores, all their algae omegas to date primarily focus on DHA only. Hopefully, we'll be seeing more combined DHA/EPA algal supplements on shelves soon.

SAY NO TO SHARK OIL (EVEN IN YOUR HEMORRHOID CREAM)

Look, I know some of you are attached to your shark oil–based remedies. But listen, sometimes we've got to consider the bigger picture. Can you imagine buying supplements made of wild elephant ivory to treat your aches and pains? There are a ton of other great supplements out there for what ails you (see Pain Relievers, page 195), but there aren't plenty more big fish in the sea. We're down to 10% of large predators left in the ocean, and a healthy population of sharks is vital to the stability of the oceanic food chain. True, some brands, such as Bell Lifestyle Products, argue their cartilage comes from by-products of the restaurant industry, not sharks illegally finned. But these days, even grocers as big as Loblaws, Sobeys and Metro are banning shark from their fish counters because of serious sustainability worries. And by the way, Health Canada tests on fish oils found the highest levels of DDT, PCBs and other contaminants in shark oil.

So, pretty please with a cherry on top, stay away from products made of shark cartilage or oils (they can be sold under trademarked names such as **Carticin, Cartilade, BeneFin and Neovastat**). Make sure your chondroitin supplements get their cartilage from somewhere else (bovine sources are at no risk of being endangered) and see page 205 for more on alternative arthritis supplements. Oh and kindly call Preparation H (which adds shark liver oil to their ointments) and tell them to stick their shark oil formulations where the sun don't shine until they reformulate. (Instead, look for all-natural anti-inflammatory hemorrhoid products that get their power from herbs, including **DermaMed Hemorrhoid Cream, Sprunk Jansen's Anusalve**, Quebec-based **Herbasanté's Hemoropax** cream, as well as all-natural cocoa butter–based suppositories by **Boiron**.)

Good news: some health stores, including Whole Foods Market, stopped carrying shark supplements (ask your local shop), and several brands, including Natural Factors, Holista and Solgar, have stopped making shark cartilage products altogether. Now if we can just convince the rest of them, such as Swiss Natural, Sisu, Organika and NOW Foods, to do the same. While we're on the topic, why don't you ask them to stop selling shark cartilage (info@swissnatural.com, orginfo.organika.com, and call NOW: 1-888-669-3663 and Sisu: 1-800-663-4163).

MINERALS

Just like the symbiotic relationship of yin to yang or Donny to Marie, your body needs essential minerals to function as much as it needs vitamins. We typically get plenty of both from the foods we eat (unless you're chowing down on Ding Dongs). Think vitally important magnesium from dark leafy greens, nuts and beans, calcium from dairy products, dark greens and canned bony fish such as sardines, phosphorus from milk, grains and protein-rich foods. Those three minerals alone are vital to bone health and so much more. Nutritionists will tell you that a healthy, well-rounded diet can give you all the minerals you need, but the truth is, most of us aren't eating a complete diet (even if you think you are), and mineral deficiencies are behind a litany of health problems in Canada today (magnesium, iron and zinc deficiencies being the biggest ones). But since this world isn't just about *your* health, it's time for the inevitable Ecoholic question: can any of our dietary mineral sources be greener?

Calcium: Ladies, is it just me or does the threat of not getting enough calcium sometimes make you feel like the world is run by the yogurt mafia? As a lactose-intolerant chick with enough grey hairs to know that osteoporosis could be just around the corner, I'm often told I don't ingest enough calcium. Clearly, many of us are feeling the same pressure since calcium is one of the most popular supplements on the market. Still, there's a lot of confusion around how much, if any, and which type of calcium you should take—a discussion that only gets more complicated when you consider the environmental implications of certain cal pills. Calcium carbonate, extracted from limestone mining or quarrying, is definitely the cheapest and most common form of calcium supplement, but it's also poorly absorbed compared with another common form, calcium citrate (which is a calcium salt of citric acid; you need some limestone powder to manufacture this one too). What about trendier forms?

Coral Calcium: For a while there, coral calcium was being touted as one of those direct-line-to-god cure-alls for everything from cancer to diabetes, but those claims got smacked down as fraudulent by the U.S. Federal Trade Commission. Still, marketers continue to upsell the benefits of the coral calcium in their water as the secret behind the longevity of Okinawans—never mind their obvious life-extending diet/ lifestyle and lifelong activity levels. Most coral calcium makers also claim that the coral they use is all on the eco up and up, but the story is always muddier than it appears.

If the calcium is sourced below sea level, a.k.a. "marine grade," then it largely involves vacuuming up weathered coral sand and broken bits near delicate coral reefs, which Reef Check says may disrupt and damage these threatened structures. Japan says it's all being gathered in accordance with local laws. Still, how pure are those deposits with so much pollution swimming around? The *Journal of the American Dietetic Association* has slammed Okinawan coral reefs for disconcerting levels of lead and mercury, and one high-profile marine-grade calcium was outed for high lead content by ConsumerLab.com (a coral cal by Robert Barefoot). Ancient coral calcium gathered above sea level is considered more sustainable, since it's mined from fossilized Okinawan deposits that have been pushed above the waterline over eons and are now on land. But at this point in their history, these are really just a type of limestone rock. And yep, according to the Japanese Ministry of Environment, they've got a lot of limestone to go around.

The biggest no-no is live coral. One company claims to have the sole Brazilian licence to gather live coral that happens to wash ashore on north Brazil's coastline, though claims that over 5,000 tons of live coral can appear on a 300-metre stretch of beach after a storm seem a little far-fetched. What I can tell you is that orgs such as Reef Check know of dodgy live coral mining that happens in the South Pacific even though no company owns up to getting their coral from there. Considering the heavy implications of getting it wrong and toying with the future of reefs worldwide, Whole Foods Market avoids coral calcium altogether, and you should strongly consider doing the same.

Algae-based Calcium: For higher bioavailability with a clearer conscience, many naturopaths point to algae-based calcium. AlgaeCal hand-harvests tennis ball–sized live algae balls that wash up on remote South American shores, has them tested for contaminants, and gets them USDA-certified organic to verify the sustainability of the harvest and the distance from pollution sources. These guys have good data backing their product as a highly absorbable bone builder, too. The big problem is that in 2011 the supplement quality watchdog ConsumerLab.com revealed that AlgaeCal contained worrisome levels of lead: 3.9 to 5.3 mcg of lead for a daily serving of three to four capsules, when California standards limit lead to .5 mcg per day. AlgaeCal isn't contesting the lead findings, but it claims the contamination is okay because the lead is naturally occurring. Sorry, but that's just bogus. FYI, some Garden of Life bone health products and certain Nature's Plus items contain AlgaeCal-based supplements (New Chapter used to but switched suppliers).

Other algae-based calcium supplements get theirs from a company that vacuums up red algae skeletons from the ocean floor off Ireland and Iceland. The supplier (Celtic Sea Minerals/Marigot Limited) also sells large quantities to the fertilizer and animal food industry, which may raise eyebrows, but certifier Organic Trust does vouch for it being sustainably harvested. FYI, while Organic Trust says it's approved this seaweed as an additive to organic products, it's false to call the algae itself certified organic, as some brands do. Some brands that use Celtic Sea Minerals algae as their calcium source include **New Chapter's Bone Strength Take Care**, as well as **Swanson's Aquamin** and **NOW Foods' Red Mineral Algae**.

MCHA Calcium: A whole slew of mid-range to high-end vitamin makers offer up bone health supplements made with MCHA calcium (microcrystalline hydroxyapatite). It's considered to be another highly absorbable form of calcium and is favoured by many naturopaths, though it's not a vegetarian pick. It comes from the bones of young New Zealand grass-fed, free-range, antibiotic- and hormone-free cattle, which naturally offer up a calcium/magnesium/phosphorus combo that boosts bone health. **AOR, Metagenics, Garden of Life, Natural Factors** and **New Roots** all make MCHA-based calcium supplements. Heads-up: ConsumerLab.com found in 2009 testing that Garden of Life Living Calcium Advanced failed to contain promised levels of calcium and vitamins K1 and K2. For more on their calcium testing see ConsumerLab.com.

MISSING IN ACTION: WHEN PROBIOTICS DON'T MEASURE UP

Look, the supplement world isn't perfect. Health Canada's Natural Health Product Directorate has been regulating natural health products since 2004, but still, some supplements slip through that don't contain what they claim on the bottle. Just spend two minutes on ConsumerLab.com and you'll notice that Kirkland Signature B-100 Hi-Energy Complex only contained 17.9% of its claimed B12 content when tested in 2010, and Joint Strength Essentials by MegaFood had no detectable chondroitin in 2009 even though it promised 400 mg.

Probably the single most disappointing category is probiotics. Since these products contain live cultures, supplements on shelves can have a problem delivering what they promise. Some had as little as 7% to 58% of the probiotics promised. Swiss Natural Sources "5" Strain Dophilus claimed to give you 6 billion, but testing turned up a piddly 0.8 billion. DDS Acidophilus by UAS Laboratories promised 5 billion at the time of manufacture but only 1.8 billion turned up; meanwhile, their Probioplus DDS passed. Otherwise well-respected Metagenics also blew it on the probiotics testing. The worst was Dr. D Chocolate Flavoured Probiotics for kids, which only had 31 million live probiotics—an upsetting 7% of what was promised. So which brands actually passed? New Chapter Organics Probiotic All-Flora, Udo's Choice (which lists both content at time of manufacture as well as amount expected before expiration), Kyo-Dophilus, Nature Made Acidophilus and Solgar, though these last two promised only a billion or less. For more tests on all sorts of supplements, see **ConsumerLab.com**.

Dietary Sources of Calcium: Ultimately, you should be aware that the medical community is now saying we may be taking too many calcium supplements and really ought to be relying on dietary sources first and foremost (think organic dairy, almonds and certain greens such as broccoli and kale, but not spinach or Swiss chard, whose calcium your body doesn't readily absorb).

- While too little calcium is linked to bone fractures and osteoporosis in women, megadosing isn't necessarily better. One large study

253

found that high levels didn't do much to prevent fractures. The research is ongoing. And of note, calcium supplements, with or without vitamin D, have been linked to a "modest" increase of heart disease in post-menopausal women, according to an updated meta-analysis by the *British Medical Journal* released in 2011. You should talk to your health practitioner about where calcium fits in your own health care plan.

- Make sure that whatever calcium you take is nestled in a whole matrix of vitamins and minerals, such as magnesium and vitamin D, as well as K, manganese, boron, zinc, etc. Any of the brands mentioned in this calcium section would qualify.
- Getting enough vitamin D is now thought to be more important to your bone health than calcium, so make sure you get enough. Talk to your health practitioner.

WEIGHT LOSS REMEDIES

We know that diet and exercise are really the only tried-and-true way to lose weight, but wouldn't it be dreamy if you could just pop a pill that miraculously slimmed you down with no effort? With 47% of Canadian adults and 63% of American adults classified as either overweight or obese, it's little wonder there are a 1,001 natural products on shelves claiming they can help melt away the pounds. And they're often the most prominently placed supplements in health stores. But wouldn't you know it, too many of them have ended up proving to be dodgy in some way or another. Health Canada actually recalled 68 specific brands of so-called natural or herbal weight loss supplements in 2009 because they were caught pawning undeclared prescription-only ingredients (including phenolphthalein, which had been taken off the market because of cancer concerns, and phenytoin, whose side effects include speech and vision problems).

But what about all those other quick-slim supplements still on shelves? A lot of them are riddled with sustainability headaches, others with contamination woes. In 2010, **ConsumerLab.com** found that a couple of herbal weight loss formulas (namely, Mega-T Green Tea and Dexatrim Max) were tainted with cancer-causing hexavalent chromium (the pollutant made famous by the film *Erin Brockovich*). And if you think for a second any weight loss pill is going to help you magically melt away noticeable amounts of fat without any effort, well, you might as well jog around the block with the word "sucker" taped on your forehead. At least that way you'll actually burn a few calories.

Hoodia: When a program as weighty as *60 Minutes* dedicated air time to the *potentially* amazing appetite-suppressing power of an African cactus called *Hoodia gordonii*, sales went through the roof. Fabulous and all, except that the Kalahari only has so much hoodia — much of which is heavily stressed. It's a protected plant in most of South Africa, Botswana and Namibia, but illegal harvesting is a massive problem. That's not to say you can't get legal sources of hoodia; the seller just has to have a valid permit approved by the Convention on the International Trade in Endangered Species of Wild Fauna and Flora (CITES). Environment Canada says illegal shipments of the diet pill are intercepted daily at mail centres, courier offices and airports in every major Canadian city. During the summer of 2006 alone, 2,000 shipments were stopped.

Note: Unilever walked away from developing a hoodia product in 2009. Why? It stopped its trials when it discovered the compound raised blood pressure levels and had no major impact on calorie consumption.

Forskolin: Another rising diet supplement is forskolin. It's made from the root of the Indian plant *Coleus forskohlii* and is unfortunately endangered in India and in China, where it also grows. The United Nations Food and Agriculture Organization says natural resources of *C. forskohlii* are being conserved through efforts to cultivate it for medicinal use, but even while cultivation is expanding, supply is still limited, so prices are high. Make sure you're not buying wild-sourced forskolin.

Other Natural Weight Loss Supplements: If you want a sustainable weight loss tool from the supplement world, swallow trendy **konjac root** before your meals (the root sort of looks like a yam and is grown in India, China, Korea and Japan). The glucomannan fibre in there bulks up in your stomach and keeps you feeling full longer (plus, it's a cholesterol lowerer). Highly touted **PGX** contains the stuff. Although really, high intake of any dietary fibre will help do the same thing and has been shown to reduce your calorie intake and food ingestion because the fibre basically fills you up. As with all fibre, drink plenty of fluids to avoid constipation and bloating, and keep in mind that your smartest weight loss plan is a diet high in fibre-rich foods (lots of whole grains, beans, veggies and fruit).

Another promising compound without environmental concerns is **fucoxanthin** or **brown seaweed extract.** This is turning up in more and more health store weight loss supplements, and the good news is that studies on humans have finally been done and the results are looking pretty encouraging. A study published in the journal *Diabetes, Obesity and Metabolism* concluded that a combination of fucoxanthin and pomegranate oil (like you'll find in **Xanthigen** and **Garden of Life's fücoTHIN**) "promoted weight loss, reduced body and liver fat content, and improved liver function tests in obese non-diabetic women."

A meta-analysis of three clinical studies on green coffee extracts (GCE), including ingredients branded as Svetol and CoffeeSlender, indicate GCE *may* promote a little weight loss, but more research is needed to draw clear conclusions. If you're still keen to fork out cash to experiment on yourself, **Genuine Health Go4Trim** contains glucomannan from konjac root, decaffeinated coffee extract Svetol, mood-boosting 5-HTP and glucose-metabolizing chromium polynicotinate.

If you're eyeballing other compounds, be sure at the very least to do a Google Scholar or PubMed search to see if you can find any clinical evidence backing claims. By and large, you'd be better off spending that time actually surfing, not Web surfing.

ENDANGERED ANIMALS

One of the biggest global threats faced by endangered animals comes from our unusual appetite for trying to cure what ails us with bizarre animal parts. Thankfully, Canada isn't really a hotbed for dried tiger penises or rhino horns like, say, Hong Kong is, but that doesn't mean it's time to get complacent about the medicinal use of threatened and endangered animals in this country. Canadian black bears, for instance, are still being poached for their gallbladders and bile; deer and seal are being illegally killed for their penises; and elk are shot for their velvet antlers. Over 600 types of traditional Chinese medicines have been stopped at the border, containing 40 different endangered species (both animals and plants). Many Canadian companies actually get a permit through the *Convention on International Trade of Endangered Species* (CITES) to legally import endangered species, but plenty are still being smuggled in, according to Environment Canada. In a precedent-setting case, one guy received an 18-month sentence in 2007 after pleading guilty to illegally importing traditional Chinese medicines from endangered turtle and tortoise shells, coral and more. Another company only got fined $1,500 for importing 6,000 packages of threatened saiga antelope horn. Bottom line: tell your TCM that you want to stay far away from anything endangered or threatened. You'll find that most practitioners in Canada feel the same way.

ECOHOLIC WEIGHT LOSS PLAN
(SHED POUNDS OF CARBON FAST!)

Do you ever eye up fat-burning products at the health store wondering if maybe, just maybe, they're the solution you've been looking for? Have you tried dieting more times than you can count but just can't stay motivated? Forget counting calories—try counting carbon instead! Yes, with my patent pending* Ecoholic Diet, you can slash your carbon footprint and lose a few pounds too! Okay, fine, so it might not attract as many followers as sexy celebrity-endorsed meal plans, but I can tell you unequivocally that the fat content of the old Atkins scheme is sure to give the planet, and some of its followers, a coronary. It's time to kick yo-yo dieting to the curb and try a way of eating (and living) that I guarantee is sustainable for both you and the ecosystem.

* Patent not really pending.

#1 Munch on less meat. Red meat in particular has a massive environmental/carbon footprint, but even pork and chicken come with carbon bloat. Instead of a burger (which gobbles 11 kg of carbon) or a turkey sandwich (500 grams of CO_2), a hummus and grilled veg sandwich has just 270 grams, and makes a tasty, filling and weight-conscious lunch. If you're willing to try going all the way veg, you'll have a team of climatologists, ecologists (and animal lovers) applauding you!

#2 Chew on less cheese. While I'm lactose intolerant, I'm not going to lie, I love my goat cheeses, and I'll gladly pop a Lactaid if you're making a veggie lasagna. But the truth is, a 2010 UN report said all animal products, both meat and dairy, cause higher emissions than plant-based alternatives. Try having two fewer portions of cheese a week, and skip rich cheese and butter in favour of yogurt, which eatlowcarbon.org notes has a smaller CO_2 footprint.

#3 OD on veggies (and eat with the seasons!). Plant-based foods, hands-down, have the slimmest carbon waistline, plus they're full of filling fibre and body-boosting nutrients to keep your system humming and jean-size dropping. Just keep in mind that seasonal fruits and veggies pack less CO_2 than the greenhouse-grown kind.

#4 Walk and bike to the store/work/woods/wherever. Working

more natural exercise into your daily routine is so much more sustainable and affordable than getting a gym membership you only use for three months (as most people do) or buying a treadmill that gathers dust. Leaving

the car at home is probably the single fastest way to wiggle into a new pair of pants and trim away pollution pounds. Plus, it will naturally weave 30 to 60 minutes of exercise into your day in small increments without you even breaking a full Zumba-style sweat.

#5 Commit to gadget-free

Sundays. Unplugging your computer/gaming machine/TV/DVD player as well as abstaining from iPhone games will get you off the couch and moving. See what's happening outside your front door and start connecting with the people and places in your community. Getting active with the support of a mini village will make sticking to the Ecoholic Diet way more gratifying.

Lung Health	263
Hay Fever/Seasonal Allergies	265
Cancer	267
Environmental Sensitivity	271
ADHD	274
Autism	278

ENVIRONMENTAL HEALTH

What goes around comes around

Let's not pussy-foot around here:

we live in a dirty world. Even if you don't reside in a smoggy urban centre, even if you live in the deep north surrounded by white, driven snow, we all have chemical contaminants floating through our bloodstreams to prove our place in the global village. Besides the broader industrial pollution we swim in every day, we're constantly inundated with a cocktail of compounds used to clean toilets, spritz wrists, retard flames, de-bug produce, bind furniture, you name it. Combine all that with other compromising co-factors swirling around in our environment, from tobacco smoke to mould, and why are we surprised that many human ailments and illnesses are influenced by, if not rooted in, our surroundings? Are we really still, well over a decade into the new millennium, taken aback by the possibility that thousands of officially "known"/"possible"/"suspected" carcinogens and hormone disruptors might just have an impact on the human body? And yet the concept is still a controversial one in many conventional allopathic medical circles. With Health Canada having taken a stand on toxins above any other environmental issue for a few years now, at least there's some official acknowledgement that, yes, Timmy, there really are toxins we shouldn't be living with. Personally, having had a brother plagued by numerous environmental ailments, I have deep respect for those with pollution-triggered conditions; you're our canaries in the coal mine. But will we heed the warning?

LUNG HEALTH

Can't catch your breath? Air outside (or inside) your home leaving
you wheezing? No one suffers the effects of air pollution faster than
someone with lung trouble. A wheezy 3 million Canadians are affected
by asthma and, yes, dust, dander and pollen are big factors in their
breathing, but a study published in the journal *Environmental Health
Perspectives* found that childhood asthma could jump by 30% in areas
with high traffic pollution. Another study published in the *New England
Journal of Medicine* in 2009 fingered long-term exposure to the ozone
in smog as the culprit behind 20% of lung-related deaths. But there are
many more elements in your surroundings that can leave you breathless,
including cleaning chemicals, perfume, formaldehyde off-gassing from
pressed wood, as well as dietary allergies. Bacteria might play a role
too. A 2010 study published in the journal *Science* concluded that
babies born via C-section (which they called "a more sterile entry into
the world") are more likely to get asthma, as are young children treated
with too many antibiotics. Thankfully, asthma cases have recently
dropped among two-to-seven-year-olds, largely because of the increase
in adults smartening up and quitting smoking (if you smoke in the
house or in your car with your child, you might as well just hand them
a pack of their own). But overall, asthma rates are on the rise, and the
number of men and women living with chronic bronchitis and
emphysema—collectively known as chronic obstructive pulmonary
disease—is also climbing.

Inhalers: Up until 2005 in Canada (and late 2011 in the United
States), asthma inhalers were actually fuelled with CFCs. Yes, *those*
CFCs that burned holes in the ozone layer in the '80s. For some
reason, asthma pumps were still slipping through the cracks years
after other products had to phase the stuff out. In the interim, the
10.7 million inhalers Canadians purchased in 1996 alone pumped out
214 metric tons of CFCs, according to Environment Canada. Today,
you can breathe easier knowing that, at the very least, your inhaler isn't
damaging the ozone layer; however, the common propellant replacing

CFCs is still a greenhouse gas—HFC134a (hence why inhalers have made up a sizable portion of GlaxoSmithKline's carbon footprint). There's no denying inhalers are necessary for countless Canadians, but it's interesting to note that numerous studies have found that overuse of some inhalers actually increases the risk of getting an asthma attack. Scientists have pegged the propensity for decreased sensitivity to certain asthma drugs on a gene variation, but how are you to know if you have that gene? Docs caution to use your inhaler only as prescribed.

Breathing Exercises: Alternative-health practitioners say you can limit the frequency and severity of asthma attacks with breathing exercises (kind of like push-ups for your lungs). This is particularly true for those with chronic obstructive pulmonary disease (emphysema or chronic bronchitis) or anyone whose asthma attacks are worsened by chronic hyperventilation. While mainstream practitioners tend not to prescribe it, the British Guideline on the Management of Asthma says the Buteyko Breathing Technique can be used to help control the symptoms of asthma. If you're curious, search for a Buteyko practitioner near you or order a DVD (buteyko.com).

Supplements for Lung Health: If you have trouble getting a good lungful of air, there are a few supplements you can consider taking to help improve your bronchial woes in the long term (remember, though: popping a supplement won't replace your inhaler when you're having an attack). Talk to a holistic practitioner about what's right for you.

- If your asthma is exercise induced, your health provider may suggest one to two grams of **vitamin C**, which studies have shown might be particularly useful in this case (one study published in *Respiratory Medicine* found results with 1500 mg).
- Fish oil may not work for everyone, but again, if your bronchial problems are exercise induced, taking 1 to 1.2 grams of EPA- and DHA-rich **fish oils** per day may help (just make sure you pick the sustainable kind; see Fish Oils, page 245).

- For mild to moderate asthma, a 2010 study published in the journal *Asthma* found that twice-daily doses of **magnesium** helped improve objective and subjective measures of asthma control and quality of life.
- On the plant-based front, the gum resin **boswellia** as well as herbal **butterbur** may reduce the number and severity of asthma attacks, but they shouldn't replace a doctor-prescribed management plan. Think of them as complementary medicine, and always talk to a herbalist or naturopath before taking them. Boswellia is near threatened in the wild, so be sure to buy it certified organic (Organic Traditions carries some).

Note: The USFDA issued a warning in 2010 against taking one particular natural supplement for asthmatics, Vita Breath, after a NYC patient got lead poisoning from the stuff. Turns out it contained more than 10,000 times the FDA's limits for lead in candy.

Diet: Some foods, such as dairy, wheat and sulphite-laced items including dried fruit, bottled lemon juice and wine, can trigger wheezing. Try eliminating one at a time and see how you feel. Also, the Canadian Lung Association warns that conventional cleaning products, paints, synthetic perfumes, air fresheners and pesticides can all worsen asthma symptoms.

Protest: Tougher air pollution laws are what will really help give your lungs a break. Email your local councillor and provincial representative about bringing in stronger emission control regs on area polluters, shutting down any coal plants that might still be active in your province, and developing better mass transit and bike lanes near you.

HAY FEVER/SEASONAL ALLERGIES

So spring has sprung, the grass has riz, and you're running out, tissue in hand, to stockpile antihistamines. Well, wouldn't you know it, just when pollen is at its peak, trace residues of over-the-counter antihistamines in waste water and adjacent river samples are also at their highest. In particular, researchers have found the cetirizine in Reactine, the acrivastine in Benadryl Allergy Relief and the fexofenadine in Allegra floating out of sewage treatment plants and making their way downstream. What are the enviro ramifications? Who knows? It has yet to be studied. In the meantime, at least Claritin's loratadine and Aerius's desloratadine weren't detected in any samples, so we can only guess that they maybe break down more readily. But wouldn't you feel better experimenting with natural, pharma-free solutions instead?

- European native **butterbur** has actually been tested against cetirizine (Reactine) and fexofenadine (Allegra) in two separate trials and has come out shining. The *British Medical Journal* study point-blank found it just as effective, without the drowsy side effects. Try this as a first line of defence against seasonal allergies.
- Naturopaths also often suggest the natural bioflavonoid **quercetin** between meals for several weeks. Studies have found it suppresses the release and/or production of inflammation-boosting histamines and leukotrienes, though studies on allergy sufferers are lacking. For better absorption, take it with bromelain, unless you're allergic to pineapples.
- There are a number of herbal formulas to help with bronchial issues such as hay fever and allergies, including **Sun Force's RespirActin**.
- Get yourself some **spirulina**. Studies have found daily consumption improves hay fever symptoms, including runny nose, congestion, sneezing and itching.
- If burning eyes are driving you batty, **Similasan Allergy Eye Relief** drops are great for calming itchy, burning, watery red eyes.
- To clear your nose, get yourself a **neti pot** and start doing regular nasal douches with salt water. Feels bizarre at first, but you'll learn to love what it does for your sinuses.

IS CLIMATE CHANGE MAKING YOUR ALLERGIES WORSE?

Allergy sufferers should really have their own mascots: Itchy, Sneezy, Wheezy, Runny, Snotty and Cranky. That last one is especially thrilled to know that allergy seasons just keep getting worse. Keep in mind that local weather triggers will vary from year to year and place to place. In 2011, an especially wet winter and spring in many parts of the country made it feel as if blooming trees and growing grass were bursting with more pollen than ever. But the overarching long-term pattern is undeniable: climate change is extending the allergy season. In a report called "Extreme Allergies and Global Warming," the U.S. National Wildlife Federation noted that across the continent, spring has been arriving on average 10 to 14 days earlier than 20 years ago. That means plants are getting it on earlier (that's what pollination is all about), and your mucous membranes are paying the immediate price. A study published in the *Proceedings of the National Academy of Sciences* in 2011 found that higher latitudes like ours are feeling the itch longer because delays in the fall's first frost are lengthening the frost-free period. That means that all you people allergic to ragweed are suffering for at least an extra week or three come fall. For 15 years, the researchers analyzed pollen data from 10 North American locations, including two in Canada, and it seems that poor Winnipeg and Saskatoon have added 25 to 27 days to their allergy calendar.

For tips on coping naturally, see Hay Fever/Seasonal Allergies, page 265. In the meantime, try keeping a lot of washable cloth handkerchiefs around so you don't single-handedly knock down a small forest with your nose-blowing needs.

CANCER

No one likes to hear the C-word, especially when it comes from your doctor's lips while you're sitting on that crumply paper in a medical gown. And yet many of us will. Over your lifetime, more than 40% of the people you know will get it. It's encouraging that cancer is increasingly beatable, but you have to wonder why we're getting so much of it in the first place. Besides bad genetics and an aging population, junky diets, heavy waistlines and couch-bound lifestyles are definitely huge factors (not to mention cancer-stick smoking and sun exposure). But even that's not the whole picture.

The U.S. President's Cancer Panel rocked the medical community and beyond when it dedicated its 2008–2009 report to reducing environmental cancer risk (deainfo.nci.nih.gov/advisory/pcp). The panel was "particularly concerned to find that the true burden of environmentally induced cancer has been grossly underestimated" and urged the president to use the power of his office to remove carcinogens from our food supply, water, air and everyday lives that needlessly increase health care costs and devastate far too many lives. Among its policy recommendations, the panel mentioned a lot of eco-friendly, natural-living tips, from prioritizing organic food and free-range meat to cutting back on your energy use to help reduce the amount of pollutants pumped into the environment. (For more tips, check out 12 Ways to Protect Your Family's Environmental Health, below.) By the way, the Centers for Disease Control note that "less than 2% of chemicals in commerce have been tested for carcinogenicity" and that exposures and risks are hard to trace when latency periods between exposure and a cancer diagnosis are often 15 to 20 years or longer. All this to say, while we wait on research to find out which chemical substances are actually cancer linked, it's best to take the precautionary approach and stick to as many naturally sourced, non-toxic products as possible.

Speaking of sourcing from nature, all kinds of natural remedies are proving helpful not just in the battle against cancer but also in potentially preventing cancers in the first place. Green tea extracts are a prime example. One such extract, EGCG (epigallocatechin gallate), was found in a 2010 Mayo Clinic trial to reduce the survival of leukemia cells in patients with chronic lymphocytic leukemia. EGCG may also help prevent the onset and growth of skin tumours and more. Research is ongoing. Another natural compound, chlorophyllin, a chlorophyll derivative, has also shown early promise, as has selenium, which Dartmouth Medical School found may reduce bladder cancer rates by 30% to 50%. What is clearer is that supplements can certainly play a supportive role in treatment. A health practitioner can help you figure out the right course of action for you. Keep in mind that some natural supplements can undermine the efficacy of chemo, so always check with your health provider.

Getting all the right nutrients through a colourful, produce-rich diet high in cruciferous vegetables (broccoli, cauliflower) and berries, balanced by whole grains, nuts and omega-3 fatty acids, and high in organic content is certainly your best foundation for health (minimize your animal fats and refined sugars, too). There's a panoply of possibilities, so speak with a doctor specializing in integrative medicine and a good naturopath to cover all your bases. Do your own research by digging for studies in the medical literature for backup. Sites such as PubMed, a free database of abstracts from biomedical literature (ncbi.nlm.nih.gov/pubmed), can be very helpful tools for educating yourself.

12 WAYS TO PROTECT YOUR FAMILY'S ENVIRONMENTAL HEALTH

Regardless of how vigilant you are around your kids, young bodies are inevitably exposed to invisible toxins in our homes, schools, daycares and backyards. What can you do to minimize your whole family's exposure to environmental factors that can compromise health? Here are my top 12 tips—many of which come recommended by the President's Cancer Panel (see page 268).

#1 Opt for fresh food over canned and packaged. Doing so has been found to reduce levels of breast and prostate cancer–linked BPA (bisphenol A) floating in our bodies.

#2 Filter your water. Even a basic pitcher filter will reduce lead levels in household drinking water, which is key since homes built before 1950 tend to have lead plumbing and those built up to 1990 often have lead solder. Plus, many Canadian communities have older sections of piping and/or solder in their water distribution systems. Note that lead levels go up in summer, when warm water is running through the pipes.

Make sure to run your water until it's fully cold to avoid drinking stagnant water.

#3 Buy genuinely natural, unscented personal care products (see chapters 1 through 5) and look for plant-based green cleaners or make your own (pick up *Ecoholic Home* for tips).

#4 Make your renos as non-toxic as can be. Choose VOC-free paints and zero-VOC furniture, and renovation materials that are either free of or ultra-low in formaldehyde (which was officially declared a known carcinogen in 2011). Also, get the vinyl floors out of your kids' rooms. Swedish researchers found that infants who lived in bedrooms with PVC/vinyl floors were at greater risk of autism. The hormone-disrupting phthalates in vinyl have been inconclusively fingered as a culprit in ADHD as well.

#5 Have a "no shoes in the house" rule. Checking footwear at the door has been scientifically proven to reduce chemical contaminants, as well as bacteria and allergens, in the home. You don't want to be tracking in persistent chemicals that your shoes picked up on the road/sidewalk/grass.

#6 Insist that your backyard and schoolyard be chemical pesticide free. Even in some provinces with bans on cosmetic pesticides, chemical weed killers are still sometimes sold in stores. Toxic chemical pest control is still very much permitted for indoor use, but that doesn't mean you should use it (see *Ecoholic Home* for tips on natural pest control).

#7 Get a radon reading. If you live in a basement apartment or if your child's room is down there, get your radon levels checked. Radon is the leading cause of lung cancer in non-smokers. Cracking windows regularly is an easy way to keep radon levels down.

#8 Go organic. Prioritize buying organic for those fruits and veggies with the highest pesticide residues (including thin-skinned fruit such as berries, as well as celery, spinach and potatoes). See Foodnews.org for a printable pocket guide to the 12 worst (the Dirty Dozen) and the cleanest 15.

#9 Stick to free-range, naturally raised meat to reduce antibiotics, growth hormones and toxic runoff from animal feedlots in our waterways. Avoid processed, charred and well-done meats to minimize your family's exposure to carcinogenic polyaromatic hydrocarbons and toxic amines. If you're barbecuing, make sure to marinate your meat/chicken/fish first since herbs, spices, wine, beer and vinegars actually reduce the toxic amines formed on the grill.

#10 Never microwave plastic. You'll just up your exposure to estrogen-mimicking, endocrine-disrupting chemicals if you do.

#11 Get a HEPA vacuum cleaner so you can trap the chemicals found in 98% of household dust inside your vacuum's filter. Be sure to vacuum behind your entertainment centre, where particularly dodgy flame-retardant chemicals accumulate.

#12 Don't smoke anywhere near your family. Cigarettes are the top pollutant in kids' lives and are fingered for all sorts of childhood problems, including asthma and even ADHD.

ENVIRONMENTAL SENSITIVITY

If the chemicals, moulds or electromagnetic pollution in your environment give you headaches, breathing problems, trouble concentrating and worse, you've likely got environmental sensitivity (ES). About 3% of Canadians have been diagnosed with environmental sensitivities, which include everything from "sick building syndrome" and Gulf War Syndrome to Multiple Chemical Sensitivities. A portion of fibromyalgia sufferers have ES, and while the propensity for fibromyalgia is thought to be genetic, chemical exposure may trigger its onset.

Thankfully, those with ES are finally getting the recognition and respect they deserve. The Canadian Human Rights Commission recognizes that the medical condition is a disability and that "those living with environmental sensitivities are entitled to the protection of the Canadian Human Rights Act, which prohibits discrimination on the basis of disability." This means, for one, that employers have a legal duty to accommodate people with ES. And happily, policies from anti-smoking laws and pesticide bans to anti-idling bylaws, scent-free buildings and greener cleaning policies in hospitals and other public buildings all work together to help protect those with ES.

Multiple Chemical Sensitivities: Does a walk down a conventional cleaning-product aisle or a bus ride with a perfume-marinated passenger make you sick to your stomach? A sizable chunk of Canadians have mild sensitivities to all sorts of chemicals in our everyday world (a whiff of mainstream laundry detergent is definitely enough to give me a mild headache), but for some the impact of pollutants in our surroundings is much more profound. So how do you protect yourself? It'll differ on a case-by-case basis, but here are some basics:

- Forget store-bought green cleaners, which can still have synthetic scents. Stick to simple bulk ingredients such as vinegar, baking soda, borax, washing soda and salt, or use specialty cloths like Blue Wonder, which require only water to get the job done. (*Ecoholic Home* has a ton of recipes for DIY green cleaning.)
- Most health store body care products still contain fragrances and synthetics that can irritate those with multiple chemical sensitivities. **Natureclean** and **Druide** both have good scent-free options, but if you're looking for seriously natural, whole plant ingredients (not lab-synthed coconut), then look for **Terressentials, Dr. Bronner** and others that meet food-grade USDA Organic standards (see Label Decoder, page 411).
- Avoid new furniture made with pressed wood, which off-gasses formaldehyde for weeks, months, years. Of the big-name stores, IKEA's furnishings are all ultra low in formaldehyde.
- New clothing, sheets, curtains and textiles are often coated with carcinogenic, allergenic formaldehyde—especially if they're not organic (see Wrinkle- and Stain-Resistant Finishes, page 305).

Buy second-hand/vintage wherever possible or wash new items several times and air out before wearing.

- Avoid dry cleaning like the plague, since they're basically dipping your clothes in chemicals (including the probable human carcinogen "perc"). When dry cleaning can't be avoided, look for alternative wet-cleaning services and cleaners that use carbon dioxide. Air out dry-cleaned clothes on your deck or balcony for a few days before putting away.
- Even VOC-free paints can be irritating since they're still made with chemical fungicides, etc. For all-natural paints, look for clay- and milk-based options.
- If you're moving, look for a place that's over 15 years old so all building materials have fully off-gassed, but not so old that mould is a concern. Also, pass on new carpeting, painting or cabinetry if looking at rentals. Forced air can be a problem, so hunt for a place with radiators (though the electric type is super wasteful and expensive in winter).
- Make sure the humidity in your home doesn't go above 50% to prevent mould growth. Get a dehumidifier to keep it in check.
- Cover your mattress and pillow with mite-proof cotton protectors.
- De-clutter your space to make it more easily dusted with a damp cloth.
- Invest in a high-quality air filter and get a HEPA vacuum cleaner. Unlike those with mild allergies or aversions, you need to make sure whatever you purchase for your home is a top performer, so do some research on allergyconsumerreview.com before you buy.

Electromagnetic Sensitivities (EMS): Is it just me, or are there few sounds in this world more annoying than the audible buzzing of a light or the high-pitched frequency coming off an old TV? Not that electrical pollution is necessarily audible. In fact, it's an entirely invisible form of pollution, and those who have electromagnetic sensitivities can experience sleepless nights, headaches, chronic fatigue, pain, tinnitus and nausea just from being near fluorescent lights, cordless phones, computers, you name it. What researchers such as Columbia University cellular biophysics prof Martin Blank say is that electromagnetic waves and radio frequencies actually trigger stress responses in cells. And that response, he adds, is activated by very weak fields—not just the kind emitted by major transmission lines, but the kind inundating your home. Magda Havas, an environmental science professor at Trent University, has been studying just that, and her research documents diabetics with blood sugar that rises in dirty-electricity environments and MS patients whose symptoms ease in "clean" environments. Health Canada, on the other hand, insists that our exposure to all this stuff is safe and that they've conducted their own studies to assess the impact of radio frequency fields' ability to cause DNA damage and affect gene expression, and there are no harmful outcomes. Until the condition is recognized by officials here as it is in Sweden (where 3% of the population is said to have EMS), I'll offer some tips for protecting yourself against the electromagnetic fields and radio frequencies those in the field call "dirty electricity."

- Unplug anything near your bed. Move clock radios to the other side of the room.
- Get rid of cordless phones and cellphones; stick with old-fashioned land lines.
- Disable dimmer switches, as they can irritate those with EMS.
- If CFLs drive you bonkers, try 240-volt halogens.
- You might consider experimenting by plugging Graham-Stetzer filters into your sockets, but warning: they'll cost you (stetzerelectric.com).

ADHD

Whether you blame MTV, video games or Google, generations X, Y and Z have all grumbled about sabotaged attention spans and crippled information-recall functions. The truth is, attention deficit hyperactivity disorder isn't something you catch from electronic games (though there's no denying they can exacerbate an existing condition). So how do you get it, and do chemical contaminants in our environment play a role?

WANT TO STAY ON TOP OF ENVIRONMENTAL HEALTH NEWS?

Hands-down, my favourite website for news isn't the BBC, the CBC or The Huffington Post, but **environmentalhealthnews.org**. It'll give you all the green news headlines from around the world as well as breakdowns of the latest environmental health science findings and scientist critiques of media coverage. The site is updated daily by Environmental Health Sciences, a foundation-funded journalism organization.

For more info on your child's environmental health, check out the **Children's Environmental Health Project** website by the **Canadian Association of Physicians for the Environment** (cape.ca/children) as well as the **Canadian Partnership for Children's Health and Environment**'s site (**healthyenvironmentforkids.ca**).

First of all, you want to make sure your child actually has ADHD to begin with. A study published in the *Journal of Health Economics* in 2010 estimates that nearly a million kids in the United States are wrongly labelled as having ADHD simply because they're the youngest in their class. Of the 12,000 kids in the study's sample, the youngest kindergarteners were 60% more likely to be diagnosed with ADHD than the oldest students in the same grade. While PET scans have revealed neurological differences in true ADHD patients, everyday diagnosis is a lot more subjective. A child will get flagged if teachers/ parents feel they can check off at least six symptoms of inattention and/ or six signs of hyperactivity and impulsiveness that are seriously affecting the child's school and home life.

Once the diagnosis is firmly established, you'll find it's even tougher to get agreement on ADHD's root causes. For the most part it's considered genetic, but what of the 30% of cases that haven't been inherited? The medical community still considers it a mystery, but early studies are raising questions about the impact of chemical contaminants on young minds. Scientists recognize the need for further research, but they do raise important alarms. Case in point: a few studies have found a link between ADHD and blood lead levels that were on the high-ish side but fell below lead safety limits of 10 mg/dl. A 2009 study published in *Pediatrics* found that kids whose lead exposure levels were in the top third were on a par with kids exposed to tobacco smoke in the womb in terms of the likelihood of ADHD, but those double-whammy kids with the highest lead levels *and* exposure to tobacco in the womb were eight times more likely to have ADHD.

If you or your child have ADHD, consider checking your child's blood lead levels, especially if you live in a pre-1976 house. If, and only if, lead levels are elevated, talk to your doc about chelation therapy. Otherwise, take precautionary measures by painting over chipped paint, filtering water that may be coming from lead pipes and removing cheap metal trinkets/jewellery that can be high in lead (see Kids' Jewellery, page 391).

But lead's not the only neurotoxin raising flags. Certain flame retardants, as well as vinyl-softening, fragrance-enhancing phthalates and non-stick and now phased-out stain-resisting chemicals, are also linked to the disorder. What can you do to avoid these? If you're planning on getting pregnant or have small children, get rid of PVC plastic (including vinyl flooring) and anything with synthetic fragrance or perfume in it, unless it explicitly says it's phthalate free. Dust and vacuum often to minimize the amount of household chemicals building up in dust bunnies. If possible, get rid of old, crumbling pre-2003 couch cushions and carpets that give off dust from banned flame retardants.

In 2010, research out of the Université de Montréal and Harvard's School of Public Health published in *Pediatrics* found that kids with above-average levels of organophosphate pesticides in their pee were nearly twice as likely to have ADHD. And we're not talking kids who grew up on pesticide-heavy farms, but kids whose exposure comes from eating pesticide-laden fruits and veggies. While, again, researchers stressed that more extensive studies were needed before strong conclusions could be drawn, they cautioned that parents would be wise to feed their children organic food as much as possible and wash all produce well.

If you or your child have ADHD, a holistic practitioner can give you some advice on potentially helpful supplements as well as other whole health strategies. Here's an idea of what you can do to get started:

- **Eat organic.** It's a good idea for the whole family but since researchers have noted that young children are the most vulnerable to the effects of these pesticides, it's particularly important to aim (as best you can) for an all-organic diet if you've got one on the way or have young children. At least get their favourite produce organic.
- **Avoid artificial food colouring.** The British National Institutes of Health (NIH) did a meta-analysis of 15 double-blind clinical trials on hyperactivity syndromes/food dyes and concluded, "It is best to avoid exposing children to artificial food colouring."
- **Dose up on fish oils or algae-based sources of omega-3.** There's a lot of evidence that the EPA and DHA in quality fish oils can help alleviate ADHD symptoms. (Veg families should look for algal sources.) See page 246 for more on picking sustainable sources.
- **Get physical.** Make lots of time for daily exercise and good old-fashioned playtime away from video games and computer screens.
- **Serve a healthy diet** low in refined foods and free of ingredients you can't pronounce, and the whole family will feel better. Try eliminating various processed foods and allergenic foods like gluten one at a time to see if any one food is aggravating the ADHD. A 2011 study published in the *Lancet* found that nearly two-thirds of kids on an elimination diet of meat, rice, veggies, water and pears saw significant reduction in ADHD symptoms compared to kids on just a general "healthy" diet.

AUTISM

Why? It's the question first asked by many parents of a child diagnosed with autism spectrum disorder. More questions flood in when they learn of the mysterious swell in the numbers of autistic children on this continent. When the U.S. government's National Institute for Environmental Health funded research to investigate the seven-to-eight-fold increase in autism cases in California alone since 1990, it concluded at the time that the rise "cannot be explained by changes in how the condition is diagnosed or counted" alone. Nor is the trend slowing. Here in Canada, an estimated 190,000 children have the disorder. If we're to find the answer, a growing number of scientists, including those at the NIEH, say research needs to shift from strictly blaming genetics, which is the conventional framework, to investigating "the multitude of chemical and infectious agents in the environment that could be involved in the rapid rise in the incidence of autism." In fact, a 2011 study on twins by University of California, San Francisco and Stanford found that genetics accounts for about 38% of autism risk. And environmental factors? 62%.

One avenue that's moved from the fringe to mainstream medical thinking involves an infant's chemical exposures while in the womb. At this point, NIEH-funded researchers are looking at 1,000 to 2,000 children as part of a long-term study trying to figure out the role of genetics and environmental exposures in all this. So far, they've largely ruled out higher blood mercury levels (though 2011 Australian research published in the *Journal of Toxicology and Environmental Health* says some may be genetically susceptible to mercury as an autism trigger), but PBDE flame retardants are looking mighty suspicious, and pregnant moms living less than 310 metres from a freeway were also found to be at higher risk of having children with autism. There's some indication that other heavy metals, including lead and antimony, can influence the severity of autism. A couple of studies have linked exposure to hormone-disrupting phthalates (including those in vinyl floors in a child's room, as well as phthalate levels in the urine of pregnant moms) to elevated chances of kids having autism or ADHD. A 2011 study found prescription antidepressant use during and even before pregnancy to be a risk factor.

What's clear is that a lone-gunman story isn't likely; it won't boil down to exposure to one single chemical, heavy metal, infectious agent or stressor. With the stew of thousands of environmental factors, including a whole host of endocrine-disrupting chemicals, floating through every room of our lives, there's probably a cocktail of co-factors involved.

Just as there's no one-size-fits-all answer to what causes autism, there's little agreement on what works for managing it. That means, for parents of an autistic child, a lot of expensive experimentation covering the full spectrum of options, from intensive behavioural therapy and a gluten-free diet to nutritional therapy and beyond. For more information, check out the Autism Canada Foundation (autismcanada.org) and the Autism Research Institute (autism.com).

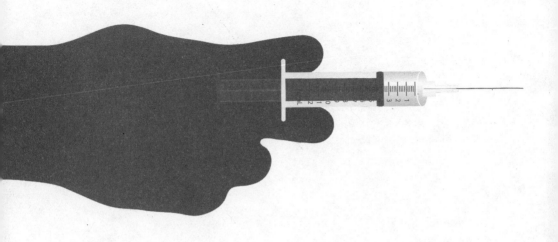

Dental Work   283

Hospitals   287

Vaccines   291

HEALTH CARE
SYSTEM

Greening the system

If you break a bone or crack a tooth,

you'd be plain stupid to run to your naturopath. No matter
how crunchy-granola you are, even if you avoid doctors like the
bubonic, you should still see your dentist twice a year for a
good scraping, call your doctor when you're pooping blood and
dial 911 when your chest hurts. That doesn't mean your dentist,
doctor's clinic or local hospital can't be greener. In fact, many
have taken steps in that direction, and are reaching for greener
cleaners as well as less toxic materials to get you healthy
without polluting the planet. For all those times when public
and private health care comes in real handy, here are some tips
for navigating your visits in the greenest way possible.

DENTAL WORK

Just the thought of sitting in a dentist's chair is enough to make many people's teeth hurt (hell, my mother-in-law's dentist did her root canal on the wrong side!), but forget about your personal pain: dentists are also giving the planet a toothache. To be honest, dentistry may never be totally green, but you can make healthier choices along the way. Many mainstream dentists are fairly dismissive of alt health considerations, but you can still insist on the dental material of your choice. You have a much better shot at getting your teeth fixed in a more earth-conscious way if you track down a holistic dentist, but they can be tough to find outside big cities (and even in them). For help with finding one, you can look up the closest member of the Eco Dentistry Association at ecodentistry.org, though plenty of holistic dentists aren't in the directory, so also try googling them in your hometown. Be sure to inquire about what exactly makes them greener and what alternatives they have available before you book. Having a recycling bin by the front desk and some natural soap in the washroom isn't enough.

Dental Fillings: Oh, the ache. As soon as it strikes, you know you have to pay the dentist a visit, but what then? We've come to realize that that shiny silver goop they've been spackling our mouths with whenever we have a cavity isn't so benign. Mercury fillings have actually been banned in Norway, Sweden and Denmark, and, in 2011, the U.S. government finally called for a "phase-down" and eventual phase-out of mercury amalgam. Soon after, the World Health Organization pushed for a global phase-down too. So far, Canada's sticking to its stance that mercury fillings are safe. Go figure. And with each amalgam filling (addition or removal) a little more mercury goes into the water system. Environment Canada has noted that dentists put over a ton of mercury into our sewers every year since 30% of dentists still aren't following voluntary standards and installing drain traps. Luckily, some municipalities, including Montreal, Calgary, Vancouver, Victoria and all of Ontario, have their own regulations mandating amalgam separators. Ask your dentist what they do with their mercury waste.

Should you take out your old mercury fillings and make a switch? Health Canada acknowledges that amalgam fillings, which are 50% mercury by weight, release low levels of trace toxic vapours, especially as we chew. (The state of Maine has even legislated that dentists hand out flyers telling patients as much.) But many say it's best to leave these things untouched. Drilling into them can send toxic fumes into your mouth, and flying bits can get embedded in your cheeks. It's a particularly bad idea if you're pregnant or nursing.

Dental Filling Alternatives: Many of us now have white, not silver, stuff filling the craters in our teeth. They may look harmless, but composite fillings are largely made of bisphenol A, an estrogen-mimicking chemical that has turned up in the saliva of people with composite sealants. The industry points to studies that say the sealant only leaches for up to a day, after which there's nothing to worry about. But do we really need more bisphenol A, a Health Canada–declared toxin, in our lives and in our bodies?

- A sensible choice would be true **porcelain**. It's used in fillings, crowns and veneers, but you'll have to talk to your dentist about its limitations (such as cracking) and whether it's right for your teeth.
- You could take your cue from hip-hop videos and fill your cavities (or root canals) with **gold**, baby. Okay, so gold mines don't have a great environmental record, but as fillings go, they're safe health-wise. It'll cost you, though.
- **Endocal** (formerly Biocalex), the holistic filling for root canals, is considered non-toxic (it's made of zinc oxide and calcium oxide), but it's known to crack. Not good.

Braces: Getting your teeth realigned is no walk in the park, yet millions of North Americans go through the pain and anguish of a mouth full of metal. Classic metal braces are made of stainless steel, but what about the clear ones? You should be aware that some clear plastic braces are made of now-notorious polycarbonate plastic. Yep, the same plastic ousted from Canadian baby bottles once it was recognized that it leaches hormone-disrupting BPA with wear and tear. While minimal research has been done on this specific end use, it's safe to assume that chewing, drinking and plain salivating with the plastic in your mouth 24/7 for two years, as clear-brace wearers do, will lead to leaching. One study, conducted by Tokyo Medical and Dental University, found that polycarbonate braces submerged in body-temperature water caused a fourfold increase in BPA over 12 months. Submersion in hot liquid for just a quarter of that time increased leaching more than twelvefold.

By the way, some clear plastic aligners designed as chic 'n' subtle substitutes for braces are also made with polycarbonate plastic. At least you remove the aligners when you eat and drink, but you're still wearing them about 20 hours a day. Both **ClearCorrect** (as of early 2010) and **Invisalign** guarantee that their devices are BPA free (ClearCorrect's are made with polyurethane), but classic stainless steel braces are still the safest (as long as you make sure your brackets aren't made of polycarbonate or bisphenol A–heavy composite resin).

Retainers and Mouthguards: There are two major types of retainers out there: wire/acrylic and clear. Acrylic resins are the most popular dental base for everything from retainers to dentures. They're generally polymers made of something called poly(methyl methacrylate) (or PMMA), which is also found in Plexiglas, acrylic paint, bone cements and butt implants (who knew?). Now, some consider PMMA safer than similar clear, hard plastic goods because it's BPA free. Thing is, PMMA is mixed in dental offices with liquid MMA to custom-make dental appliances such as retainers, and MMA isn't just a skin irritant and allergen that can trigger asthma and nausea in dental technicians; it can also contain 6% to 8% phthalates (dodgy plastic softeners linked to various health concerns and banned from kids' toys), according to an EU Commission report on plastics in medical devices. Health Canada is actually restricting several phthalates from items chewed or sucked on by children under four years old, but medical devices such as mouthguards and retainers aren't affected by phthalate regs.

Regardless, acrylics are generally a hell of a lot better than cheaper vacuum-formed clear retainers made entirely of PVC, which can have a much higher percentage of hormone-disrupting phthalates. The EU has raised concerns about the leaching of DEHP phthalates into the mouths of those wearing PVC retainers day in, day out—ingesting, by one estimate, 10 mg of DEHP a day.

- Ask your dentist for a retainer made of somewhat pricier polypropylene, which is considered one of the safest plastics, or a monomer-free option.
- Looking for a little extra dental protection on the field/rink/ court? Athletes will definitely want to stop sucking on mouth-guards made of either PVC or polycarbonate. You'd be better off with one made from safer ethylene-vinyl acetate (EVA), inert silicone or a monomer-free acrylic such as **Flexite**.
- Night clenchers will want to make sure your night guards are made of polypropylene and/or EVA. You can also ask about night guards made of monomer-free acrylics such as Flexite.

Dentures: Can you believe they used to make dentures out of wood? Would hate to see the splinters from one of those bad boys. Today, the pink plastic that mimics the look of natural gums is mostly made of acrylic resin. See "Retainers and Mouthguards" above for a full breakdown on the pros and cons of acrylics, but just keep in mind that the material used can cause allergic reactions in some. Also, soft acrylics in some denture linings are going to have more phthalates than harder ones. In fact, the reason soft acrylics can grow to feel harder in your mouth over time is that those plasticizers leach out, say researchers. Kind of creepy.

Because of sensitivities to the MMA monomer used to make acrylic dentures, there are more and more "acrylic-free" and/or "monomer-free" plastics on the market. Options without irritating

monomers include **Valplast** flexible partials made with a biocompatible nylon thermoplastic (meaning it shouldn't mess with your body)
and **Flexite,** made of monomer-free acrylics. You can also ask about
metal bases made of biocompatible nickel-free metals (specifically,
chrome cobalt). You wouldn't think so, but they're said to be quite
comfy. By the way, if you can't afford anything beyond basic acrylic,
just soaking new acrylic dentures in warm water for 24 hours reduces
the amount of monomer leaching from them, so ask if your dentist
did so and then do it again anyway when you get home.

X-rays: The silver used to process that image of your pearly whites
with traditional X-rays is actually the source of hazardous waste that
can contaminate water supplies.

Look for a dentist who uses digital X-rays. All the cool dentists are
doing it. They definitely cut back on toxic waste, and they're said to
reduce patient exposure to radiation by as much as 80% (though some
say that number is exaggerated).

HOSPITALS

You've heard the old health care adage "Do no harm"? Well, while
hard-working pros are trying to keep us healthy, hospitals themselves
have, for decades, been making the planet sick thanks to their
hazardous waste, toxic chems and giant greenhouse gas footprints.
None other than the World Health Organization teamed up with
Health Care Without Harm to tell hospitals to get it together and
lead by example (check out noharm.org/us_canada/issues/climate).
Whether you're a patient worried about leaching medical equipment,
a health care worker wanting a greener work environment, a fretting
family member craving healthier food in the caf, or just a concerned
community member hoping your local hospital can be a less polluting
neighbour, speak up! If you're a patient, let the patient relations
peeps know it's time for health care facilities to help heal the planet.
They may just have initiatives on the go they can tell you about.
Certainly organizations such as the Canadian Coalition for Green

Health Care have been helping hospitals across the country shrink their energy use, switch to less toxic cleaners and reduce their hazardous waste.

Medical Devices: You go to the hospital to get healthy, so you wouldn't expect that some of the medical devices being used contain some pretty scary toxins. Well, while mercury has been ousted from thermometers, dilators, defibrillators, blood pressure monitors and feeding tubes can all contain mercury and end up as toxic waste. And most hospitals also still use controversial PVC drip bags/catheters/

DISHING UP SUSTAINABLE HOSPITAL FOOD

Nothing like walking into a hospital cafeteria and seeing fried chicken and reconstituted potatoes on the menu. Aren't these places supposed to be shining beacons of good nutrition? The U.K.'s Department of Health issued a sustainable food guide for hospitals encouraging them to prioritize local foods in season, as well as organic produce, fair-trade food options, environmentally conscious meat and dairy as well as sustainable fish. Here in Canada, the majority of hospitals have yet to make changes, but according to the Canadian Coalition for Green Health Care, more and more are starting to move towards more sustainable food procurement. One national hospital-purchasing organization is working with over two dozen member hospitals to boost local food purchases across the board. St. Joseph's Health Centre in Guelph buys local, sustainable meats for both patients and the caf, as well as, whenever possible, local produce, and organic coffee. Scarborough Hospital has partnered with Local Food Plus to offer more fresh, regional, sustainable and ethnically diverse food made from scratch.

Are you a patient or family member craving greener choices? Don't be shy. Put in a request for things like organic milk, fair-trade coffee, free-range, antibiotic-free chicken and seasonal, local produce from your hospital. For ideas and tips, check out **healthyfoodinhealthcare.org**.

feeding tubes/etc. PVC is made with hormone-disrupting phthalates that are banned from baby toys in the United States, Europe and now Canada but medical devices won't be covered by the ban here. One phthalate (DEHP) is such a worry for newborns that a Health Canada expert committee noted that babies and moms-to-be should be kept away from suspect drips, but nothing has formally been done to stop its use across the country. Health Care Without Harm says over 80 hospitals from San Fran to Sweden and Slovakia have taken steps to eliminate PVC. Why is Canada so slow to catch on?

- Ask your hospital if it's got PVC-free (or at least DEHP-free) options, particularly if you've got young children receiving treatment. To be frank, they probably won't have any, but you'll be letting them know there's demand.

Cleaning Products: There's no arguing that hospitals need disinfectants that get the job done. Hospital-acquired infections are serious business, and keeping surfaces properly sanitized is part of keeping you healthy. What isn't necessary are all the lung- and eye-irritating, smog-inducing VOCs emitted by most of their cleaning products. Yes, they're trying to reduce the spread of viruses, but they aren't exactly helping patients with compromised immune systems and chemical sensitivities. Some, like the University Health Network (a network of three major hospitals in Toronto, including Toronto General and Princess Margaret), have already phased out the worst offenders. UHN is using EcoLogo-certified cleaners as we speak.

- Tell your hospital's patient relations department about greener Health Canada–approved cleaning products certified by EcoLogo or Green Seal (ecologo.org; greenseal.org).

Medical Imaging and Nuclear Tests: There's no denying that advancements in medical imaging tests and nuclear medical exams have made diagnosing and treating diseases such as cancer way more precise. The problem is that these tests also carry long-term risks. According to the President's Cancer Panel report of 2008–09:

"Many referring physicians, radiology professionals, and the public are unaware of the radiation dose associated with various tests or the total radiation dose and related increased cancer risk individuals may accumulate over a lifetime. People who receive multiple scans or other tests that require radiation may accumulate doses equal to or exceeding that of Hiroshima atomic bomb survivors. It is believed that a single large dose of ionizing radiation and numerous low doses equal to the single large dose have much the same effect on the body over time."

In the United States, Americans are said to get nearly half their total radiation from medical imaging, compared to only 15% in the '80s. Here in Canada, there have been significant investments in diagnostic imaging since 2000, which has elevated the number of scans Canadians get, according to the Health Council of Canada. A 2010 HCC reported cited "inappropriate [use] and overuse of diagnostic imaging" and raised concerns about implications for patient safety. Saskatchewan, for instance, found that anywhere from 30% to 50% of imaging exams were unlikely to contribute diagnostic info "proportional to their cost and the radiation exposure for patients." Case in point: less than 2% of CT scans for headaches actually find the root of the problem.

Some things to keep in mind:

- While MRI testing is radiation free, CT and PET scans will expose you to ionizing radiation, with potentially harmful side effects.
- Children's bodies are more sensitive to the effects of radiation, so be extra cautious about their exposure.
- To reduce your exposure to radiation from medical sources, the President's Cancer Panel recommends you talk to your health care provider about the need for tests and procedures that involve radiation, your personal radiation history, the benefits of the procedure and alternative ways of getting at the same information. Also start keeping a record of all the imaging and nuclear medicine tests you receive, for future reference.

How to Help: Want to get involved? There are so many great organizations working on this file, including the Canadian Coalition for Green Health Care, which has helped health care organizations eco-fy their purchasing, buildings, cafeterias, waste and much more (greenhealthcare.ca). Healthcare-EnviroNet is another great resource for the medical community, linking to tons of info on pollution prevention strategies and green purchasing (www.c2p2online.com). If you're a front-line worker, you can really help drive change from the inside (see theluminaryproject.org for inspirational examples). No enviro rep on staff? Start your own green committee. If you need backup, look into the Health Care Without Harm's Nurses Workgroup (www.noharm.org/us/nurses).

VACCINES

Parents have a cribful of stressful decisions to make when raising a child, but for many the choice of whether or not to vaccinate is one of the most agonizing. A full quarter of moms and dads call the decision "difficult" and a third who have already immunized or plan on immunizing their child were/are nervous about it, according to a study by the Ontario College of Family Physicians. No wonder stats reveal only 75% of Toronto kids are up to date on their vaccines, when 90% is considered the desired target for "herd immunity" to prevent outbreaks of whooping cough, diphtheria, polio, measles, mumps, rubella, etc. I'm not stepping into this heated debate since it's an extremely personal choice and neither route is entirely risk free. But be sure to weigh both sides, using your critical judgment. If you're uncomfortable with trace mercury preservatives in vaccines (a.k.a. thimerosal) and are looking for more information about each vaccine and its contents, here are some things to consider:

- Single-dose vaccines, which means most vaccines in Canada, don't require preservatives. Some might have residual amounts if thimerosal has been used in the production process but not added to the final product. Check phac-aspc.gc.ca/im/q_a_ thimerosal-eng.php for more info.
- Multi-dose vaccines (which can treat 10 people with one vial), such as the flu shot and most but not all hep B vaccines, do contain

thimerosal to prevent contamination. The amount of mercury per dose varies from 2 to 50 µg per 0.5 mL dose. Ask for details. Check phac-aspc.gc.ca/im/q_a_thimerosal-eng.php for info.

- There are two thimerosal-free influenza vaccines approved for sale in Canada (including Influvac). However, last time I checked, they aren't often available for publicly funded programs. Preservative-free FluMist immunizes without needles; it's a nose spray. This one shouldn't be given to kids or adults with asthma or those who are allergic to eggs since it's grown in chick embryos.
- Ask your doc about whether the vaccine contains an adjuvant (an antigen-booster). Many don't, but if they do it's often an aluminum salt. Vaccines for measles, mumps, chicken pox and more are adjuvant free.

SHARK OIL IN VACCINES?

H1N1 adjuvanted vaccines contain a deepwater shark liver oil called squalene. This isn't a health concern so much as an environmental one: deepwater shark are destructively bottom-trawled and have extremely low reproductive rates. The Shark Safe Network estimates that GlaxoSmithKline's 2009 orders for 440 million doses would involve 4,400 kg of shark oil. GSK is looking for shark-free alternatives. By the way, in the case of the H1N1 vaccine, the un-adjuvanted version had 50 µg of thimerosal versus 5 µg in the adjuvanted one. The Public Health Agency of Canada said both contained less mercury than a can of tuna.

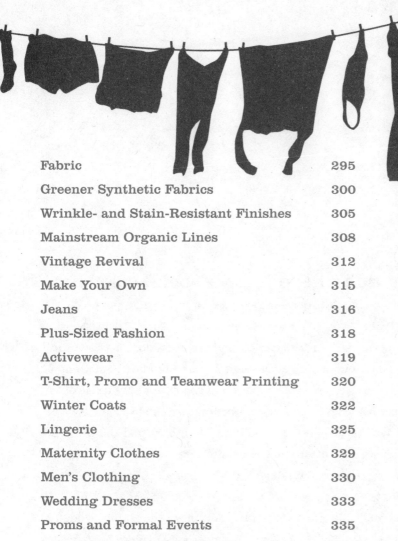

Fabric	295
Greener Synthetic Fabrics	300
Wrinkle- and Stain-Resistant Finishes	305
Mainstream Organic Lines	308
Vintage Revival	312
Make Your Own	315
Jeans	316
Plus-Sized Fashion	318
Activewear	319
T-Shirt, Promo and Teamwear Printing	320
Winter Coats	322
Lingerie	325
Maternity Clothes	329
Men's Clothing	330
Wedding Dresses	333
Proms and Formal Events	335
Clothing for the Chemically Sensitive	338

CLOTHING
Fashion faux-pas

You don't have to be a social scientist

to know that clothing can really say a lot about a person—
especially if you're wearing a Vegans Are Cuter T. But slogan
or not, our garments of choice also say a lot more between the
lines about our society's penchant for the Big Macs of clothing—
cheap, nearly disposable apparel churned out at breakneck
speed with little consideration for total planetary costs. We're
mall deep in the stuff, but I'm happy to report that the world of
eco-conscious clothing has expanded like a smartly dressed
Chia Pet. Despite a dip during the recession, the fashion
forecast is looking up. So don't be shy, ask for eco-clothing
when you walk into a store and scan for green content when
you eye up a new shirt. Yes, it can cost a little more for fabrics
that don't ravage the planet with pesticides, petrochemicals and
poverty-pushing salaries. Just buy fewer outfits, remembering
that quality items last season after season (call it the Slow
Clothes Movement)—something a $29 pair of harem pants can't
promise. And if your budget just doesn't permit, bypass cheaper
mall stores for thrift and vintage shops, hold clothing swaps
with friends and scour green websites for off-season sales.
Those are my tricks.

FABRIC

How green is your fabric, really? There are two staples in our collective closets: cotton and, well, a gloop of synthetics. While retailers try to convince us that the first is a "natural" fibre, how natural is it when cotton is the most chemical insecticide–heavy crop on the planet and almost half (49%) of the world's supply comes from genetically modified seeds born of a lab and patented by the multinational Monsanto? (Did I mention that a jaw-dropping 93% of American cotton, our most local source, is genetically altered?) U.S. farmers have sprayed so much of the pesticide Roundup on Monsanto's Roundup Ready cotton that surrounding weeds have grown resistant and farmers are now battling monster weeds, some with stems four inches around. Meanwhile, Cornell researchers have discovered that Chinese farmers growing GMO cotton were using alarmingly more pesticides than conventional cotton growers. That wasn't supposed to happen. And that's the whole thing with GMOs— you never know what the future holds.

But who needs farmed cotton to get dressed when you can weave fibres with petrochemicals? Crude oil–and natural gas–derived fabrics such as polyester, nylon and acrylic account for 50% of all fibres used in the textile biz, and that adds up to 38 million tons of synthetic fibre annually. Beyond the impacts of drilling for the oil itself, you've got to factor in the high energy demands of making fibres out of oil (how the heck do they do that anyway?), plus all the climate-cooking carbon dioxide as well as polluting hydrocarbons and nitrous oxides emitted into the atmosphere when this stuff gets processed. FYI, acrylic is 30% more energy intensive and sucks up more water than polyester, and nylon production is even worse for potent greenhouse gases such as nitrous oxide.

But just because conventional textiles are so darn dirty doesn't mean we should assume eco-fabrics don't have a ring around their collar. When I was writing the first *Ecoholic* book, the green community was celebrating the availability of any and all green textiles, including bamboo, soy and corn-based Ingeo, as in "Yippee, they exist!" At that point, we hadn't really stopped to analyze the impact of making the fabrics themselves. Sigh. I hate it when things lose their lustre. Here's a second look at eco-fabrics; call it hindsight with 20/20 vision.

Hemp: Still considered the king of green since even non-organic hemp is so pest resistant that it's automatically low pesticide, and hemp is also less water intensive than cotton, which is a huge bonus. Plus, this high-yield crop actually grows faster than weeds—pretty awesome. Most of it's cultivated in eastern Europe and China. Too bad none of the hemp grown in Canada is being processed into hemp fabrics (it all goes to food). We're still waiting on a "dirt to shirt" all-Canadian hemp garment (are you out there?). Keep in mind that if your hemp is butter soft, it's chemically processed. If that's the case, make sure the chemicals are processed in a greener closed loop, as is the case with Lyocell (see Tencel/Lyocell, page 304) as opposed to, say, rayon or viscose (see viscose/rayon from bamboo, page 301).

Linen: Woven from flax/linseed fibres, linen is one of the most ancient and reputable eco-fabrics you can find. It's inherently low pesticide and involves minimal processing, making it the lowest-carbon fabric in town. "Organic linen" is rarer but guarantees that it's chemical pesticide free. Canada is the world's top linseed grower, but ever since the last flax-fibre processing plant here closed in the '50s, we haven't produced any domestically grown linen. Such a shame, though hopefully the locavore movement can turn that around. Europe dominates high-grade linen production, though more and more cheap linen is coming from China. No surprise there.

Organic Cotton: Natural go-to fabric. Yes, cotton is quite water intensive to grow, but organic cotton is free of all the chemical pesticides and fossil fuel–based fertilizers involved in conventional cotton growing. Unlike bamboo or soy, it doesn't require any chemical processing to take it from picked cotton to woven fibre, either. Organic cotton is grown in India, Turkey, Syria, Tanzania, China, the United

States and beyond. The Stockholm Environment Institute found that organic cotton has quite a low carbon footprint.

Better Cotton: Have you seen this label on tags yet? The Better Cotton Initiative started in Switzerland in 2005 but is now catching on with major retailers, who are promising to use more and more of this greener cotton. Basically, cotton grown under these principles isn't organic but farmers must commit to minimizing chemical pesticide and herbicide use as well as using water wisely and maintaining soil fertility. Better Cotton workers have the right to unionize and enjoy some minimal workplace protections, such as being paid the legal minimum wage in whatever country they're in, with no forced overtime. It's not organic, fair-trade cotton by any stretch of the imagination, but it is more conscientious than regular cotton. Adidas will be using 100% Better Cotton by 2018. H&M says it'll only use Better Cotton, organic cotton or recycled cotton by 2020. Bettercotton.org

Wool: These days, more and more wool comes from sheep that *haven't* had a flap of their hiney painfully sliced out to prevent flystrike (maggots) in a controversial procedure called mulesing. That's because over the last couple of years, the Gap, H&M, Nike, Hugo Boss, Abercrombie & Fitch and Pierre Cardin have joined about 60 other companies in a boycott of Australian merino wool from mulesed sheep (although several unnamed European retailers quietly lifted the ban as long as the sheep were given pain relief). Initially, the Australian wool industry promised to voluntarily put a stop to mulesing by 2010, but the year came and went and they abandoned their commitment. As a result, under pressure from PETA (People for the Ethical Treatment of Animals), more retailers, including Talbots and Ann Taylor, brought in mulesing-free policies that same year.

But wool's problems don't end at mulesing. Too many sheep-shearing countries continue to treat their sheep with polluting pesticides (over 14,000 pounds of insecticides were applied to sheep in the United States in 2000 to control pests, according to the Organic Trade Association) and feed them groundwater-contaminating antibiotics as a growth booster.

Organic wool guarantees happier, drug- and pesticide-free sheep—and your sweater will carry less guilt, too. It's tougher to find though.

Silk: Lots of high-end designers blend silk into their green lines because it's a natural fibre. It's also renewable (unlike crude oil–derived synthetics) and biodegradable in the long term. Nonetheless, conventional silk involves boiling moth cocoons in a highly caustic solution with the moth inside (they do this before the moth has a chance to emerge and tear the cocoon fibres). Extracting and weaving silk fibres is also a seriously labour-intensive process (you need 3,000 cocoons to create one pound of silk fabric, according to one silk manufacturer) and since it's being done in Asia, you can assume fair wages are not happening. Not that all silk is made this way. Some companies claim they use fair-trade silk, and many more offer types of peace silk (where the moth emerges from the cocoon to live a full life, maybe start a family and settle down before the cocoons are collected), including **wild silk**, **tussah/tussore** and **ahimsa** silks, which are supposedly processed in a more natural way. Some people claim to have organic silk, but certification is rare so you'll have to press the company for details about what exactly they mean by "organic."

CANADA'S NEXT TOP (ROLE) MODELS: 15 FAB GREEN CLOTHING DESIGNERS

Back in 2004, when I first started writing the Ecoholic column and people wrote in with questions like "Where can I find clothing that doesn't make me look like I'm entering a potato sack race?" I was sort of at a loss. There wasn't much being offered on most Canadian shelves other than a little baggy hemp here and an oversized cotton T there. But oh baby, have we come a long way. With well over 50 amazing Canadian designers working with eco-fabrics these days, it was a challenge to keep this list to 15. Nevertheless, here's a taste of fashion leaders who are sticking to planet-hugging textiles. You'll find tons more awesome brands listed throughout this chapter, including in Vintage Revival, Menswear, Activewear and more.

Atelier B: Cool Quebec-made streetwear with hip techy edge for women and men. **atelier-b.ca**

Device Clothing: Vintage-inspired modern classics. Made in Toronto from 99% eco fabrics, $80 and up. **devicedesignco.com**

Elroy: One of the most sizable and established collections of super-fly eco-dresses/blazers/coats/skirts/tops/pants and more. It's designed in Canada, though it's made in women's co-ops in Indonesia. Accessibly priced along the lines of Banana Republic. **elroyapparel.com**

Lav & Kush: The flirt of sustainable fashion, offering sexy dresses, tops, skirts and more, ranging roughly from $60 to $150. Made in B.C. **lavandkush.com**

Lilikoi: Pretty printed dresses, skirts and tops mostly from a mix of bamboo rayon and organic cotton (starting from $60). Made in Nelson, B.C. **lilikoiclothing.com**

Lindsey M Collection: Fun, easy and saucy line with plenty of wearable dresses, skirts and soft tops, accessibly priced from $40 to $140. Also from Nelson. **zenessentials.ca**

Nicole Bridger: The stylish drape-master and winner of the 2010 Fashion Takes Action Design Forward Award makes all her stuff in B.C., with higher price point. **nicolebridger.com**

Nixxi: Trendy structural silhouettes in soft organic textiles, out of Salt Spring Island. From $70 for tops, up to the $400 range for winter coats. **nixxi.ca**

oöm Ethikwear: These conscientious Montrealers focus on stylish printed cuts for women, men, kids and babes at awesome prices. **oom.ca**

Paper People Clothing: Creatively recycled Toronto designs that turn unloved sweaters into one-of-a-kind body-hugging styles, and vintage bedsheets into breezy summer dresses. **paperpeopleclothing.com**

Peridot Kiss: Comfy chic, feminine styles, all in hemp jersey, from Vancouver. From $60 to $200 (**peridotkiss.com**). The same designer also does higher-end, fashion-forward **Red Jade** with organic cotton, merino wool, silk, Tencel, hemp and more. **redjade.raiment.ca**

Preloved: The pioneers of recycled vintage, reconstructing sweaters, skirts, dresses and much more, all made in Toronto to a code of conduct and sold around the globe. Tops in the $50–$80 range, dresses higher. **preloved.ca**

Thieves: High-end cuts and fashion-forward styles for men and women, shown at NY Fashion Week 2010. Higher price point, from $150 to $400. **thieves.ca**

Voilà Par/by Andréanne: This Manitoba-based Aboriginal clothing company offers breezy, eco-friendly, fair-trade skirts, dresses, tops and more, from $50 to $140. **mjannecouture.com**

WE3 (Twigg & Hottie): An offering of mostly stylish basics and layering pieces in eco-knits from Vancouver, with prices starting around $70. **we3.ca**

GREENER SYNTHETIC FABRICS

Move over polyester, hello plant-based synthetics! This disparate gang of green fabrics are all part of the hunt to replace the 38 million tons of petroleum-based synthetics made every year. Why do I call them plant-based synthetics? Well, let me put it this way: you won't see a weaver in rural China weaving creamy soft fabrics out of little soybeans or bamboo stalks. They need some heavy-duty processing to get that silky drape of synthetic naturals that we've learned to love. The whole class of textiles made from tree pulp, cornstarch, soy, bamboo, seaweed, you name it, can be lumped together as "regenerated fibres." Those regenerated fibres are either factory made of plant cellulose from, for instance, tree pulp (such as rayon, viscose, Lyocell, bamboo, Tencel and modal) or plant proteins (such as soy and corn fabrics, as well as old WWII versions made of skim milk protein and peanuts). You might see the protein types referred to on clothing websites as "Azlon fabrics."

FYI, scientists are busy trying to concoct some eco-friendly ways to make wool with the protein in scrap chicken feathers and linen out of wasted rice husks. Not sure how long it'll be before you see these on shelves, though you can find a growing number of clothes made of leftover shellfish shells (it's called chitosan/chitosante).

Viscose/Rayon from Bamboo: Used to be you'd pick up a shirt or dress that said "100% Bamboo," as though it came straight from the stalk, direct from the lush plantations of China. Well, turns out it's not quite that clear-cut. In 2009, the fraud-busting Competition Bureau stepped up to clarify that the only fabrics that can label themselves "bamboo" are those that are mechanically processed the old-fashioned way, the way linen is processed from flax. Everyone else making textiles with chemically processed bamboo pulp would have to call a spade a spade and label it "rayon (or viscose) from bamboo." In 2010, the U.S. Federal Trade Commission (FTC) sent out letters to Walmart, the Gap, Sears and a good 50 indie bamboo clothing producers sternly warning them to stop misleading customers. It added: "There's also no evidence that rayon made from bamboo retains the antimicrobial properties of the bamboo plant, as some sellers and manufacturers claim." In Canada, brands can still claim to be antibacterial or biodegradable or whatnot as long as they back it up with hard data.

Bottom line: unless that bamboo shirt looks and feels like linen, it's a type of rayon. Rayon, or viscose, is kind of like the bologna of clothing—made from otherwise natural base ingredients but processed with questionable synthetics. Rayon is always made from some sort of woody pulp (be it pine, spruce, hemlock, jute or bamboo), dissolved in a caustic soda then spun in a chemical solution of carbon disulphide (a reproductive toxin). For every kilogram of rayon produced, about 20 to 30 grams of carbon disulphide and 4 to 6 grams of harmful hydrogen sulphide are emitted, so a rayon factory can release a good 15 to 40 tons of carbon disulphide each and every day, according to a World Health Organization report on the chemical. Not good for workers or for those living near factories, especially considering that the clothing brand Patagonia's own investigation into bamboo fibres noted that most rayon factories recover only 50% of this solvent. Patagonia is one of a growing list of companies that are opting out of, or discontinuing their use of, bamboo.

So, does bamboo have any legit green value? The plant certainly does grow like a weed, with no (or next to no) chemical inputs. Its root structure helps prevent erosion and detoxes water. Moreover, bamboo forests are great carbon sinks (like all forests, really). Though clearing natural forests or farmland to establish bamboo plantations doesn't offer much biodiversity, growing the bamboo generally isn't the main issue (especially if it's certified organic and/or FSC certified). Compare it to the toxic-pesticide and heavy-water inputs needed to grow conventional cotton and it'll win every time. But we expect more from our "green" fabrics. And rightly so.

Here are some tips for picking the right rayon from bamboo, or any other source for that matter.

- Some newer bamboo-rayon manufacturing plants are borrowing the more benign techniques used by Lyocell (See Tencel/Lyocell, page 304). Essentially, they claim to be closed loop, recycling nearly all of their solvents and processing their chemicals in-house. Some bamboo brands that maintain they use closed-loop, organically grown bamboo include Canadian indie **MiiK** (which offers figure-flattering dresses, tops and more for women as well as basics for men; miik.ca), flirty U.S.-based **Jonäno** (jonano. com) and basics from Bamboosa.com (100% of the sodium hydroxide and 74% of the carbon disulphide is recovered and recycled for further use). Those that also use Lyocell's gentler solvents (namely, N-methylmorpholine N-oxide) in a closed loop should label themselves as "Lyocell from bamboo."

- Look for bamboo that's Oeko-Tex Standard 1000 certified, since the audited international standard tells you the factory itself minimizes air and water emissions and energy consumption, prohibits child labour and more. (Note: Oeko-Tex 100 only tells you there are no chemical residues such as formaldehyde on the finished fabric.)

Soy: This is another ultra-soft darling of eco-designers. It's made with soy proteins in soy husks left over from manufacturing various soy foods. Unlike corn, bamboo or rayon, people aren't expressly growing soy for the clothing biz. It's a waste product, so this gives it a leg up. It's murky as to whether soy is being processed as a rayon or in a greener way, like Lyocell. I'd expect the Competition Bureau to crack down on fabrics calling themselves "soy" just like they did with bamboo. When they do, manufacturers will have to tell us if their soy is a rayon/viscose or Lyocell, which will be helpful. The big problem is that soy is largely genetically modified; an astonishing 91% of American soy is GMO. Just like GMO cotton, genetically modified soy is notorious for breeding pesticide-resistant superweeds that end up putting farmers on a pesticide treadmill where they need more and more chems. Organic soy fabric guarantees your outfit is GMO and pesticide free, but it's tough to find.

Corn (Ingeo/Sorona): Ingeo's maker (agro giant Cargill) says manufacturing this fabric produces 60% less greenhouse gas than making regular polyester and consumes 50% less non-renewable energy (i.e., fossil fuels). Like soy, one of the main problems with this one is that you can't guarantee it wasn't made with genetically engineered corn, since 73% of American corn is GMO. And since only the kernel is used, the rest of the corn is wasted. The process is more wasteful than soy fabric creation. Plus, conventional corn is a pesticide- and fossil-fuel fertilizer–heavy crop and there's no organic corn fabric yet being made. Still it's certainly better than petrol-based synthetics like nylon and acrylic. FYI, DuPont-made Sorona fabrics are petroleum based mixed with 37% corn-derived fibres.

Tencel/Lyocell (Eucalyptus): You've probably seen these fabrics listed on the tags for all sorts of clothing but never really paid much attention. Silky soft Lyocell is generally considered a greener rayon, made from eucalyptus pulp from European plantations (yes, trees were cut down to make this fabric) and processed with gentler solvents in a mostly closed-loop system (where solvents are continuously recycled). In the case of Tencel branded Lyocell, 99.6% of the non-toxic solvent is reused. It's also made with Forest Stewardship Council–certified pulp, so the eucalyptus sourced has a sound rep. Some Lyocell factories do use a formaldehyde treatment to avoid pilling, but it's certainly not necessary, and the Tencel brand (used by Patagonia and Modrobes) says it's free of it. You can find Lyocell made out of bamboo, seaweed (a.k.a. Seacell) and more.

I wouldn't be surprised if the Competition Bureau ordered companies claiming their clothes are made of "eucalyptus" to change their tags to say "Lyocell or Tencel from eucalyptus." If they did it for bamboo, they should do it here too. Either way, both are a decent pick. FYI, the Competition Bureau smacked down Lululemon in 2007 for claiming their Vitasea Seacell threads were somehow nourishing your skin. Totally bogus.

Modal: This material is showing up on more and more fabric tags, especially on buttery soft undergarments and lingerie. Modal is basically beech-pulp viscose and isn't as green as Lyocell or Tencel. One of its makers, Lenzing, tells me that about 90% of the carbon disulphide (see Viscose/Rayon from Bamboo, page 301, for details) involved in making it is recycled—at least at *their* factory. Lenzing's modal gets its Austrian beech pulp certified by PEFC, which is a pretty weak certifier according to Greenpeace and other forestry activists. Interestingly enough, Lenzing says a by-product of making modal is tooth-friendly sweetener xylitol. Can't guarantee other modal is produced to the same standard.

FASHION WEEKS THE WORLD OVER GO GREEN

In the world of catwalks, darling, spring and fall are the only two seasons that matter. It's when fashion houses the world over roll out their finest threads. Move over, Gisele and Naomi, the earth is starting to get central billing. Hell, London Fashion Week cleared prime runway time for a sustainable catwalk show for the first time ever in 2010, featuring high-profilers such as Stella McCartney and Vivienne Westwood alongside more indie names. New York's Eco-Fashion Week, a.k.a. The GreenShows, is growing an ever higher profile. And though Toronto Fashion Week is largely content with rocking the traditional fashion runway (Toronto has done very little to set an example by greening itself or its designers to date, say insiders), Vancouver's become the hub for forward-thinking eco-fashion in Canada, and Montreal's not far behind. In 2010, Vancouver kicked off its first-ever **Eco Fashion Week** and season after season their runway designs are so hot they're bowling over fashionistas from around the globe. See for yourself: **ecofashion-week.com**.

WRINKLE- AND STAIN-RESISTANT FINISHES

Ever since the ancients evolved the urge to dress to impress, we've been manufacturing devices to rid our clothes of creases. Then, in the 1950s and '60s, wrinkle-resistant duds swept in to free battalions of housewives from ironing duty (notwithstanding those wacky moms still ironing underwear and sheets). So what magical substance, pray tell, makes a shirt stay mysteriously crinkle free?

Formaldehyde: Formaldehyde resins were the original wrinkle reducer (invented by the French in the early 20th century), and they are still commonly used. Thankfully, today's formaldehyde-based finishes release lower levels of the toxin than they used to, but totally formaldehyde-free options haven't caught on as broadly because, well, they cost more. Everything from rayon and wool to cotton and corduroy is regularly treated with the stuff. But while it keeps your sheets and

305

shirts pretty, formaldehyde has been classified as a known human carcinogen by the International Agency for Research on Cancer, and it's also quite the allergen. Some people have worse reactions to formaldehyde than others (picture burning, watery eyes, wheezing and, most commonly, contact dermatitis). It's especially bad news for the chemically sensitive. Washing said item doesn't help matters much, since permanent-press finishes are designed to be, well, permanent (though levels are reduced the more you wash). The amount of formaldehyde released from clothing goes up a notch in humid conditions or if you're sweating. Wouldn't you know it? North America allows four times more formaldehyde on clothing than Japan does.

Teflon: Yes, Teflon has uses beyond making your eggs glide. It's found on clothing, too. You can purchase plenty of stain-repellent khakis, button-downs, even motorcycle jackets coated with the stuff. The key ingredient that goes into the Teflon finish, PFOA, has been deemed a probable cancer causer and major American companies have agreed to phase it out by 2015, but the agreement is voluntary and definitely not global in scope. Kind of unnerving considering that many researchers argue coated textiles might be one of the largest ways we're exposed to the chemical. By the way, the U.S. Environmental Protection Agency pushed manufacturing giant 3M to phase out the super-bioaccumulative carcinogen—and Teflon cousin—PFOS from popular wrinkle and stain protector Scotchgard. But if you have pre-2002 textiles treated with the stuff, I'd consider nixing them in a hurry.

Nano Finishes: These days, you'll find that more and more companies claim to have freed themselves of all of the above by going high-tech. That's right, kids, the new and highly untested world of nanotechnology (where scientists play with molecules, oh, 100,000 times smaller than the width of a human hair) is coming to keep creases and ketchup blobs at bay. Gone are the stiff coatings of yore. Thanks to nanotechnology, the treatments are infinitesimal enough to attach to individual fibres without anyone noticing a change. It's the same tech that lets you put today's zinc oxide sunscreen on your nose without making you look like a goofy '50s lifeguard. The headache here stems from the brand-spanking newness of the field. A recent report by the U.K.'s Royal Commission on Environmental Pollution flagged serious concerns about nano materials used in consumer products. Experts warned that it could take several decades before we understand the environmental and health repercussions of releasing these materials.

Nano-Tex, which supplies a stain-, static- and stink-resistant fabric protection to the Gap, Old Navy, Sears, Tilley, New Balance, Adidas and Victoria's Secret, says it's free of the loose nano molecules that could get out and cause problems, such as nano silver and carbon nanofibres. Their Duro-Block finish for home textiles is even certified by the green Cradle to Cradle gurus at MBDC (McDonough Braungart Design Chemistry is a global sustainability consulting and certifying firm).

Still, Nano-Tex reps admit some of their older clothing finishes do contain PFOA (though those should have been phased out of all their brands by the end of 2010). Beware of fraud: a 2010 study published in *Particle and Fibre Toxicology* found half of the store-bought shirts labelled as "nano silver" did not contain any silver or have any antibacterial properties. Definitely better for the environment, of course, but you're still being had. And those fabrics that did contain nano silver particles released the tiny metals into human sweat. Not good.

- In general, you'd be, ahem, hard pressed to find a "self-maintaining" shirt that gets the green thumbs-up from enviros. Go the old-fashioned route and get out that ironing board when creases have you frowning (though, since these little appliances are big energy hogs, be sure to shake and hang-dry freshly washed and/or dried duds ASAP to minimize ironing).
- If you're really stain-prone, tuck a funky lobster bib in your bag for sloppy meals, or just do what I do and get yourself a top-notch natural stain-buster like Pink Solution's laundry bar. Because let's face it—clothes aren't meant to be life-proof.

MAINSTREAM ORGANIC LINES

Shopping malls aren't exactly beacons of sustainability. Racks of rock-bottom prices filled with clothes shipped from China and Bangladesh might as well be disposable since you know they ain't gonna survive till next season. But at the very least, a surprising number of retailers are offering *some* organic and greener fibres. Okay, fine, most are still stitching their threads in Asia and Latin America under questionable labour conditions according to sweatshop activists (for local, organic and sweatshop free, you generally have to support indie designers or go fair trade; see page 311). Zara used to be a big organic-cotton buyer but then they dropped off the green map, and by the way, Zara's main Brazilian supplier was busted and charged for using "slave labour" in 2011. Here's a rundown of some conventional producers with organic lines:

Aritzia: This hip Vancouver-based chain has an in-house eco-label Community. Well-cut organic hoodies and flowy tops plus hemp coats are all on offer, though at higher price points more on par with indie Canadian designers. Most of it is made in China. communityclothing.com

American Apparel: Over 40 locations from Victoria to Halifax, and a strong selection of organic-cotton tanks, Ts, zip-ups, kids' and dogs' apparel, as well as racy organic thongs and underwear, all for the same price as their regular versions! They also buy 30,000 pounds of "Cleaner Cotton" (a low-pesticide and GMO-free program led by California's Sustainable Cotton Project) and weave it into their non-organic line. All woven and made in their solar-panelled L.A. factory under fair labour conditions. americanapparel.net

Banana Republic/Gap: You can find a surprising amount of clothing made of 90% Tencel, Lyocell and not-as-green modal at Banana Republic (Gap's Lyocell is more blended with regular rayon). Too bad the handful of clothes with organic-cotton content only contains 5% of the pesticide-free stuff. Note: it's easier to search by fabric on the U.S. site. FYI, parent company Gap has become, among the big brands, one of the most responsive to allegations of worker abuse and systemic problems, but recent, serious problems with worker treatment in supplier factories in Cambodia, Bangladesh and El Salvador have arisen. bananarepublic.gapcanada.ca

Le Château: This discount trend-pusher may not make clothes that last, but they do offer nearly two dozen jackets, slacks, blazers, skirts and more made out of Tencel/Lyocell or bamboo rayon, though they're often blended with conventional cotton and spandex. Lechateau.com

Lululemon: This Vancouver-headquartered yoga sensation offers some organic yoga pants, tanks and thongs, but you have to label-snoop to find them. Too bad they shut down their all-eco Oqoqo offshoot stores. Most of their stuff is still manufactured offshore (for more on their factories see lululemon.com/legacies/factories). Lululemon.com

H&M: H&M's organic selection really ebbs and flows, sometimes going down to just a few basic organic Ts and socks, although their 2011 Conscious Collection had over 30 pieces. Regardless, they claimed a top spot as the world's fifth-highest user of organic cotton in 2009, and they're promising to only offer cotton that's either organic, recycled or classified as Better Cotton (see Better Cotton, page 297) by 2020. Just beware: they were caught labelling clothing made with genetically engineered Indian cotton as organic in 2010 and a couple of supply factories in Cambodia, where workers reportedly earned 30 cents a day, had mass staff fainting in 2011. The organic agencies certifying the cotton, including Ecocert, were fined. hm.com/ca

Nike: No all-organic items in the store when last checked—but Nike had 5% organic cotton woven into all their cotton apparel by 2011 and now aims to weave 10% organic cotton in there by 2015. It's actually been among the world's top three organic-cotton buyers a few years in a row. They're also PVC free and use a little recycled polyester. If you love the swoosh, keep putting pressure on them to do better. Sweatshop-wise, though, I've gotta say, Nike's been pretty good about leveraging their buying power to address labour rights or enviro violations that have inevitably arisen at supply factories in recent years. Big switch from the '90s. nike.ca

Roots: Of all the big cross-Canada mall stores, Roots has the most organic fabrics inside, including caps, Ts, tanks, sweaters, sweatpants and more, from $25 to $70 (though many items are only partly organic, so read the label). Canada.roots.com

Sears: This ain't your grandmother's Sears catalogue selection. Sears.ca has a large number of organic-cotton clothing items for adults and children under their in-house Nevada and Jessica lines, though Sears's Bangladeshi clothing supply factories have been marred by problems. Better to stick to the Canadian-made brands they have on offer, including urban casualwear by **EcoGear** and **Tees 4 Trees** as well as GOTS-certified organic, Indian-made dresses and yoga-inspired wear by **Yes Lifestyle Organics**. Sears.ca

Tristan: On the racks of this Montreal-based chain you'll find a healthy sprinkling of shirts, dresses, Ts, jackets and pants made of greener fabrics such as Tencel and Lyocell, as well as modal and bamboo rayon, all for the same prices as the rest of their clothing. Look out for a few "made in Canada" tags here, too. Tristanstyle.com

Walmart: Weirdly enough, this activist target turned over a green leaf in the mid-2000s and became the world's top buyer of organic cotton three years in a row, before dropping to hover in the top five. As with the other chains, I can't tell you the workers were paid fairly to sew this stuff, especially when Walmart's organic clothes all retail, shockingly, for under $10. Maybe it's no surprise that Walmart was inducted into the International Labor Rights Forum's 2010 Sweatshop Hall of Shame, though, like the Gap, years of public scrutiny has encouraged Walmart to become one of the more responsive brands in terms of corporate accountability. Still, serious concerns with suppliers in Bangladesh, China and Sri Lanka have continued to surface in recent years. Walmart.ca

Fair Trade: So how do we find organic clothing that's also fair to global workers in mainstream stores? Start asking for clothing that's both fair trade *and* organic in one. U.K. shops big and small, from massive Marks & Spencer to indie People Tree Clothing, carry the combo, so it's definitely

JUST BECAUSE IT'S GREEN DOESN'T MEAN IT'S NOT MEAN: SWEATSHOPS

Does an organic tag at a three-for-one panty sale guarantee that what you're buying is truly sustainable? Can you crank out a legit pair of green jeans for $59.99? Truth is, eco-friendly and worker-friendly aren't necessarily one and the same, and sweatshop activists worry that workers will be forgotten when a fancy "organic" label gets slapped on clothing. We can't forget that the lowest-price-for-the-quickest-turnaround business model still applies to organic T-shirts when they're made en masse. Pressure to meet those conditions has certainly been enough to drive organic-cotton farms and mills out of the United States to cheaper pastures in India, Turkey, Pakistan and China, where labour rights abuses are common. It'll definitely surprise most of you that many organic standards don't say a peep about working conditions (Europe's further ahead on this one, thankfully, and the Global Organic Textile Standard, or GOTS, does do some monitoring around workplace conditions). Plus, even if a company has a firm workplace code of conduct to improve conditions for the workers sewing their clothes, that code doesn't extend to field workers growing, picking and processing the cotton. Pretty appalling, really. Even organic farm workers in California are scraping by on minimum wage without benefits or health insurance, according to a 2005 University of California, Davis study.

Still, the certified-organics system can be pretty transformative since it forces manufacturers to keep traceable, audited records of all their ingredients, making abuses such as child labour way less likely, according to Textile Exchange, a California-based not-for-profit that works with industry to boost organic-cotton use in apparel. For its part, Textile Exchange is encouraging conversations with its corporate members about farm worker rights and creating sustainable farming systems by pushing for long-term contracts between corporations and farmers.

doable. We just need to create demand here at home. In the meantime, vote with your dollar by supporting the fair-trade organic options at Ethicalocean.com (just punch "fair trade clothing" into the search engine), Elroyapparel.com and jeans from Goodsociety.org, as well as clothing from Fibrethik.org, globalgirlfriend.com, lizalig.com and Bono-affiliated edun.com. For lots more suggestions, check out the Shop With Conscience Consumer Guide at sweatfree.org/shoppingguide.

By the way, fair-trade certification has, by and large, only applied to the cotton itself. Fair Trade USA finally brought in standards for the whole garment, from seed to sewing machine. Look for the tag **Fair Trade Certified Apparel**. You'll find a list of products that carry the label, like **Maggie's Organics** at transfairusa.org/products-partners/apparel-linens. FYI, while the term "fair trade" mostly applies to imports from developing countries, some Canadian brands such as mjannecouture.com say they're fair trade, which, in the Canadian context, basically means that everything's done above board. **oöm Ethikwear**, for instance, has all their clothing sewn by social enterprises in Quebec. Why is "socially responsible" clothing necessary in this country? Well, Canada has its own share of under-the-table sweatshops and documented reports of "home workers" doing piecework for brands for long hours at less than minimum wage. The surest way to guarantee your Canadian-made clothes are fairly made is to buy union (canadianunionapparel.com).

VINTAGE REVIVAL

Blame it on *Mad Men*, blame it on "the downturn," blame it on our boredom with generic mall clothes. No matter how you stitch it, previously loved apparel has become one seriously hot commodity. And the planet is smiling about it. Over the last few years, there's been an explosion in vintage boutiques across the country, continent and globe. Pretty awesome considering that second-hand clothes are, hands-down, the greenest threads you could possibly sport. As the peeps at green.ebay.com note: "When you choose to reuse an item, you aren't asking the planet to come up with the raw materials required to make a new one. In most cases, the greenest product is the one that already exists." Yes, choosing a second-hand sweater over a new one saves enough energy to do 68 loads of laundry. As pimply teens in Montreal, my friends and I did all our best shopping on Mont-Royal, the old heart of the city's second-hand scene, knowing we could score original pieces we'd never spot in dime-a-dozen chain stores. These days, however, the options for second-hand lovers are dizzying, from high-end glam consignment shops to indie designers reworking old finds.

Vintage: Boutiques specializing in vintage finds offer a carefully hand-picked treasure trove of outfits from the 1920s through the 1980s or sooner depending on the store. Some specialize in hipster looks while others stick to classic designer labels and cocktail attire. Their finds are plucked anywhere from specialty rag houses to auctions, estate sales and collectors. The world of vintage has become so competitive that store owners guard their sources as state secrets. I'd give you a listing for each city, but there are too many nationwide. Just google them in your hometown.

Consignment: Consignment shops let people sell their unwanted and gently used clothes, shoes, sunglasses and purses in their space, with the store taking a cut. Most of them offer up quality designer labels at a deep discount. If you've out-shopped your budget, this is a good way to unload pricey pieces and make a buck off items that are otherwise gathering dust in your closet. There are probably a few consignment shops tucked away somewhere in your hometown. Here's a wee sampling from coast to coast: **Green Goddess** in Vancouver (greengoddessfashion.com), **Rewind Consignment** in Calgary (rewindconsignment.com), **Fashionably Yours** in Toronto, **Retro Ragz** in Montreal and **Elsie's Used Clothing** in Halifax.

Thrift: Your most affordable option. This category includes your basic Goodwill, Value Village and Salvation Army shops, which get bags full of donations dropped off. Thrift shopping involves a bit more time scouring the racks, but you can find some great scores for a couple of bucks. If you're doing the donating, you just have to determine who you want to have first crack at your clothing. Goodwill and the Salvation Army are registered charities. Value Village is a for-profit business, although it does buy second-hand clothes in bulk from charitable orgs such as the Canadian Diabetes Association—you know, the ones that call your home for clothing donations. VV says over the last 10 years it's purchased $1 billion worth of clothing from 140 such charities. You could also bypass the big boys altogether and donate your unwanted clothes to an indie organization that will distribute them to someone who needs them. Many women's shelters will gladly take drop-offs of clean seasonal clothing, and they're not alone.

If your aim is to donate to charity, be wary of clothing drop boxes in mall parking lots and whatnot. Many of these are actually for-profit businesses that, at best, market the fact that they give a tiny percentage of their profits to charity. The good news, for Torontonians at least, is that since 2007 all bins have to clearly identify if they're a genuine charity or not.

Reconstructed Vintage: My personal fave. Instead of buying new fabric, designers take old sweaters, trench coats, aprons, blouses, scarves, you name it, and stitch them together to create something completely new and different. The brand **Preloved** is Canada's most famous example. It's now available in indie boutiques the world over, as well as in Anthropologie stores across North America. To be honest, Canada is teeming with fabulous designers working with second-hand discards and factory surplus as a base. Montreal is positively brimming with innovative reconstructed vintage designers, including international sensation **Supayana**, which uses a mix of recycled, vintage deadstock, organic cotton and mill-end fabrics (supayana.com), sexy originals from **Dita & Bella** (ditabella.com) that rework recycled clothing and organic cotton, as well as super-funky **Myco Anna** (mycoanna.com) and **Creations Encore** (creationsencore.com). Some sizzling hot talent out of Ontario includes **Paper People Clothing** (see Canada's Next Top Role Models, page 298; paperpeopleclothing.com), **Embody** (embodyclothing.com) and **Precocious** (precociousboutique.com), which makes some lovely feminine cardigans, shrugs and T-shirt dresses (love 'em, own one), as well as patchwork queen **Susan Harris** (susanharrisdesign.ca). Out west, **Adhesif** (adhesiveclothing.com) styles things up with a mix of recycled, factory surplus and new. On the opposite coast, **Orphanage Clothing** is stitching kick-ass rock 'n' roll styles from old Ts, dress shirts and more (orphanageclothing.com). If you're looking for leather, Quebec's **Cokluch** creates super-sexy fitted jackets and more with recycled leather (cokluch.com). Meow.

HOT ECO-FASHION BLOGS

Want to get hip to all the latest green fashion designs, finds and news? Here are some of your top gateways:

Ecouterre.com: This top U.S. blog for sustainable fashion devotees was founded by the same peeps who do design-friendly **inhabitat.com**.

Fashiontakesaction.com: Not a blog, but this is Canada's only non-profit focused on sustainability in the fashion industry. Sign their Resizing Fashion's Footprint pledge!

Forthoseabouttoshop.ca: Canadian blog about fashion with a purpose.

Threadbanger.com: DIY fashion how-to blog.

Socialalterations.com: A self-described education lab for socially responsible fashion.

MAKE YOUR OWN

I used to have an eensy-weensy teeny-tiny clothing business back in the day. I mostly sold T-shirts to my local feminist bookstore and made pants out of tapestry fabric for my friends. All the evening sewing classes in the world couldn't make me very good, and really the best part was wearing the clothes myself. While I'd rather stick a pin in my eye than sew a collared button-down shirt from scratch (once was enough), pants, skirts and tube dresses are easy-peasy to make, so take it from me and start with those. Just head to a Fabricland, Fabricville or an online source, not for the fabrics but for the patterns. And feel free to alter a pattern's shape to make it cooler, snugger, billowier, you name it. Just make sure you don't use unsustainable fabrics.

- Ask your local fabric stores if they carry any eco-fabrics such as Lyocell, organic cotton, Tencel, even viscose/rayon from bamboo (see page 301).
- Rummage around for cool organic and eco textiles online: delyla.com (out of Montreal), efforts.ca (Toronto based), manoir-inc.com (Quebec), nearseanaturals.com, tenfoldorganic.com, seworganic.com, organiccottonplus.com, pmorganics.com as well as a small selection at organicbynature.ca, mahadevidesign.com and schoolyardstudio.com.
- You can find hemp fabrics at bigger hemp supply shops, or head online to rawganique.com for pretty hemp fabrics, yarns, twine, webbing and more.
- Search second-hand shops for cheap clothes you can cut up and re-work. I often reconstruct random outfits with a chop here and a seam there. It's way easier than sewing from scratch, plus it takes tired old outfits and recycles them.
- Need some inspiration and ideas on how to reconstruct old clothes? My favourite book on this is *Generation T: 108 Ways to Transform a T-Shirt.*

JEANS

Finding just the right jeans to flatter your butt and slim down your planetary footprint can be as challenging as learning to love acid wash again. The vast majority of denim is stitched with pesticide-heavy cotton, then doused with bleaching agents, enzymes, dyes, chemical softeners, stain resisters and UV protectors. And the more "distressed" the look, the more chems your jeans were treated with. Many of those pollutants are seriously contaminating waterways in denim districts like Tehuacán, Mexico, turning local creeks blue and ravaging irrigated crops. Sandblasting is one of the very worst processes for the workers' health, triggering a lung disease called silicosis. H&M and Levi's surprised everyone when they announced plans to eliminate sandblasting from their denim lines by 2011. Hopefully, more brands will do the same. By the way, Levi's cancelled its organic line but says it's moving to Better Cotton (see Better Cotton, page 297).

Green Jeans: Luckily, there are now a slew of sexy organic-cotton jeans kickin' about. Some are more sustainable than others. Remember, the darker and less processed the denim (i.e., no whiskering, fading, sandblasting), the greener the jean.

Second: Finally, some made-in-Canada organic jeans! Second's sexy women's cuts (they're famous for their, albeit non-organic, stretchy yoga jeans) now come in half a dozen organic styles—all at the reasonable price of $120. These Montreal-made jeans are processed using 50% less water and are treated with non-toxic, chemical-free dyes. Even their non-organic jeans are more consciously dyed (yes, the yoga ones, too). With their organics anyway, make sure to size down since they stretch out. secondclothing.com

Good Society: The name says it all. This internationally acclaimed Canadian-based company is hell-bent on making stylish, feel-good jeans out of 98% organic cotton. Their mill even teaches Indian farmers how to go organic. Natural dyes used, and sewn under fair labour conditions. A portion of the proceeds goes towards children's and women's orgs in India. Jeans go for $110. goodsociety.org

Loomstate: Making fashion-forward organic denim since 2004. Used to be made in America, but now Loomstate jeans are sewn in factories around the world, though the company claims to have high labour standards. More men's styles than most brands. $160 and up. loomstate.org

Rawganique: Okay, so these guys make better men's cuts (like carpenter-style) than women's, but hey, they're all made with hemp and organic cotton, and if trendy isn't your thing, women should sneak a peak too. At under $100, the price is right. rawganique.com

Nudie: This Swedish men's line offers some super-stylish Turkish organic cotton sewn in Italy for about $200. nudiejeans.com

Reco Jeans: Ultra-faded men's and women's cuts made with 60% recycled cotton and 40% conventional cotton. Designed in NYC and made in China. Prices range from $99 to $129. recojeans.com

$$ **Second-hand:** The most affordable and sustainable way to score a pair of eco-jeans is to scan local second-hand shops. They're dirt cheap and no cotton had to be grown, sewn or flown in.

PLUS-SIZED FASHION

Ever feel as if all the coolest eco-fashions are biased towards skinny minnies? Totally unnecessary when there are some kick-ass green designers gearing their cuts for curvy fashionistas. **Diane Kennedy** offers plus-sized dresses, gauchos, tunics, leggings, jackets and more in soft organic cotton and certified-organic bamboo in up to 3X (dianekennedy.ca). Two more B.C.ers stitching up a full range of sizes are **Mandala Sky**, which does sexy beach goddess looks in up to 2X (mandalasky.com) as well as **Chloe Angus**, with multiple collections (chloeangus.moonfruit.com). Want to kick it up a notch? **Mewv Sustainables** has curve-licious organic-cotton/Tencel/bamboo dresses in up to size 26—but they ship from the United States (saffrona.com/mewv). On the more relaxed end of the spectrum, you can find hemp and organic-cotton casuals in up to 3X at Rawganique.com out of Victoria. Probably the easiest place to track down plus-sized eco-fashions across the country is Sears, which carries **EcoGear**'s plus-sized recycled-cotton/pop bottle line and **Yes Lifestyle Organics** (sears.ca). By the way, you can score plus-sized sportswear in recycled, high-performance fabrics from the Oregonians at teamestrogen.com.

ACTIVEWEAR

If you're running, jumping or bending yourself into a pretzel in Lycra, spandex, nylon or any high-tech fabric, you're essentially sweating in petrol. Even the most organic tech clothes will need to blend in a bit of the bad stuff to give you the stretch you want, but at least they're slimming down your oil dependency. Downward dog devotees (a.k.a. yogaphiles) already know they can score an ever-shrinking handful of organic cotton blends (for men and women) at their local **Lululemon** chapter (lululemon.com), but who offers more warrior-worthy organic threads that are strictly made in Canada?

Designed for Vancouverites wanting to bust out of the Lulu uniform, **Tonic Lifestyle Apparel** offers an eco-line of workout wear available at yoga studios across the country. Though Tonic isn't all green fabrics, it is all made in Canada, unlike Lululemon, which is stitched in 11 countries around the globe—Canada being just one of them (mytonic.ca). **Respecterre** makes a whole whack of outfit possibilities for any workout with organic and fair-trade cotton and rayon from bamboo, all woven and stitched in Quebec (respecterre.com). Bonus: they offer men's and women's options. Out of the Prairies, Alberta-based **Lucid Lifestyle** has several sports tops and bottoms for women (lucid-lifestyle.com). For something with a little more visual interest, Toronto-made **Squeezed** has great yoga pants and camis with built-in shelf bras, all with pretty silk-screened designs (using water-based inks), from organic cotton with a little spandex (squeezed.ca). Victoria-based **Salts Organic** has several styles of yoga capris, leggings, Ts, tanks and more made of bamboo and organic cotton (saltsclothing.com). For a little more hippie in your yoga or dance wear, check out west-coasters **Maha Devi Design** (mahadevidesign.com). The peeps behind **EcoGear**'s Ts also started a great yoga line called **JuteStyle**, made of viscose from fast-growing jute. It's available at Sears (eco-gear.ca; sears.ca). Active dudes should really dig **Beta** (betaclothing.ca). For high-tech teamwear made of recycled fabrics, check out Teamwear Printing, page 320.

POP BOTTLE CHIC

I know I've slammed synthetic clothing made of petroleum, but there's always an exception to the rule. If you're buying a synthetic fabric, find one with high recycled content. **Modrobes** has some as do Mountain Equipment Co-op (mec.ca) and Patagonia (Patagonia.com/ca). Yes, melting down pop bottles to recycle them is energy intensive, but it's less energy intensive than making new synthetic clothing, and by making the switch, Toronto-based Modrobes claims to have saved 14,422 metric tons of CO_2 and 160 metric tons of liquefied petroleum gas (a reduction of 16.6% from 2006), and water consumption in the manufacturing process has declined by 40% since 2007 (**modrobes.ca**). There is some question as to whether recycled plastic fabrics give off antimony (which leaches from plastic bottles into, say, water when it's in bottle form), so not everyone will embrace them. Still, they have a lot of fans. Also, be sure to look for companies that take back synthetic clothing for recycling, such as **Patagonia** (since 2005, it's taken back 45 tons of clothes and made 34 tons into new clothes).

T-SHIRT, PROMO AND TEAMWEAR PRINTING

Back before I was putting green advice into print, I was hawking my own T-shirts at local shops. At the time, my day job involved fighting for sweatshop workers' rights, so my main focus was making sure the workers who knit the fibres and stitched the shirts were fairly paid. You can imagine my horror, years later, when I found out that the ink used on the majority of North America's screen-printed Ts—you know, the kind that cracks after a few washings—is most often made with PVC. Yep, that polluting, heavy metal–laced, hormone disruptor–off-gassing devil of a plastic. This isn't great news if you've been screen-printing T-shirts in your home.

- **Look for PVC-free, water-based inks.** It's becoming more and more common.
- **Ask how the screens are cleaned.** Do they wash their screens

with air- and water-polluting lacquer thinners, bleach and
petroleum-based mineral spirits, or low-VOC biodegradable
solvents? (An important question since 60 mL of toxic solvents
typically go down the drain for every 12 T-shirts printed, according to one greener printer, Toronto-based T-ShirtGuys.)

- **Ask about embroidered logos instead.** This ink-free system
involves a mechanized needle and thread and is extremely
durable. It'll cost you upwards of $2 per logo. Embossing logos
is also plastic free and will work on leather jackets/bags or
cotton/polyester shirts.

- **Pick the greenest fabric.** Hemp has the smallest eco-footprint,
but most manufacturers blend it with conventional cotton. I'd
choose straight-up organic cotton over bamboo or soy blends
because it's subject to much less chemical processing and is
more durable.

- **Make sure it's sweatshop free.** You definitely want to make sure
your shirts were stitched in a respectable working environment.
Major blank T-shirt companies, including Gildan, Russell
Athletic and Fruit of the Loom, have all been at the centre of
anti-sweatshop campaigns in the recent past. Though they're
now working with labour rights orgs to improve conditions,
there's still a long road ahead, according to the Maquila
Solidarity Network (see maquilasolidarity.org for more info).

Sustainable Options: Anyone printing on blank Ts today has a
refreshing number of choices at hand. Quebec-made **Rêv-Evolution** is
OÖM Ethikwear's all-organic promotional blank clothing line, and 1%
of your purchase price goes to social causes that they support (oom.ca).
Then there are the stylishly conscientious Ts, hoodies, dresses and
more from social enterprise **Me To We**, all made in Canada using
either organic cotton or viscose from bamboo. And 50% of profits go to
charity partner Free the Children (metowestyle.com). **Pure Blankz**
(pureblankz.com) offers certified-organic cotton, fairly made blank
shirts from India coloured with natural and low-impact dyes.

321

American Apparel is a sweatshop-free L.A.-made option that offers a wide selection of blank organic-cotton Ts, tanks, V-necks and long-sleeves in a rainbow of colours at wholesale price. Though not everyone's a fan of their notoriously raunchy ads. For a good selection of ethically sourced promotional wear including jackets, athletic apparel, hoodies, polos, Ts and kids' options made in a range of eco fabrics, hop on B.C.-based Fairware.com. These guys supplied Oxfam Make Trade Fair Ts.

Got a team to outfit? If you don't have a large order (some companies have 48-unit minimums), **Stormtech** (stormtech.ca) makes a couple of high-performance technical Ts and polos out of 50% recycled quick-dry polyester. Trimarksportswear.com carries recycled tech tops, polos, fleece and jackets.

The greenest of the green should scour second-hand shops for used blank Ts and print on those instead.

WINTER COATS

Deep in the grip of a Canadian winter, the tug-of-war between warmth and fashion can be struggle enough for most without throwing in an extra element like sustainability. But we can't hide our heads in the snow forever, people.

High-tech Outerwear: You may be toasty with them on but winter coats can leave the planet out in the cold. Just ask the maker of some of the greener winter coats around, Patagonia. The do-gooding company did a footprint assessment of some of its jackets and confessed that while many of them contain high recycled content, they're still coated with some sketchy finishes. The Nano Puff Pullover, for instance, may be fully recyclable (if you send it back to the company), but its shell and zipper are treated with a durable water-repellent finish that degrades into PFOA—that now-infamous non-stick chemical used to make Teflon that is polluting bloodstreams the world over.

Patagonia actually had to remove the word "eco" from its Eco Rain Shell Jacket after it came clean on the fact that it too contained PFOA. A company rep says the lack of PFOA-free waterproofing finishes has been a massive industry-wide problem. Patagonia says it should be totally PFOA free by fall 2013 but that in the meantime the maker of its rain jacket recycles 99% of its solvents. To be honest with you, **Patagonia** is still among the greenest options for technical outdoor wear since they have the highest recycled content and planet-friendliest policies. **Mountain Equipment Co-op** also carries a few water-resistant recycled-polyester shells and coats (including kids' versions), as well as lots of insulating layers made of recycled polyester. Those fabrics use as much as 75% less crude oil than virgin fibres while keeping trash out of landfills (a couple are 100% recycled). MEC's working on sourcing more polyester fibres that are free of the heavy metal antimony. If you like stylish cuts mixed with high-tech performance, you should jump on **Nau**'s website since these guys rock waterproof 100% recycled–polyester shells as well as waterproof recycled pol/organic cotton–blend jackets with fashion-forward designs (nau.com).

Fashion Jackets: Looking for something with less tech and more pizzazz? While plenty of eco-designers are stitching lightweight spring/fall jackets, there hasn't historically been much on offer for winter. The good news is that your options for earth-and-ego-friendly winter outer-wear have improved over the years. At least fewer mainstream mall stores are painfully mulesing their sheep (see Wool, page 297) for their wool coats, but that doesn't mean the wool is green. I'd rather see you in an organic wool coat (lined with hemp/silk) by a green Canadian company like **Nixxi** (nixxi.ca) or a recycled-wool coat from Aritzia's **Community** line, especially their Canadian-made jackets. For snuggly sass, Aritzia also has cool green parkas made of hemp and recycled fibres (vegan alert: most are stuffed with real down. Keep your eyes peeled for a microfibre fill made from PrimaLoft ECO, which is 50% recycled fibres).

Speaking of hemp, **Hemp HoodLamb** offers somewhat, um, edgier options complete with a rolling-paper dispenser and music pockets with earphone loops in the neck, all in a water- and wind-resistant hemp/organic-cotton shell with snuggly synthetic "fur" or fleece lining, also made of hemp fibres. You can score men's and women's models from

323

hemp shops such as Toronto Hemp Company, or head online to their Canadian distributor's site (freshheadies.com). **Rawganique** carries a line for men and women called Nova Scotia Winter Extreme Hemp Jacket lined with wool and organic-cotton flannel, as well as a Tofino Organic Cotton Corduroy Jacket (rawganique.com). By the way, hemp is naturally more water resistant than cotton and has been used for ages in sails. For a selection of vegan peacoats, classy throwbacks like the Audrey and tailored parkas for both women and men, check out **Vaute Couture** online: vautecouture.com. This Chicago/Brooklyn-made line is constructed with combos of windproof velvet shells (made with 90% recycled fibres), 100% closed-loop, zero-waste recycled-satin liners and/or shells, and some recycled Primaloft stuffing, depending on the coat. Leather lovers will drool over Quebec-based **Cokluch**'s super-hot recycled-leather jackets (cokluch.com).

$$ All of this out of your budget? For the biggest, widest selection of toasty/trendy and inevitably green jackets at the best prices around, go to Craigslist or Kijiji in your hometown/province. Seriously. You'll find pre-loved coats from every brand under the sun (last checked, even a hemp Aritzia coat), all deeply discounted and the deepest shade of green you can find, since you're reducing, reusing and recycling in one fell click. Or scour thrift and vintage stores near you to find the perfect coat for the season.

? GREENWASH ALERT: WHEN THE FUR FLIES

I remember being five years old and having a lucky charm that I rubbed and rubbed as though it were a magic rosary straight from the land of unicorns and fairies. Then one day I realized where it came from: a dead rabbit. It was like waking up and realizing you're Glenn Close in *Fatal Attraction*. Plenty of animal lovers were equally horrified when they spotted the Fur Council of Canada ad campaign pushing the green side of fur. The question is, is fur green? Do a little trolling on Furisgreen.com and you'll notice that the lore of the noble Aboriginal trapper is the primary marketing tool. One "educational" image of a Cree trapper in front of a tent-side fire asks, "When his family has eaten the beaver roast, should he throw the fur away?" Yes, it's true that Aboriginal hunters are wonderfully holistic when it comes to making use of the entire animal, but I don't know any tony uptown wives who are eating mink tenderloin for dinner. You? No one's arguing that traditional Native rights to trapping and living off the land should be taken away (though the Canadian Federation of Humane Societies does say humane trapping standards need to be strengthened). But 85% of the world's fur comes from farms, not Native trappers. Hardly natural when you cram thousands of mink and foxes into steel cages and feed them bits of slaughterhouse by-products. Now, according to Fur Commission USA, the use of slaughterhouse leftovers as feed for mink is one of the main reasons farmed mink can be considered "sustainable." By that logic, it would be peachy green to skin all the house pets who are fed a steady stream of low-grade abattoir off-cuts.

One industry claim that you do have to credit is that fur is durable and recyclable. Pre-loved proponents argue that wearing second-hand fur—either in its original design or recycled into new purses, belts or even earrings—is as green as wearing Goodwill wool or cotton. But sporting them could still land you a pretty icy reception in many circles that feel supporting the aesthetic of fur, even the recycled kind, is just plain wrong. I have to admit, while it may be green, vintage fur makes me a tad uneasy. Of course, I wear 1970s vintage leather, so I'd have to confess to being a full-on second-hand hypocrite.

By the way, not all fake fur is actually fake. Some retailers, including Urban Outfitters, have been caught selling real fur–lined hoodies that were labelled "faux." Test your fake fur by pulling out a few hairs and holding them with tweezers while trying to light them. If it smells like plastic, it's fake. Time to make a stink.

LINGERIE

Let's cut the funny business: where can a Canadian girl find cute green underpants? Everywhere you look, you'll find a sea of synthetic, petroleum-based satins, shiny polyester/nylon blends, and pesticide-sprayed cotton sewn by workers 10,000 miles away and likely paid far too little for their fancy stitch work. If you're not a fan of high-waisted beige briefs, your only other green option, until recently, was to forgo the whole panty scene and go commando. A little chilly in winter. No surprise to anyone, naughtily progressive Europeans were the first to really take to organic knickers and nighties. That means we had to pine with envy at the plethora of options available across the pond, such as **Enamore**. Now, you can find a handful of kimonos/camis and even lace-hemmed bras made out of ultra-soft modal spun from farmed beech trees (for more info on Modal, see page 304) at mainstream lingerie shops such as La Senza and La Vie en Rose for cheap, but they're neither local nor fair trade.

VICTORIA'S SECRET:
WHAT'S THAT OFF-GASSING FROM YOUR BRA?

Does your new lingerie get you hot and bothered? Get in line. One woman filed a lawsuit against Victoria's Secret in 2008 after her Very Sexy Extreme Me Push-Up and Angels Secret Embrace bras triggered welts and serious itching. Regardless of how the case turns out, it would be wrong to assume Victoria's Secret should be the sole accused when the whole clothing industry coats its products with irritating, carcinogenic formaldehyde finishes. Make sure to hand-wash items at least once in soapy water before you wear them.

Greener Undergarments: Pop by your local independent lingerie shop and ask them if they carry any lingerie or undergarments made of ecological fabrics such as organic cotton or Lyocell/Tencel (for eco-assessment of fabrics such as bamboo, modal, Lyocell and more, see pages 300–304). Indie shops often carry collections such as **Hanky Panky**'s organic Cotton with a Conscience line (hankypanky. com), **Eberjey**'s Green Goddess and Dream in Green lines made of bamboo rayon (eberjey.com), **Huit**'s Biotiful organic bras and undies (huit.com), as well as Montreal-based **Blush Lingerie**'s modal pieces, which are also available at big-name stores like Urban Outfitters (blushlingerie.com). Keep your eyes peeled for lacy thongs and hot pants in organic cotton and modal by **Lululemon**.

Want to get up close and personal with more locally made eco designs? Do a little online shopping for playful **Candy Pants**, which has frilly, flowery and basic cuts (candypants.ca). They're made in Canada from organic cotton with stretchy bamboo binding. B.C.-based **Devil May Wear** serves up super-cute and colourful undies out of bamboo jersey, soy and organic cotton, as well as conventional nylon lace (devil-may-wear.ca). **Nomads Hempwear** offers basic bras and undies made out of soy and organic cotton in seven colours (nomadshempwear.com), while Quebec's **Abaka** clothing line has a couple of printed underpants made of bamboo and cotton (abaka.ca). For all y'all who prefer to sleep in a tank instead of an itchy lace number, get some soft **BamJamz**. This line is one of the only companies out there sewing sleepwear (think sleep leggings and strappy tunics) with FSC-certified bamboo (mixed with organic cotton), and it's all Canadian made (bamjamz.com).

Want a hit of Technicolor? Saunter into any **American Apparel** chain store and you can score a sweatshop-free pack of organic thong/ boy-cut/basics in a rainbow of shades, or some two-tone unisex organic baby-rib briefs. In the sassy 'n' sporty category, **Patagonia**'s Active Hipster and Active Boy Shorts moisture-wickers are made with recycled polyester (patagonia.com/ca). Virtual shops including Rawganique.com, Organiclifestyle.com and Notjustpretty.com carry a bunch of different knickers and camis, though they're mostly basic cuts in beige or black organic cotton. Ditto for Grassrootsstore.com.

Burning for some classic glamour? Trawl vintage stores for genuine silk slips, robes, even kimonos from decades gone by. That's where you'll score the greenest and classiest sex appeal. Of course, if you're crafty, you could always sew your own from vintage linens or Ts with a little guidance (just google "sew your own undies").

GOOD REASONS NOT TO BUY TONS OF CLOTHES YOU DON'T NEED

I hate to be a total Debbie Downer, but I've got to say that as much as I love, love, love green fashion and support you supporting it, you need to keep in mind that buying a lot of stuff you don't need is always wasteful. So yes, buy quality, buy green, buy fairly made, and buy pieces that will last season after season. But every new item we purchase, however green it may be, has an impact, so you want to make sure you invest wisely. Case in point: Patagonia is a great, progressive company that's put a lot of effort into greening the footprint of their clothing and of their company as a whole, but still, every article they make requires energy, water and carbon inputs. You can just imagine how much more bloated clothing's footprint could be if an effort wasn't being made. Here's a sampling of what Patagonia found in their Footprint Chronicles (**patagonia.com/us/footprint**):

	CO_2 (from making it to shipping it)	DISTANCE TRAVELLED (from field to store)	ENERGY CONSUMED	WATER CONSUMED
DRESS (made with organic cotton and recycled polyester)	31 pounds (14 kg)	26,313 km	35 kWh (like burning a CFL for 81 days)	N/A
BUTTON-DOWN SHIRT (made of organic Pima cotton)	18 pounds (8 kg)	17,703 km	11.5 kWh (like burning a CFL for 27 days)	2,304 litres (growing cotton in water-stressed region)

	CO$_2$ (from making it to shipping it)	DISTANCE TRAVELLED (from field to store)	ENERGY CONSUMED	WATER CONSUMED
ORGANIC-COTTON JEANS	85 pounds (39 kg)	16,206 km	48 kWh (like burning a CFL for 110 days)	180 L
HIKING BOOTS (greener leather; 50% recycled rubber outsoles)	66 pounds (30 kg)	28,823 km	33 kWh (like burning a CFL for 76 days)	160 L

MATERNITY CLOTHES

The way fashions are cut these days—think forgiving, billowy tops—there's really not much need to buy a closetful of maternity-specific clothing anymore (at least when it comes to clothing for your upper body). Plus, how eco is it to invest in a whack of maternity clothing you may not have a chance to wear again after nine months? **Nicole Bridger** knows her clothes can work as double agents with both your pre- and post-baby bod, so half of her regular line is actually labelled as maternity friendly (nicolebridger.com). Sweden's maternity sensation **Boob** makes all kinds of style- and ethics-conscious dresses, tops, tanks, skirts, leggings and pants out of mostly organic cotton, and no doubt you could keep wearing many of these after the baby arrives. You can score Boob items at dozens of boutiques and online retailers across Canada (see the store locator at boobdesign.com). **Momzelle** makes cool nursing-compatible tanks, dresses, long-sleeves and more in either organic or non-organic cotton designed to flatter postpartum figures. And 98% of it is made in Quebec (momzelle.com). Still, your most affordable and environmentally conscious pick involves hand-me-downs from previously pregnant pals and family members. Remember to pay it forward and consider donating your pre-loved maternity clothes to women's shelters and homes for pregnant teens.

$$ We all have ghosts in our closets. A shirt you spent too much on but never wore, a skirt you never really fit into to begin with, and pants you outgrew months after you took them home. Give those fashion memories a new lease on life by holding a frock swap. Gather a group of your friends and colleagues (making sure that there are multiple people of the same size coming), set a five-piece donation minimum (this shouldn't be hard for most of us), ask people to bring clean clothes, shoes and accessories in good condition, and start swapping. Let everyone showcase their items one at a time, Vanna White–style, to see if there are any takers. A simple game of rock, paper, scissors should decide any duels. Donate leftovers to your local Goodwill or women's shelter.

MEN'S CLOTHING

Let's face it, guys—there are a hell of a lot more green designers making clothes for women than there are for men. Sorry about that. That's not to say there aren't some great sources for planet-friendly dude-gear. I've rounded up some tip-top earth-conscious clothing companies that go out of their way to make sure you're not feeling neglected.

Ts and Tops: Want some cool Canadian-made basics? **OÖM Ethikwear** is a conscious Quebec-made source for graphic Ts, V-necks, polos, long-sleeves, zip-ups, even body-hugging vests, all made of 100% organic cotton or recycled cotton and recycled polyester (oom.ca). For more pointed political graphics on organic Ts, polos and long-sleeves, check out fairly traded **Me To We Style** by Free the Children (metowestyle.com) as well as Montreal's gritty **New K. Industry** a.k.a. **NKI** (newkindustry.com). Vancouver's **Nate Organics** has a creative collection of organic cotton Ts and hoodies (nateorganics.com). Another Canadian-made brand, **Guats** "active lifestyle clothing," gears its graphic hoodies and Ts towards outdoorsy snowboarders/freeskiers/kiteboarders/snowshoers, you name it (guats.com). Toronto-made **EcoGear** offers all kinds of T-shirts, hoodies and sweatpants using

35% recycled pop bottles and 65% pre-consumer cotton clippings, thus avoiding the water-intensive cultivation of new cotton (though melting pop bottles into fibre is indeed energy intensive); available at sears.ca. Nelson's **Nomads Hemp Wear** offers a few shirts and hoodies (nomadshempwear.com). Online retailer **Ecocentrik Apparel** carries a good spectrum of brands for men, with free shipping over $100 (ecocentrikapparel.com)

Casuals: A man can't go out in the world in T-shirts and polos alone. On the Canadian-made front, **Atelier B** designs dope men's gear, including sweaters, vests, jackets, zip-ups and more (atelier-b.ca). **Thieves** offers sophisticated, urban cuts for trousers, shirts and sweaters (thieves.ca). B.C. board maker **Sitka** does button-downs, jackets, pants, shorts, Ts and more in organic cotton and bamboo (sitkasurfboards. com). **Patagonia** and **Mountain Equipment Co-op**, of course, offer tons of organic-cotton and recycled-poly options in casual, functional styles (mec.ca and Patagonia.com/ca). Companies making hot organic men's jeans include the Canucks behind **Good Society,** as well as **Loomstate** and **Nudie** (for websites, see Green Jeans, page 317). Some American brands offering a good selection of casual button-down shirts, sweaters, jeans and way more include elementecowear.com and plaid-heavy hornytoad.com (head to **Horny Toad**'s website for a huge list of stores carrying them across Canada). Oregon-based **Sameunderneath** also has a few great pieces, including pants, jackets and tops (sameunderneath.com).

Men's Underwear: Boys, your goods needn't be relegated to conventional cotton briefs any longer. Everyone from Calvin Klein to Emporio Armani are making underwear out of ultra-soft modal now. It's not the greenest of the green, but this beech-wood-pulp fabric isn't bad (see Modal, page 304).

Rawganique carries boxers and briefs made out of organic cotton and hemp (rawganique.com). **American Apparel** also has fairly made, organic-cotton, tighty-whitey-style briefs in all sorts of crazy colours

331

(americanapparel.net). You can score sexy Quebec-made **Abaka** bamboo briefs through Stilleagle.com or Abaka.ca. If you can get your hands on a pair of **Baskit Pure** organic-cotton briefs, these are pretty rockin' too (baskitwear.com). **Mountain Equipment Co-op** makes some moisture-wicking briefs out of heavy metal–free recycled polyester (mec.ca). Patagonia carries comparable recycled polyester boxers and briefs in basic as well as pretty loud patterns (patagonia.com/ca).

Suits: Though the eco-world is supposed to be an egalitarian place, this is one instance where men get screwed. Planet-conscious girls can get dolled up much easier than tree-hugging boys, but that doesn't mean you've got no options. At least you can find flax-based linen threads in many men's stores come summer; they're just not necessarily sweatshop free. For top style and ethics, it's Toronto designer Sonja den Elzen of **Thieves** to the rescue (thieves.ca). She's whipped up a couple of exceedingly well-tailored cuts, including, last checked, a washable, single-breasted tailored jacket of a hemp/wool/Tencel blend, lined with hemp silk. **Ecogir** (ecogir.com) makes some cool certified-organic as well as recycled pop bottle–polyester suits, though you'll only find some of their machine-washable recycled polyester–wool suits at sears.ca (where they're actually called the Boulevard Club "Traveller"), as well as **Tip Top Tailors** (where you'll find a couple eco suits under their Bellissimo line; tiptop.ca). Rawganique.com has certified-organic hemp dress slacks and matching suit jackets (in nearly half a dozen styles), as well as oxford shirts in several hues and even hemp ties. Liveco.ca also carries a small selection of men's hemp sports jackets. Getconscious.com offers hemp herringbone suits. The crispest, classiest dress shirts are made by **Boll Organic** (bollorganic. com). In the cool, too-bad-it's-hard-to-find-in-this-country category are "music tape blazers" made of 100% recycled-polyester post-industrial music cassette tapes by **Soho's C-Pas** (collectionpas.com). Definitely pop by their store if you're ever in New York City though.

Don't forget, you can hit vintage shops for swank retro suits, or for really fancy occasions, try renting a tux or a suit instead of buying one new. Of course, the dry cleaning solvents used between rentals might not be all that green, but that's tough to avoid.

WEDDING DRESSES

So you're getting hitched but you'd rather not sell out your earthly convictions just to look glam at the altar. Congratulations! Now let's make sure they sing "Here comes the bride, all dressed in chartreuse hemp" as you walk down the aisle. First thing you gotta know is your fabrics. Pretty much every wedding fabric on the market (organza, chiffon, satin, tulle, lace) comes in pricier silk, cheaper petroleum-based nylon or chemical-intensive rayon versions. You might think of going with silk since it's a natural fabric, but keep in mind that silk isn't for vegans (moths are typically boiled in their cocoons so they don't emerge and rip the fibres) and has other ethical considerations (see page 298). If your tulle, chiffon or satin isn't real silk, it's probably wood pulp–based rayon (a chemical-intensive polluter; see page 301 for more on rayon) or petrol-based nylon. You can also assume all that intricate beading found on most conventional wedding dresses was put there by the tired hands of a very poorly paid worker. And just because yours comes from Italy doesn't mean it's above the fray. Several investigations have found the fashion capital to be rife with networks of underground sweatshops staffed by Chinese migrants.

So what should an earth-lovin' bride-to-be look for? Look for a dress made ethically by an eco-conscious designer. Hemp/silk blends are a big fave among green bridal designers (though, again, they're not vegan). Hemp, a naturally low-pesticide crop that requires much less water than cotton, when blended with unbleached silk has a lovely sheen that's absolutely perfect for a wedding dress. If you're a veg-friendly girl and supporting silk freaks you out, fear not: some producers create all-hemp or organic-cotton sateen versions.

Green Wedding Dress Designers: One of Canada's best-known wedding designers, **Adele Wechsler**, has fabulous Eco Couture collections made of certified-organic hemp/silk, vegetable dyes and remnant fabrics, all fairly made in Canada and tailored to different personality types (adelewechsler.com). She makes both bridal gowns and cocktail dresses. I'm a huge fan of Vancouver's **Pure Magnolia** eco dresses starting at $450 for short styles. They even rent wedding gowns for $300 or they can redesign old dresses! (puremagnolia.ca) On the more casual side, Rawganique on the west coast carries simple organic-hemp and hemp jersey wedding dresses, some lined with wild silk (rawganique.com).

You can find a burgeoning assortment of wedding dresses from the United States on the web (and keep in mind anything made in North America doesn't get slapped with duty at the border). The broadest selection comes from **Olivia Luca** (OliviaLuca.com) of Portland, Oregon—maybe because this company makes it ridiculously easy for you to design your own dress. The site allows you to stipulate absolutely everything, including your skin tone, bodice style, skirt length and shape, sash and, of course, fabric (think organic-cotton sateen, fair-trade silk, hemp/silk charmeuse, hemp/Tencel blends, soy silk, bamboo and more), all with just a few quick clicks. It even offsets the CO_2 involved in shipping. New Mexico–based **Conscious Clothing** (Getconscious.com) has several pages of lovely wedding dresses on its site (not to mention plenty of flower girl and bridesmaid designs), starting from around $600.

$$ Budget-friendly Options:

If you've got a design in mind and a good tailor at hand, you could always create your own green dress from scratch. **Near Sea Naturals** has a great selection of hemp/silk, hemp/silk charmeuse and peace silks (nearseanaturals.com). They'll send you samples for about 50 cents a swatch. Other virtual green fabric sources: efforts.ca, picknatural.com, rawganique.com and envirotextile.com. AuroraSilk.com has several peace silks to choose from and even lets you custom-dye your batch with natural hues. Tammachat.com has some fair-trade organic silks by the metre that haven't been processed or dyed with chemicals, in creamy shades. For more fabric sources, see Make Your Own, page 315.

GIVE IT AWAY NOW: DRESS DONATIONS

Once you've wowed the crowds with your stunning, ecologically conscious attire, you can ensure your dress/party purse/shoes keep giving by paying it forward. For bridal gowns, track down the Brides' Project (**thebridesproject. com**). This group sells previously worn dresses (including maternity bridal gowns) for a good price to brides on a budget and donates the cash to cancer charities. All non-bridal dresses (including old bridesmaid, prom and formal dresses) should be donated to the Corsage Project, which gives gowns to high-school girls who can't afford their own prom dresses (**corsageproject. ca**), or Inside the Dream (**insidethedream.org**). That way, next prom, students who can't afford to buy their own duds can still get all gussied up the green way, with pre-loved glamour.

The greenest dresses are also the chic-est form of post-consumer recycling. I'm talking vintage. If Mom's or Nana's dresses aren't to your taste (or if your mom spilled, say, red wine down the front of hers), start rummaging through vintage shops. You're sure to spot some unique beauties with a little patience.

Hate the retro look? Buy (and sell!) used dresses, shirts, veils and more at smartbrideboutique.com. Craigslist.org, Ebay.ca, Etsy.com and Kijiji.ca all offer lots of designer dresses worn for one brief day (hell, some never even made it to the altar). You'll find some serious scores here for anywhere from $100 to $1,000.

Lastly, even "sample sales" can qualify as recycling. Those sample gowns made for runways, ad shoots or showrooms may be gently used, but boy, do they make for great bargains.

PROMS AND FORMAL EVENTS

My prom experience is limited to what I saw in *Pretty in Pink*. Being the Debbie Downer, establishment-hating teen that I was, I opted out of the festivities. (Thankfully, I figured out how to party and still be political by first-year university. Phew!) Before we get to green

335

prep tips, I've gotta give you props for even thinking about the environment when most of your classmates are probably dedicating their brain space to stressing about whether they can walk in stilettos without wiping out and plotting ways to sneak in booze. That's not to say green teens don't worry about all of the above. But it is big of you to try to figure out how to have a good time without giving the planet a hangover. So how do you do that? Well, you do what everyone else does, only a little greener.

Unless you plan on streaking the event, you'll need some clothes. There's one area where you can wear your principles on your sleeve. Girls, pass on the high-priced mall-bought sweatshop gowns and check out the hot green dresses at eco-retailers (see pages 298–300). Guys, you can either go for a rental tux (which covers the first two Rs of environmentalism, as well as being your cheapest bet) or pimp out with an eco suit (see Suits, page 332). Not one for blending in? You'll find some seriously original one-of-a-kind dresses, retro suits, accessories and even shoes if you do some hunting in vintage shops.

Green Prom Tips:

- Sass up your ensemble with a sustainably farmed, socially and environmentally responsible corsage (look for suppliers at sierraeco.com/florists.asp). That way, you won't be boogying with a bloom grown in the "sweatshops of the fields" and sprayed with the most toxic pesticides.

- Girls probably wear more makeup on prom night than any other day of the year. Too bad most of the stuff at the beauty counter is loaded with Mean 15 ingredients (see page 8)—even the ones marketed as "natural"! Genuinely natural makeup can be pricey, but you can doll yourself up with fairly affordable products from **Pure Anada** (thepureboutique.com) or a less natural but even more affordable and still phthalate-, paraben- and petrochemical by-product–free **Sula Beauty** (sulabeauty.com). From drug-stores like Shoppers Drug Mart you can find **Organic wear** by

Physicians Formula, which makes great all-natural mascara and decent blushes and bronzers.

- Skip the typical pre-prom energy-gobbling fake-'n'-bake sessions. If you want to look a little more tanned, use some natural bronzing moisturizer from Nature's Gate. See page 54 for more on natural tanning creams.

- Hoping to get your hair done up by a pro? Just say no to air-polluting, smog-inducing aerosol hairspray (pumps are better), and look for a greener salon near you (see Hair Salons, page 144).

DRESSED TO THRILL: GORGEOUS GREEN DRESSES

So you've got a big event and need to get gussied up. I don't know about you, but this is when I start fruitlessly raking through my closet, fully aware that I have absolutely nothing to wear. I'm all stocked up on casual dresses and skirts, but when it comes to formal attire, I'm at a loss (clearly, I don't get out enough). What's a planetarily conscious girl to do when she needs or just plain wants to take it up a notch? You can find some dresses made out of eco-fabrics such as Tencel at some mall stores, including H&M and Banana Republic, but those aren't exactly original or known for their fairly paid workers. If you want true green Canadian style, prowl around your local eco-boutiques (see Directory), hop on **chartreusestyle.com, ecocentrikapparel.com** or **notjustpretty.com,** or search for "eco apparel" at **mudsharkstreetwear.com**. Or why not go direct to the sexiest designers in the nation? Check out the one-of-a-kind, sophisticated dresses from **Elroy (elroyapparel.com)**, **Thieves (thieves.ca)**, **Red Jade (redjade.raiment.ca)**, **Two of Hearts (two-of-hearts-clothing.com)**, **Nicole Bridger (nicolebridger.com)**, **Nixxi (nixxi.ca)**, **Kali Clothing (kaliclothing.ca)**, **lilikoiclothing.ca**, as well as **miik.ca, Cherrybobin.com, Rescued-designs. com** and **Sarahstevensondesign.com**. **Dianekennedy.ca** does plus sizes—up to 2X or 3X. So does **Chloe Angus (chloeangus.moonfruit.com)**. For more bodacious plus-sized dress options online, head to **saffrona.com/mewv,** though it's not Canadian like the others.

CLOTHING FOR THE CHEMICALLY SENSITIVE

Canada's teeming with clothing that would make any green fashionista weak in the knees. All marvellous, unless you're chemically sensitive. One problem is that a lot of organic cottons are blended with small proportions of petroleum-based synthetic Lycra to give them some stretch. Some people with multiple chemical sensitivities (MCS) can handle a little Lycra, while others, not so much. But if you're really sensitive, your biggest beef may be with the dyes. Nearly all of the companies I mention in this chapter use low-impact, synthetic fibre–reactive dyes (as do Patagonia's and MEC's organic lines). That means they don't get their hues from heavy metals or toxic dye fixers (mordants) and generally use less energy and water in the dying process, but they're still petroleum based. It's tough to get really punchy reds, blues, purples and other great colours from nature (at least when it comes to clothing)—sorry. The bad news is that if your reactions are severe, you might simply have to stay away from this stuff. At least organic companies, unlike mainstream clothiers, don't usually apply formaldehyde as an anti-wrinkling agent, or other finishing chems (see page 305)

Although natural (that is to say, plant-, mineral- or insect-, yes, *insect*-based) dyes are generally easier for those with sensitivities to handle, granola-heads might be surprised to learn that some natural dying techniques employ not-so-eco heavy metals as mordants. You might or might not have a problem with them. Fabrics that have been simmered with clay, onion skins, tea, mud or walnut husks are the most benign, but they're hard to find. Earthcreations.net carries a selection of organic-cotton/hemp clothing in 17 clay-dyed pigments. Another excellent option would be colour-grown cotton, from plants cultivated for thousands of years to grow in earthen shades of red, green, yellow and brown. CottonfieldUSA.com is a decent source for organic clothing made from these fibres. They offer more conservative styles with a looser fit, if that's your thang.

Then, of course, there are the recycled and reconstructed vintage options I absolutely love (reduce, reuse!) by hot Canuck collagers including Preloved, Adhesif, Paper People Clothing and Precocious (see Reconstructed Vintage, page 314). But vintage fibres *can* be a nightmare for the chem-sensitive, since you can't know what synthetic soaps and softeners they were washed with. Still, I know plenty of people with mild chemical sensitivities who sport vintage clothes exclusively. Just wash them a few times in baking soda and borax, or soak them for a few hours before you wear them.

Otherwise, you're stuck with beige. Luckily, rawganique.com offers most of its organic-hemp styles in "natural." B.C.-made **Salts Organic**'s hoodies and tops in natural hues are unbleached and undyed (saltsorganic.com). Out of the United States, **BGreen** (bgreenapparel. com), **Blue Canoe** (bluecanoe.com) and LotusOrganics.com carry a small handful of all-natural, undyed, Lycra-free organic items. **American Apparel** makes some plain beige 100% organic-cotton tanks, girlie Ts and even thongs. Scan the selections at organiclifestyle.com and grassrootsstore.ca too (the former even has some colour-grown cotton and Oeko-Tex 100 bamboo, which means it shouldn't have any chemical residues on it; see Label Decoder, page 411).

Some combo of the above options should keep you from running off and joining a nudist colony, anyway. Besides, who knows what disinfectants *they* use?

Leather   343

Vegan Footwear   346

Athletic Shoes   348

Footwear Protection   349

FOOTWEAR
You've got sole

Shoes have been the ultimate foot

soldiers in the battle of ethics. Hell, Nike essentially spawned the mass anti-sweatshop movement of the '90s when the atrocious conditions of its shoe factories were discovered (says a lot about a sneaker). And thanks to that movement, most major running shoe companies have greened the chemicals they expose workers (and the planet) to. But that doesn't mean the rest of the shoe biz has stopped using dangerous toxins as solvents in their glues, primers, degreasers and more. The industry says it's using more water-based glues but, sadly, too many in the footwear biz are still stuck in the past, clinging to solvents that are made of about 80% harmful VOCs (volatile organic compounds) such as acetone and neurotoxin toluene, which are either harmful to workers, raise smog levels or, in toluene's case, both. The first step on the path to a greener shoe may be demanding they be made with water-based glues, but there are a lot more steps in the journey.

LEATHER

We can't talk shoes without covering the most pervasive footwear fabric on the planet: leather. The question of whether leather can be green is a tough debate because while the meat-raising sector has a massive environmental footprint (and an appalling animal-welfare record), many would point out that leather itself is a waste product that would be tossed otherwise, so we might as well use it. They do make a good point, though you also have to consider where the funds from that leather are going. If it's supporting cattle ranchers responsible for tearing down the rainforest to make way for more cows, that leather is seriously tainted. In a 2009 investigative report by Greenpeace International called "Slaughtering the Amazon," the world's largest leather supplier, Brazil's cattle giant Bertin, was called out for illegal Amazon-clearing practices. And guess who was buying from Bertin? Running shoe giants Nike and Adidas/Reebok as well as Clarks, GEOX, Timberland and more. The report prompted Timberland, Adidas/Reebok, Nike and Clarks to demand an immediate moratorium on Amazon destruction from its suppliers. Bertin eventually backed the moratorium as well, but in a 2011 follow-up report entitled "Broken Promises," Greenpeace outlined how JBS (which took over Bertin) was still buying from illegal ranches invading indigenous land and was on Brazil's slave labour blacklist. But this time brands were helping Greenpeace put pressure on JBS.

Even if your leather doesn't come from illegally cleared rainforests, you still have to consider all the heavy-duty toxins used in processing it. The tanning and dying of leather are, by and large, horrifyingly toxic processes, especially if they're done in developing countries such as India and China, which have few enviro standards. Actually, 80% to 85% of the world's leather is tanned with chromium. Now, not all forms of chromium are readily toxic, but the Danish Environmental Protection Agency tested 43 leather products in 2001 (including 10 pairs of shoes) and found that over a third contained the worst kind, hexavalent chromium, the known carcinogen made famous by the film *Erin Brockovich*, on the leather itself. The good news is that HC was below detection limits in all baby shoes tested. But even when HC wasn't detected, a 2009 report by the Swedish Society for Nature Conservancy found extremely high levels of trivalent chromium in shoes, which, when incinerated or dumped in landfills, can oxidize into the highly toxic hexavalent form. The environmental organization suggested that because of the risk, leather products should be designated hazardous waste and managed accordingly.

The org also happened upon some pretty toxic metals, including arsenic, lead and mercury, in some of the leather footwear (all used as leather preservatives), as well as formaldehyde. These days, you'll find more and more footwear with stink-busting, antibacterial finishes. Always ask what chemical's being used to kill the stench. High levels of a bioaccumulative, seriously toxic fungicide/bactericide (2,4,6-Trichlorophenol) was found on one of the shoes tested. Another shoe contained the highly allergenic mould inhibitor dimethyl fumarate.

Ecoholic Leather Options: Now, what if you could replace toxic hues and use vegetable dyes instead? And in place of neurotoxin-laced glues, use water-based ones and recycled rubber or cork footbeds? Well, lo and beyond, there's a whole world of such fashionable, earth-friendly footwear at your feet. My personal fave is **El Naturalista**. This super-cool Spanish company produces kick-ass fairly made boots, shoes and sandals, all with veg-dyed leather and natural rubber or mottled recycled-rubber soles (elnaturalista.ca). **Think!** is the slightly less fly German-made equivalent, with natural tannins from ground bark extracts of plantation trees and mostly cork/natural latex foot beds (carried by Walking On A Cloud stores). For a chunky, funky Canadian-designed shoe, sandal or boot, check out Ontario-based **Groundhogs**. These guys use semi-vegetable tanned leathers, natural latex, recycled rubber and cork soles, with coconut and tree resin buttons and buckles (groundhogshoes.com). The last two of these companies really focus on women's gear, though.

Terra Plana, on the other hand, has everything from women's pumps to cool unisex sneaks in a mix of materials including vegetable-tanned leathers, organic cotton, recycled quilts/heels/plastic bottles, soles made from reconstituted natural latex and rice husks, and insoles made of 70% recycled polyurethane and natural cork. They're made in China but are third-party monitored (terraplana.com).

Fair-trade African-made **Oliberte's** leather shoes and sneakers don't come from factory-farmed animals but from free-range ones that lived on small, family-run farms. The soles are made of natural rubber tapped in Liberia. And the company is Canadian (oliberte.com). Speaking of fair-trading Canadians, I'm also digging the colourful loafers, boat shoes, sandals and lace-ups by **soleRebels Canada**. These guys are officially fair trade–certified and crafted in Ethiopia of stuff like organic cotton, recycled tire soles, free-range leather and jute (solerebelsfootwear.co). Of the big brands, Timberland has a green collection of men's and women's shoes, sandals and boots called **Earthkeepers** that incorporates materials such as leather from silver-rated environmentally responsible tanneries (tanneries get ranked for green performance by the Leather Working Group) as well as canvas that's made of organic cotton and recycled PET, 100% recycled PET linings, organic cotton laces, and soles that are in part made of recycled rubber (timberland.com).

For more conservative but high-comfort walking shoes, **Mephisto** is still the go-to company (mephisto.com). They stick to natural rubber soles, water-based glues and veggie-dyed leather, as well as natural, sustainable cork insoles. I looked more closely at **Ecco**, another line of extra-comfy shoes and boots. Turns out they use *some* latex/recycled soles, *some* veggie tanned leather but no veg dyes. Soles fused without glues (ecco.com). Chunky **Kalso Earth Shoe** footwear isn't veg-dyed but they do use water-based glues, their footbeds and footbed liners contain some recycled milk jugs, and their soles are biodegradable plastics and starch (kalsoearthshoes.com).

Locavores will like that there is at least one company constructing stylish footwear on Canadian soil: **La Canadienne**. They manufacture some shoes in Europe, but otherwise it's maple leafs all the way (made in Canada, that is; as a Montreal-based company I'm sure they'd prefer I said they're Habs all the way). They're not particularly green, though they use chrome-free dyes, which is a healthy start (lacanadienneshoes.com).

By the way, if you can't imagine buying shoes without trying them on, Walking On A Cloud and SoftMoc are two mainstream mall chains that carry several of the greener brands mentioned here.

VEGAN FOOTWEAR

Tortured is the ecologically conscious soul who wishes to wear fashionable yet ethical footwear. Somehow, finding a shoe that meets all your needs (sweatshop free, eco-friendly, cruelty free and stylish) seems like too much to ask. What if you want something beyond hemp sneaks? Well, the classic vegetarian pick has always been faux leather, traditionally made from PVC. I bought a sexy pair of pleather boots over a decade ago, thinking I was doing a good deed by sparing a fuzzy animal's life. Alas, this toxic plastic is reviled by the eco-community for its polluting manufacturing process, the hormone-disrupting plasticizers that off-gas from it and the dangerous chems emitted if, at the end of their life, your boots are burnt in a crappy municipal incinerator. The last few years have seen a rise in the use of PU (that's polyurethane to you, mister) as a replacement for PVC in the faux leather biz. It doesn't have the same haunted rep, but making this stuff is still far from holy. In fact, Greenpeace ranks it as the second-worst class of plastic, tied with Styrofoam and bisphenol A–laced polycarbonate. But it's still considered moderately greener than PVC. You can find pleather shoes made of PU at the cheapest mall shoe stores (though most of the time they're just vaguely labelled "synthetic," so it's impossible to know if they're PVC or PU). The problem is, you're treading deeper into serious sweatshop territory and much higher chances of dodgy solvent-based glues (if a new shoe smells strongly of plastic, that's a dead giveaway).

There's actually a large and fabulous selection of vegan men's and women's shoes at online boutique ethicalocean.com. As well, look for specialty vegan shops such as **Karmavore** in New Westminster, B.C.

(karmavore.ca), **Nice Shoes** in Vancouver (gotniceshoes.com), Leftfeet.ca out of Toronto or **Duckie Shoes** in Montreal (duckieshoes. blogspot.com; the first three have good online shopping). Planet-conscious, fair trade–certified solerebels.com carry a lot of vegan sandals and funky loafers. For the absolute largest source of people-and-planet-friendly vegan shoe brands, check out mooshoes.com. This adorable New York–based shop and virtual boutique sells everything from hot high heels to classy guy gear and claims to get 70% of its stuff from unionized European factories. Here are some more vegan brands that will leave you and the planet truly footloose and fancy-free.

- **Novacas** is a PVC-free, worker-friendly company with stylish women's and men's lines out of Portugal with a couple of Canadian retailers. novacas.com

- **Neuaura Animal Friendly Footwear** comes from an environ-mentally responsible, unionized factory in Brazil, and is made with cotton canvas, jute, recycled Ultrasuede and synthetics such as polyester and PU. neuaurashoes.com

- Brazilian-made **Melissa** flats and flip-flops are made of "recyclable" plastic at a virtually zero-waste factory (just don't expect your local recycler to accept them). melissa.com.br/en

- Wanna skip the plastic and play Imelda Marcos without buying 5,000 pairs of shoes? **Mohop** makes sexy, sustainably sourced wooden sandals that come with five sets of adjustable ribbons that let you deck your foot out in an infinite number of styles. mohop.com

- Italy's **Charmone** makes sexy, sweatshop-free, vegan, PVC-free dress shoes and sandals for women with a mix of organic cotton, micro-suede, recycled wood and some polyurethane. charmone.com

- **Jambu** isn't all vegan but it has a trail-rated women's and kids' vegan line made with natural rubber outsoles. jambu.com

- Canada's own **John Fluevog** makes a handful of über-original vegan women's and men's options. fluevog.com

- Tough **Dr. Martens** also come vegan. drmartens.com

- For more basic hemp clogs, hemp oxfords and hemp sandals, check out rawganique.com.
- **Toms** super-simple and ultra-popular "buy a pair, donate a pair" slip-ons now come with vegan options (tomsshoes.ca). This company does use leather for their "classic" insoles, but their vegan picks are made of either hemp/recycled-plastic-bottle twill or pesticide-free cotton. Toms partners with humanitarian and health organizations to give away a pair of shoes to a child in need for every pair of shoes purchased. By 2010, Toms had given away over a million shoes to needy kids.
- For vegan sneakers, see below.

ATHLETIC SHOES

Whether you like your techy footwear for jogging or just kicking around the neighbourhood, it's time to add a little green bounce to your step.

Running Shoes: The race for the greenest performance running shoe is on, and new additions keep arriving, so here are some things to keep in mind.

All the major brands are marketing their greening initiatives, such as PVC phase-outs, but Brooks is certainly in the running for top spot with its **Green Silence** line. An impressive 75% of it comes from post-consumer recycled sources, plus it has biodegradable insoles, midsoles and collar foams. Brooks's green trail-running line **Cascadia Six** is made of 50% recycled content. Plus, both lines use safer dyes and water-based glues. Moreover, many of their other shoes have biodegradable BioMoGo midsoles and petroleum-free HPR (High Performance Rubber) green soles (brooksrunning.ca).

New Balance shoes are all totally PVC free, any polyester used in meshes, linings and laces is at least 35% recycled, and their PU synthetic leather is made with 30% fewer solvents and/or 25% recycled content. Their leather tanneries have to score a bronze for enviro performance (versus silver for Timberland) and they're "increasing the use of water-based adhesives wherever applicable," whatever that means. Bonus: they now offer cool 95% recycled sneakers called **newSKY** (newbalance.ca).

When it comes to hiking boots, trail runners and more, **Patagonia**'s got a good selection made with partly recycled insoles and outer soles, though its non-sporto shoes often offer greener materials such as hemp (Patagonia.com/ca).

Sneakers: There are a whack of great green sneaks on the market. Simple Shoes may be gone but you can score cooler, fair-trade veg or free-range leather sneaks from solerebelsfootwear.co or oliberte.com. We still love **Adbuster**'s classic, fairly made, all-hemp-and-natural-rubber Blackspot Sneaker in, well, black and fiery red (adbusters.org/culture-shop/blackspot/sneaker). For more selection, **Autonomie Project** makes a dozen vegan, organic and sweatshop-free sneaks and even offers custom screen-printing options (autonomieproject.com). I've got a pair from another great company, **Veja**, made with family-farmed, fair-trade, certified-organic cotton and wild-tapped Amazonian rubber, and they also offer snazzy leather options with eco-tanned leather that uses veg extracts such as acacia, but Vejas are hard to track down outside Montreal (veja.fr).

In the totally mainstream, not particularly fairly traded camp, Keds makes a couple of 100% organic shoes in its Champion line, as well as the Green Label line with organic-cotton uppers, recycled-rubber soles, "non toxic" dyes and recycled insoles.

FOOTWEAR PROTECTION

It's almost a national ritual: shoe store clerks bully you into buying shoe protector you don't really want, and then you go home and gas your boots as far away from heat and open flames as you can get, wondering "Is this going to kill me?" There's got to be a better way. Most shoe-proofing sprays come with pretty much every warning label imaginable, including "extreme danger," "very flammable," "poison" and that yield-shaped explosive symbol. I've spotted products with all of the above that tout their

15% beeswax and silicone content, as though that undoes all the danger at hand. Oh sure, they all say they're ozone friendly and CFC free, but guess what? *Everything's* been CFC free for, oh, two decades, so it's just basic greenwash. I'd rather see them say low-VOC, since all those aerosols are heavy in smog-inducing, volatile organic compounds that seriously pollute the air we breathe. They're also responsible for headaches, dizziness and eye/nose/throat irritation.

Worse still, lots of shoe sprays and waxes contain bad-news PFOAs, the very bioaccumulative, environmentally persistent fluorochemicals used to make Teflon and all sorts of stain- and grease-resisting finishes. This stuff binds to our livers, kidneys and blood, and Environment Canada's found it in our caribou, belugas, seals, waterways, sewage sludge, you name it. EC is bringing in a risk management approach to eliminating exposures, but in the meantime, look for PFOA or PFC (perfluorinated chemical) free.

Granger's proofing line is water based, but it mostly claims to be green by offering protection that outlasts the competition. A little digging tells you their G-Max Universal Waterproofer is made with ethanediol, a.k.a. ethylene glycol, an antifreeze which, while biodegradable, really shouldn't be swallowed. Their G-Wax Leather Conditioner contains a petroleum distillate (hydrotreated naphtha) that is classified as toxic to fish and shouldn't be dumped down the drain.

You'll find lots of silicone-based waterproofing products on the market, but unless you know they're free of environmentally toxic and bioaccumulative D4 (cyclotetrasiloxane, octamethylcyclotetrasiloxane), which the feds are restricting, you'll want to keep your distance.

I don't care how natural it is, I don't have to tell you to stay 10 feet away from totally unnecessary mink oil. It's scraped from the dead hides of farmed minks and, according to one manufacturer, only about 3 to 10 grams can be obtained per mink. That's a lot of dead mink on your toes. It's still sold as a leather conditioner and waterproofing agent, and to add insult to injury, you can even buy mink oil aerosol—if you want to add hazardous VOCs to the mix.

By the way, I don't want you using Bear Guard either. It's made with wild Maine beeswax, which is lovely, as well as (gulp) bear fat.

Ecoholic Options: Phew! That's a lot to avoid. So what should you be looking for? Look for brands that explicitly say they're free of fluorinated chemicals. **Nikwax** is one of them. This water-based U.K. line is made with a purportedly non-toxic, biodegradable polymer that's free of petroleum distillates and solvents (the very stuff that gives off VOCs, many of which are potent greenhouse gases). Nikwax says if they were manufacturing with run-of-the-mill petroleum-distillates or aerosol products, they would have put 500 tons of VOCs and propellant gases into the atmosphere by now. Plus, they say, by extending the life of your shoes (including suede), boots, coats and tents, you're buying less gear. Nikwax is available at Mountain Equipment Co-op and other outdoor suppliers. This one's not tested on animals, either.

Canadian-made **Clapham's Beeswax Leather Dressing** with beeswax and carnauba isn't perfect but it's certainly greener than mainstream picks. It also uses cattle-derived neatsfoot oil and petroleum-based mineral oil solvents, but those solvents are free of carcinogenic aromatic hydrocarbons. Check with your local Home Hardware or Lee Valley Tools or see Clapham's store directory (claphams.com).

Jewellery	355
Diamonds and Other Gems	358
Engagement Rings	359
Natural and Repurposed Jewellery	361
Purses and Bags	363

JEWELLERY
AND ACCESSORIES
The devil's in the details

One thing I learned from

Anthropology 101 is that while chimps make tools and apes
have a pretty decent vocabulary, we humans really distinguish
ourselves from our fellow mammals through personal adornment.
You don't see monkeys with handbags or gorillas wearing
wristwatches (although I did see a squirrel monkey steal my
brother's sunglasses once). Either way, wildlife globe-wide are
certainly feeling the effects of having their habitat gouged to
dig up the minerals we use as body decoration. And the earth in
general is feeling the pinch of cramped landfills and the toxic
pollutants we use just to churn out all the cheap accessories we
buy and toss every year. But have no fear, accessory lovers, you
can still drape yourselves with options that are much gentler
on the planet and still look smashing in the process.

JEWELLERY

From cheap charms to outrageously expensive bling, jewellery is, hands-down, the single biggest fraud in your possession. Oh sure, it's all sparkle and shine on the outside, but it's riddled with dark secrets lingering just below the surface. Whether you're talking gold, silver, platinum or gems such as diamonds, you've got to dig up a lot of earth to get at it, and doing so is not only incredibly scarring to the physical landscape, frequently in already fragile ecosystems, but it creates massive amounts of waste, groundwater contamination and pollution.

Gold, Silver and Platinum: Gold is definitely the most notorious bad boy in the precious metals sector. And with good reason. A single gold ring, for instance, leaves behind 20 tons of waste rock. And because cyanide is often used to extract that gold from surrounding rock, the average large gold mine uses over 1,900 tons of deadly cyanide a year (the cyanide also commonly releases a great deal of mercury from the gold ore, as it's been found to do in mines in Nevada and elsewhere).

Though gold gets most of the flack in the jewellery racket, it's not for lack of bad behaviour amongst other metals. South Africa's platinum mines, where 80% of the world's platinum comes from, have been fingered for unacceptable air pollution levels, as well as illness and even death amongst its migrant workers. Even under our own noses on Canadian soil we have trouble keeping a grip on pollution. At Placer Dome's now-shuttered Equity Silver mine in B.C., 42 million tons of tailings (waste rock) will need pollution control measures for centuries to come in order to limit harmful acid mine drainage of heavy metals, and the pollution of local lakes and streams remains an ongoing issue, according to a report by BC Wild and the Environmental Mining Council of B.C.

In 2010 an industry-commissioned report revealed that Canadian mining companies operating abroad have the worst environmental and human rights record among all global mining nations, stating "Canadian companies are more likely to be engaged in community conflict, environmental and unethical behaviour." According to the report, written by the Canadian Centre for the Study of Resource Conflict, gold and copper mines were some of the worst.

Greening the Jewellery Business: In 2004, Earthworks kicked off its famous No Dirty Gold campaign, and since then the big guys in the jewellery world have started to improve their ways a little. In the 2010 follow-up report, Earthworks noted that over 60 jewellery companies (representing $14.5 billion in sales), including Birks and Tiffany & Co, had committed to sourcing cleaner gold by endorsing a set of Golden Rules for responsible mining. Does that mean buying from these retailers ensures you're supporting clean gold? Let's not get too far ahead of ourselves. Not everyone that signed on had strong scores, but the commitment is a healthy start. For all the details on who's committed to what, check out the Tarnished Gold report at nodirtygold.org.

You might come across jewellers who claim to work with fairtrade metals. Ask them where the mine is located and what makes it fair trade. If they source from Colombia's **Oro Verde**, they definitely get the green light. I love Oro Verde's artisanal mining approach that takes careful consideration of environmental and social criteria. The people who work the land have collectively owned it for generations and are vested in its sustainable future (go to greengold-oroverde.org for more info).

Recycled Metal: No new metal is ever going to be totally green, so what are tree-hugging lovers to do when they want to give their partner something pretty? Repurposed or vintage metals will be your greenest pick, followed by recycled metals. Of course, it takes some energy to melt metal, but it's significantly lower impact than digging up new ones.

- Hunt down jewellers who offer primarily recycled gold, platinum and other metals. For conventional jewellery from reclaimed metals, check out online shop **Brilliant Earth** (brilliantearth. com; see Engagement Rings, page 359, for more info) and **Leber Jeweler** (leberjeweler.com).

- For more creative designs, take a peek at all the fab Canadians working with recycled metals, such as the reclaimed-steel designs of theraveniron.com or personalized fingerprint jewellery from recycled silver by **Dimples** (dimplesforever.com). Lots of indie retailers, including Web-based Ethicalocean.com and bricks-and-mortar **Distill** in Toronto, carry lovely recycled-metal options too. **Organic Metal Gallery** actually refines and recycles its own metals in house (on top of selling fair-trade metals (organicmetalgallery.com). For really cool recycled-copper-pipe jewellery, browse **Winterchild Jewellery's Old Tin Roof** line (winterchildjewellery.ca).

- **Etsy.com** is a treasure trove of recycled-jewellery options. You'll find a bunch of unique Canadian designers on the site who offer a large handful of recycled/reclaimed-metal options, including **Jake + Cleo** (jakecleo.etsy.com), **Anjastudios** with recycled silver collected from old circuit boards and photographic supplies (etsy.com/shop/AnjaStudios), **Bella-Bijou** (bellabijoutoo.etsy.com), which uses recycled and reclaimed metals and ethically sourced stones whenever possible, and, in part, **Organikx** (mixed with fairly traded artisanal silver; organikx.etsy.com).

- **TerraCycle** is a multi-talented upcycling company (they do everything from office supplies to worm poop fertilizer made with recycled packaging) and now they're in the jewellery biz! They make recycled-sterling-silver pendants and earrings with fake diamonds (a.k.a. cubic zirconium) and certified-conflict-free Canadian diamonds starting from $20 up to $220. You can score some at sears.ca and walmart.ca.

CERTIFIED-RESPONSIBLE JEWELS?

Considering the heavy tarnish marring the jewellery biz these days, the industry really needed a certification system to help polish up its image. Enter the Responsible Jewellery Council. The non-profit says it will certify members for ethical, social and environmental practices in the diamond and gold sector. And, hoorah, every jeweller and their uncle is signing up. Marvellous and all—except instead of being an independent third-party, multi-stakeholder organization like the Forest Stewardship Council, the Responsible Jewellery Council is more of an industry-only backroom club that certifies, well, not that much. It's been heavily critiqued by eco-org Earthworks for its weak environmental and social standards and failure to provide proper independent verification of compliance. It certainly doesn't certify completely traceable member supply chains the way the FSC does for wood or the Marine Stewardship Council does for fish.

All in all, it's been lumped with Walmart's Love, Earth jewellery line for being a particularly bejewelled form of greenwash. Love, Earth broke a lot of hearts when a *Miami New Times* exposé in 2011 revealed that the gold chains and earrings "committed to protecting the environment" actually came from the second most polluting mine in the United States, as well as sweatshops in Bolivia. Sigh. Why does love always end in pain?

We'd rather see more jewellers join Tiffany & Co. in working towards a true third-party seal by participating in the Initiative for Responsible Mining Assurance (IRMA) for large-scale mining. In the meantime, don't be lulled into thinking "responsible" jewellery is always as it seems.

DIAMONDS AND OTHER GEMS

This is where bling gets its name, from the sheer eye-popping dazzle power of cut gems. But from Burmese rubies to African diamonds, these villains of the jewellery world have attracted as much bad press as a roomful of fallen dictators. You shouldn't be able to buy conflict-fuelling blood diamonds anymore, right? The 75-country-strong Kimberley Process Certification Scheme was supposed to clean all that up. And it has, over the last decade, helped a few countries that were the most severely affected by diamond-fuelled wars to boost their official conflict-free diamond revenue, but as the NGO Global Witness notes: "Despite the existence of the Kimberley Process, diamonds are still fuelling violence and human rights abuses. Although the scheme makes it more difficult for diamonds from rebel-held areas to reach international markets, there are still significant weaknesses in the scheme that undermine its effectiveness and allow the trade in blood diamonds to continue." Critics charge that its monitoring is weak, human rights standards aren't being upheld, and it's failing to crack down on seriously offending members such as Zimbabwe and its violence-plagued diamond fields.

Canadian Diamonds: Wanting to forgo blood diamonds from abroad, lots of conscious lovebirds look to Canadian diamonds. I hate to break up the party, but I do have some mixed news about these stones. Sure, northern miners are paid a tidy sum for their services and Canadian mines are heavily regulated on all fronts compared with Third World mines. But critics say the environmental problems still exist. Just ask Mining Watch Canada. This NGO published a report detailing the lake draining, wildlife disruption and undermining of Native peoples that happens when you dig up environmentally fragile ecosystems. For more dirt, check out There Are No Clean Diamonds: What You Need to Know about Canadian Diamonds (miningwatch.ca).

Sustainable Gems: The cleanest, greenest diamonds and gems you can find, in order of sustainability, are: 1) vintage, 2) lab created, and 3) fair trade (keeping in mind that Canadian diamonds are often called "fair trade," so this is a fuzzy topic). For more retailer options, see Engagement Rings, below.

ENGAGEMENT RINGS
Either someone popped a question or you're just about to and are hunting for the right ring. *Mazel tov.* The traditional route is to fall face-first into the hands of the marketers behind De Beers' diamond

monopoly and friends. The same ones who convinced us all over half a century ago that diamonds are the very best symbol of "forever" and inched out all the other stones and plain bands that had been the norm.

Vintage Jewels: You can stick it to the diamond monopoly and score yourself a stunning one-of-a-kind stone by going the vintage route. I was committed to going ring free until my guy and I stumbled across this amazing 1920s art deco ring in an antique furniture store, of all places. Reaching for an antique means no new metals had to be extracted and refined, and no new stones had to be bloodily yanked from the ground. It's essentially footprint free. You can find stunning originals at antique jewellery markets as well as antique jewellery auctions like the ones offered by **Waddington's Auction House** (waddingtons.ca).

New Rings: GreenKarat says nuh-uh to Canuck stones, and will custom-make rings with lab-grown diamonds, fair-trade or recycled stones, petrified wood or even the lovely pebble you kept from the park where you first made out. Plus, you can send them a broken gold chain or your grandma's old gold bracelet that's too small for you and they'll melt it down into a new ring (Greenkarat.com). **FTJCo** out of Toronto offers engagement rings that set Canadian diamonds in fair trade–certified Oro Verde gold and platinum from Colombia, where workers are paid decently, no cyanide or mercury are used, and "minimum-impact practices" are in place (ftjco.com). If you're set on getting a new diamond, **Brilliant Earth** (see page 356) uses recycled gold and platinum with Canadian gems and ethical diamonds from Namibia as well as some fair-trade **Pride Diamonds** from **Sierra Leone.** They also offer lab-made diamonds now, so if, like J.Lo, you enjoy a pink, blue, yellow or orange hue, then this is your best bet. The company, which offers custom engagement/wedding rings and more, also carries True Blue fair-trade sapphires from Australia, Sri Lanka and Malawi, ethical emeralds from Colombia, as well as fair-trade gold from the Oro Verde mine in Colombia (brilliantearth.com).

Another American, **Leber Jeweler**, offers similar options online (leberjeweler.com), and **Artisan Wedding Rings** has comparable choices but with more Celtic styling (artisanweddingrings.com). Plenty of local artisanal jewellers, like **Organic Metal Gallery** in Toronto, will help you create your own custom ring with Oro Verde or recycled metals and pre-loved stones, so be sure to inquire and, as always, press for details.

Not that you have to go the metal/gem route. **Touch Wood Rings** out of B.C. custom-makes beautiful commitment/anniversary/engagement/wedding rings out of any of a dozen kinds of trees, often blown-down or bug-infested on their 50 acre lot, or some kind of scrap wood or wood sent to them by those requesting rings (touchwoodrings.com).

NATURAL AND REPURPOSED JEWELLERY

I'm a jewellery fiend, but the kind I fawn over doesn't sparkle or cost a week's salary. Not when there are countless creative options handmade by local artisans. Remember when green jewellery was limited to woven-hemp stuff that smelled like patchouli? I'm happy to report we've gone way beyond that now.

Recycled and Found Objects: There are just so many indie jewellery crafters working with vintage bits—from retro dominoes (oddbirddesigns.com) to every vintage doodad under the sun (samanthanemiroffjewellery.com). I couldn't list them all if I tried, but here's a small sampling, starting with a really beautiful collection of necklaces and studs by Vancouver's **Type B** made with vintage ephemera pressed between recycled glass from discarded picture frames. It's all held together with nickel- and lead-free silver solder (lovetypeb.com). With a more modern take, Gatineau-based **Fani Song** presses photos of trees, cities and more between recycled glass jewellery (she does it with custom photos too; fanisong.com). Speaking of glass, Ecstatic.ca offers some chunky spiral bracelets and necklaces with recycled glass beads. Montreal's **Okzoo** recycles used plastic bags, processes them with non-toxic water-based glues and makes super-fly earrings, cuffs, necklaces and more (okzoo.etsy.com). Ecocessories.ca has a pretty collection of necklaces, bracelets and earrings made with recycled beads and vintage brooches. You can also mail her your old broken jewellery and she'll rework it into a new design. **MarchelloArt** does really neat rings and bracelets out of bent antique cutlery (etsy.com/shop/MarchelloArt). **Ten Thousand Villages** has a selection of necklaces and bracelets made of rolled-up recycled newspaper beads.

Reclaimed Wood: Not to give away all my secrets, but if there's one piece of jewellery I wear all the time it's **Contexture**'s Coffee Cuff bracelet that doubles as a coffee-cup sleeve (of course, you should be bringing your own mug, but if you're caught needing a paper cup, this sleeve will save you one piece of garbage). It's handmade in Vancouver out of reclaimed architectural veneer offcuts (contexture.ca). Other Canadian jewellers working with rescued wood? Out of B.C., the clean, carved designs of **Billy Would** (billywould.com), the modern cuts of **Dominic Design** (dominicdesign.ca) and the crafty visions of **Créations Nabel et Sylkel** (nabel-sylkel.com; you can order a ton of their reclaimed-wood necklaces, bracelets, earrings and more at ecocentrikapparel.com). (See Engagement Rings, page 359, for more on Touch Wood Rings.)

Nuts and Seeds: For real. Jewellery made of dried nuts and seeds is great because nothing had to be cut down, refined, welded or processed to get it to you. Probably my favourite are designs made of the tagua nut. This "vegetable ivory" is harvested from the forest floor in South America and sort of looks and feels like its namesake ivory (though it can be dyed all sorts of colours). Pueblito.ca has probably the biggest collection of fair-trade tagua, coconut, acai seed and *totumo* (dried gourd) necklaces, bracelets and earrings, and even watches. Ecobling.ca has a bunch too, as do **Ten Thousand Villages** stores.

When I was a teen, I used to love spending hours in bead stores concocting necklaces and earrings. Unfortunately, most of those beads were probably made cheaply in China. These days you can find natural tagua nut, coconut and sometimes recycled-glass beads in your local bead shop, but for the greenest DIY jewellery in town, try hunting down your own vintage beads. Sift through your jewellery box for broken pieces to unstring. Troll thrift stores for old jewellery you can rip apart and reconstruct your way. Antique hardware from junk shops is another treasure trove of re-stringable knobs and doodads (I've even made necklaces out of antique cabinet knobs). Or save yourself some time and sift through the countless salvaged beads, charms, buttons and more at Ontario-based **Supply Treasures (etsy.com/shop/supplytreasures)**.

PURSES AND BAGS

Someone once said handbags are the eyes to a woman's soul. Okay, fine, I said it. And they're more like a sneak peek into a woman's life. Are you a free spirit with a bag swirling in chaos? A no-nonsense clutter-hater with a clutch organized to a T? A nurturer with Band-Aids, tissues and organic hand sanitizer? Regardless, it's time to look beyond the contents and consider whether the bag itself reflects your values. Truth is, conventional purses don't say much good. High-end designers Gucci, Versace, Prada and others have been caught using Italian sweatshops populated by Chinese migrant workers. On the contaminant front, the Center for Environmental Health out of California tested purses and wallets from 100 top retailers in 2010 and found disturbingly high lead levels, up to 100 times worse than Cali's lead limits for children's articles. Tainted purses were found at Aldo, H&M, Sears, Benetton, French Connection, Walmart, Nine West, Steve Madden and more. Faux leather PVC materials were the biggest culprit, but leather was culpable too. A settlement agreement was signed with over 40 major retailers who agreed to limit lead in leather, vinyl and painted surfaces on purses and all sorts of accessories by the end of 2011.

Happily, you can still capture your style and ethics in one lovely handbag.

Recycled Materials: Quebec-based Eco-handbags.ca has every possible style made from dozens of different types of recycled and eco materials, including old seatbelts/sails/tarps/wrappers/slides/CDs/ sweaters/cans and way more. You have to see it to believe it. They even have green travel, laptop and diaper bags. I particularly love the dinged-up-skateboard clutches lined with silk. Also on the found object trajectory, **Noelle Hamlyn** is famous for her vintage books-turned-handbags, a.k.a. Pocket Book Purses (noellehamlyn.com). My own pick on my perennial wish list happens to be **Jack & Marjorie** bags. This duo stitches totally original purses, clutches and messenger bags for men and women from recycled military surplus materials (think military tents, wool blankets, duffle bags, parachutes, rifle-sling straps). All bag linings are organic-cotton twill, and any leather used is either vegetable dyed or reclaimed from upholstery samples (jackandmarjorie. com). Confession: I've got three of their cloth bags already. Want to go veg without fretting about lead or hormone-disrupting, plastic-softening phthalates? Famously vegan Matt & Nat bags do have recycled linings but the outside is still regular polyurethane plastic. Greener Quebec designer **Ressac** is doing cool bags for men and women with flat bike tubes (ressac.ca), as is U.S.-made **English Retreads** (englishretreads. com). **Mari Cla Ro** does backpacks, bike bags, laptop bags and more from truck tarps, seatbelts and inner tubes (they do recycled leather versions, too) (mariclaro.ca). If you'd prefer something with more of a natural-fibre look, Canadian **Echoes in the Attic** does pretty stuff with salvaged textiles (echoesintheattic.com) and **Fluf** does modern graphic-printed sacks in organic cotton and hemp (fluf.ca). For a great selection of all kinds of natural-fibre bags, including laptop bags, purses, courier bags, reusable shopping bags and more in cool cork, jute, hemp and organic cotton from all kinds of designers, check out ethicalocean.com.

Leather: Craving a leather purse without the guilt of having a fresh cow on your arm? Canada's chock full of recycled-leather handbags. Vancouver-made **Ashley Watson** bags has well over two dozen styles of large recycled-leather bags in all sorts of cuts and colours (ashleywatson. net). **Ora Bags** are a little better priced and offer up interesting recycled-leather backpacks as well as signature bike bags that strap to your handlebars (orabags.com). **Erin Templeton** is another excellent Van-city designer of oversized recycled-leather bags (erintempleton. com). You'll totally covet the oversized '80s recycled-leather options from **Baggage** (often with straps made of old-school braided leather; baggagehandbags.ca). I definitely dig Quebec-made **Cokluch** printed clutches and bags (cokluch.com). Another Quebec-based bag master is **Rachel F**, who also makes printed recycled-leather bags in both small and larger versions (rachelf.ca). Some winter accessories use recycled fur.

Personal Care Products	369
Diapering	377
Clothing	388
Jewellery, Charms and Trinkets	391
Health	392

KIDS AND BABIES

Greeneology

You might go your whole life stewing

in chemicals and breathing in toxins and, quite frankly, not give a bleep. But the moment a baby pops onto the scene, many otherwise nonchalant folks become strident environmentalists. To a growing number of parents, pollution is personal. In the first **Ecoholic** book I told you how 287 chemicals had been detected in umbilical cords. Well, we're now up to 358. And a 2011 study revealed that virtually all pregnant moms tested (and by that I mean 99% to 100%) have everything from non-stick and flame-retardant chemicals to oldies but nasties such as DDT and PCBs coursing through their bodies. Now, before you panic, keep in mind that certain exposures we just can't avoid; even polar bears and dolphins test positive. But we can certainly slash the pollutants we put into the world and, thankfully, whittle down our children's chemical body burden through the choices we make every day. So here's some fresh-baked info on raising your kids with fewer questionable synthetic ingredients, not to mention the straight goods on avoiding poseur naturals that are sadly rampant in the baby care world.

PERSONAL CARE PRODUCTS

Parents always have a back-burner list of at least a dozen worries to triage in their brains. So when the federal government steps in and says relax, we're taking the harmful lead out of kids' products, the bisphenol A out of baby bottles and unpronounceable phthalates (that's THAL-ates) out of toys, you can let out a little sigh of relief. Unfortunately, it's still not time to break out the bubbly (god, I'm such a party-pooper, aren't I?). Sorry, folks, gotta stay vigilant until Health Canada starts banning toxins in body care.

There is no excuse for having any of the Mean 15 ingredients (see page 8) with health ramifications in children's products. Come on, are we really going to let them get away with banning phthalates from toys and bibs but not from the lotions and powders that we dust and rub on our kids every day? Especially when a study published in the journal *Pediatrics* found that the more lotion, shampoo and powder are used on babies, the higher the levels of phthalates in their pee. In fact, breakdown products of phthalates were found in the urine of 90% of 163 babies tested. The situation was even more glaring in infants under eight months old. But Health Canada so far is sticking by its line that as long as the baby doesn't suck or chew on it (as it does with a toy), those phthalates aren't a concern.

Wonder what they make of the fact that Denmark, in 2011, announced it wants to ban four phthalates from all consumer products in direct contact with the public, young and old alike? Or a 2010 study out of Mount Sinai School of Medicine in New York that tested phthalate levels in the urine of pregnant moms and found that mothers with higher levels ended up having children who, four to nine years later, had more behavioural issues such as attention problems and aggression? If ever there's a time to be beyond cautious, it's with developing bodies. If that's out to lunch, I'll pack myself a picnic. If you're with me on this, let your MP know, since Health Canada is now considering whether or not to take further action. By the way, tell them you want to see estrogenic parabens banned from personal care products too. In late 2010, Denmark became the first country in the

EU to ban propylparaben and butylparaben preservatives from lotions and other baby products. This was just one year after the Danish Ministry of the Environment reported that the amount of propylparaben and butylparaben absorbed from oil-based creams, moisturizers, lotions and sunscreen "can constitute a risk for oestrogen-like disruptions of the endocrine system." Your move, Health Canada.

Baby Shampoos and Bubble Bath: Tub time can already be a drag in many households, so who needs the extra worry that they're dipping their kids in a chemical bath? In 2009, the Campaign for Safe Cosmetics made a big splash when it commissioned independent lab work on 48 conventional baby products and found that 67% tested positive for the probable carcinogen and liver/kidney toxicant 1,4-Dioxane, and 82% had disconcerting levels of carcinogenic/skin-sensitizing formaldehyde. FYI, neither of these ingredients are listed on the label because they're by-products. And did I mention that the last time California's attorney general found 1,4-Dioxane in personal care products, he sued the companies for failing to warn consumers that they contained a carcinogen? See page 125 for more on that. By late 2011, Johnson & Johnson was still using formaldehyde-releasing preservatives, so the American Nurses Association and three dozen health and parents' groups wrote to J&J again, asking them to quit it. Finally, in fall 2011, J&J said they were phasing out the formaldehyde releasers worldwide.

J&J wasn't the only brand implicated. Huggies Naturally Refreshing Cucumber & Green Tea Baby Wash, L'Oréal and Suave Kids products, as well as Barbie/Dora/Hot Wheels/Sesame Street/Tinker Bell bubble bath all tested positive for 1,4-Dioxane and formaldehyde. Aveeno Baby Soothing Relief Creamy Wash didn't have formaldehyde but did contain 1,4-Dioxane. Testing by Organic Consumers Association in 2009 also slapped Disney body washes on the red list. Now, both Johnson & Johnson and Huggies Natural Care Baby Wash had reduced Dioxane levels from 2007, but they certainly haven't eliminated them. At least major health store brands that were caught with these chems on their hands such as Nature's Gate are now purifying their ethoxylated ingredients so they're 1,4-Dioxane free.

If formaldehyde and 1,4-Dioxane don't show up on the ingredient list, how can you avoid them in the stores?

- **Stay away from formaldehyde-releasing ingredients** such as quaternium-15 (biggest culprit), imidazolidinyl urea, DMDM hydantoin, diazolidinyl urea, methenamine and Bronopol, a.k.a. 2-bromo-2-nitropropane-1,3-diol.
- **Avoid ingredients with** *–eth* (like sodium laureth sulphate) or *PEG* in their name (they're commonly contaminated with 1,4-Dioxane). Note: big-name health store brands that still contain these ingredients now vacuum-strip the ingredients to make sure they're 1,4-Dioxane free.
- **Check out the rest of my Mean 15 list** on page 8 and avoid these like the plague (get a printable pocket guide at ecoholic.ca).
- **Seek out clean, green, naturally derived shampoos/soaps.** There are dozens of Canadian-made lines to pick from. The ones you'll find in health stores across the country include **Druide** (baby soaps, shampoo, bath potion, lotion, oil, balm) and **Green Beaver Jr** (toddler/kid line of shampoo, bubble bath, soap, lip balm). Though not local, Australia's **EcoKid** has a good line of children's hair care products (including styling aids for young hipsters), which my niece Brianne has given the thumbs-up (the shampoo/conditioner left her wavy mane soft and tangle free) (ecokidorganics.com).
- **For top-notch natural purity, look for whole, plant-based** ingredients that you could, at least in theory, eat and that haven't been synthesized in any way (see Naturally Derived, page 14). **Terressentials' baby line** and **Earth Mama Angel Baby** products (with pure organic olive oil castile soap) are USDA-certified organic (which means they're at least 95% organic and meet organic food standards), as is **Dr. Bronner's Baby Mild** liquid and bar soap. All Things Jill's line **Peas in a Pod** Organic

Baby Wash + Shampoo is a good Canadian choice (she also does bum spray, powder, lotion, balm, shampoo/body wash plus mama stuff; allthingsjill.ca). **Matter Company's Substance Mom and Baby** line is either totally natural or naturally derived, depending on the product (mattercompany.com).

- There are countless awesome local, indie baby care brands you can find in baby shops, green stores and online sites in your neck of the woods. Just make sure you scan the ingredients well before you believe natural claims.

- Don't bother with bubbles. Bathing in plain warm water skips one tier of product exposure, since even those sudsers found in green brands can be irritating for some babies (cocamidopropyl betaine was labelled allergen of the year in 2004 by the American Contact Dermatitis Society). Plus, they just won't give you the same long-lasting bubbles as the chemical stuff. But if you insist on looking for bubbles, check out **Green Beaver Jr Bubble Bath**, which contains Canadian-grown organic cranberry and raspberry seed oil.

- Plain water is fine for newborns. You don't actually need soap unless your little one is already hitting the gym or working the coal mines.

Moisturizers, Oils and Jellies: If your kid's outer layer needs extra moisture, skip the complicated ingredient–heavy formulas that only up the chances of taking in unwanted synthetics. And definitely walk right past those drugstore-brand baby oils and lotions that are really no better than a rubdown from Esso thanks to ingredients such as mineral oil, petroleum and petrolatum. Note that Baby Magic scented lotion had such high formaldehyde levels when tested by the Campaign for Safe Cosmetics that it would need to be sold with a warning label in Europe. Actually, it'd have to be yanked from shelves in Canada if someone were to, say, police Health Canada's Hotlist. Just a thought.

And honestly, I'm not even going to advise you to spend your money on fancy natural lotions when really all you need is straight

TANGLED UP IN BLUE: TOXIC HAIR DETANGLERS

Detanglers are really popular with parents trying to comb through their child's mane without eliciting howls, but what's in 'em? Several Johnson's No More Tangles detangling sprays will leave the planet in tears thanks to slippery, environmentally persistent and bioaccumulative siloxanes like cyclomethicone that cause problems for fish downstream (see Mean 15, page 8). Suave Kids Detangling Spray is coating your child's follicles with an oil slick of petrochemicals and formaldehyde-releasing preservative DMDM hydantoin. L'Oréal Kids Tangle Tamer spritzes out parabens and lots of other junk.

So what's a comb-wielding parent supposed to use instead? For one, you can stop by your local health store to scour for more natural detangling options, including **Green Beaver Jr. Conditioning Detangler for Toddlers and Kids, Natureclean's Treehouse Leave-in Detangler,** or, out of the United States, **TruKid Dancing Detangler** and **California Baby Calming Hair Detangler** (the first two being Canadian). Though honestly, all you need is an empty spray bottle, 1/4 to 1/3 cup (60 mL to 80 mL) of any natural hair conditioner you already have kicking around your tub and 2 cups (500 mL) of hot water. Shake until well mixed, then spray away without having to sink your money into a specialty product. By the way, 2-in-1 shampoos like Natureclean's Treehouse aren't going to cut it on kids' hair that is prone to tangling. My niece was my official tester and gave it a major thumbs-down.

coconut oil (ideally organic, fair trade) or a nice unscented oil like organic grapeseed/safflower/jojoba. Call them your natural baby oil that's awesome on big kids too. They're both super nourishing and you can guarantee there's no junk hiding in there. Frankly, though, if your child's skin isn't visibly dry, you really don't need to slather on anything. Just let the poor kid's skin breathe.

Diaper Rash, Cradle Cap, Cuts and More: If your wee one's skin is irritated, you want to make sure you're not adding to the problem by bringing more suspect synthetics into the mix. Take, for

373

instance, greenwash king Gentle Naturals' line of eczema baby washes. They contain sodium laureth sulphate and PEGs (all prone to 1,4-Dioxane contamination) and mildly estrogenic parabens, for gerber's sake. So what are some truly natural skin soothers? The B.C.ers at **Dimpleskins Naturals** make great genuinely natural specialty healing products, from their **Sniffles Eucalyptus Rub** to their **Boo Boo Goo Soothing Salve** with calendula and vitamin E (works wonders on, well, boo-boos, scabs, eczema and more). Their **Bum Bum Balm Diapering Salve** gets great reviews from parents, too (dimpleskinsnaturals.com).

Speaking of irritated behinds, there are lots of other great diaper rash salves out there, so what should you look for? Well, whatever you do, skip all the petroleum-based mineral oil/paraffin, silicones and parabens in most diaper rash cream (see Mean 15, page 8, for more info). Sure, mineral oil and paraffin are harmless to the end user, but we wage wars, both ecological and national, in its name. Totally unnecessary on a baby's bottom. By the way, even pseudo-natural brands such as Aveeno contain all of these.

Instead, look for all-natural bases such as quality food oils, beeswax and shea butter, together with healing, antibacterial, anti-inflammatory herbs such as calendula, myrrh, camomile and/or marshmallow root. Some all-Canadian winners include **Lalabee Bottom Balm** (lalabee-bathworks.com), **Matter Company's Substance Nappy Rash Ointment** and **Butterfly Weed Herbal Hug Nappy Rash Ointment** (also by Matter Company; mattercompany.com), **Bare Organics Baby Balm** (bareorganics.ca) and **Lunar Eclipse Diaper Rash Ointment** (lunareclipse-babies.com). **Miessence's Baby Barrier Balm** isn't Canadian, but it's USDA-certified organic (that means it's at least 95% organic). Method Baby's Squeaky Green Diaper Cream should lose the silicones (such as dimethicone) and phenoxyethanol preservative and then it might get a thumbs-up. I'm not crazy about Weleda's Calendula Diaper Care either since many of its ingredients are potential skin sensitizers, even if they're essential oil based (such as geraniol and limonene).

If you still want zinc in your cream, **Burt's Bees' Baby Bee Diaper Ointment** is a good choice, though it isn't Canadian. **Live Clean Baby Diaper Ointment** is a decent Canadian-made option with zinc that gets good reviews from Ecoholic parents (though I don't love all their baby products since they contain synthetic fragrance and many are heavy in unsustainable palm ingredients; see Mean 15, page 8). Really, though, some parents have better luck just sprinkling their baby's bottom with straight cornstarch or arrowroot powder (both of which you should be able to buy organic from the health store). For cradle cap, get yourself an all-natural calendula oil or cream.

GOO-GOO GREENWASH: PSEUDO-NATURAL BABY PRODUCTS

No one wants to slather their baby with toxins, and companies know it. That's why you can't walk down a drugstore aisle without tripping on exaggerated green baby claims. Aveeno Baby Wash & Shampoo says "Natural Care Formula" on the front but only has a handful of genuinely natural ingredients. Gentle Naturals eczema cream, shampoos and cradle cap treatment are loaded with parabens, petroleum-based mineral oil and ethoxylated ingredients. Huggies Natural Care Baby Wipes may have phased out their parabens, but they still contain formaldehyde-releasing DMDM hydantoin. Jeez, Huggies Naturally Refreshing Baby Wipes are even worse, with several parabens—including two banned in Denmark. And Canus Li'l Goats' product may contain "fresh" goat milk but why does it have to bury it in petroleum, synthetic fragrance, parabens and formaldehyde-releasing diazolidinyl urea?

The lesson here is: don't believe the hype. Everyone's weaving the word "natural" into their baby product packaging because they know it'll make them a few extra bucks. Green diapers are even more mired in greenwash (see page 375). The only way to know for sure is to read the fine print and look at ingredient lists. If the company isn't willing to cough up specifics about what makes their product natural or organic, move on to one that is. Simple as that.

Sunscreen: The best way to protect babies from the sun is simple: keep them out of it (for the most part). But that's pretty much impossible as soon as your kids know how to use their own two feet. When you're slathering your child with sunscreen, make sure you're avoiding the estrogen-mimicking chemical sunscreen ingredients found in drug-store brands (see Sunscreens, page 44). And that includes Aveeno Baby Sunblock Lotion, which talks up its skin-soothing colloidal oatmeal but still contains dodgy oxybenzone (see page 9 for more info). Aveeno Baby Natural Protection Mineral Block is a better drugstore choice since it uses natural sunscreen ingredients zinc oxide and titanium dioxide, but, for the love of chemicals, why does it insist on using Mean 15 preservative BHT as well as lots of petroleum-based ingredients? Ditto for other poseurs including Neutrogena Pure & Free Baby Sunblock. Johnson's Baby Daily Face & Body Lotion does use "100% naturally sourced sunscreen ingredients," but does it have to contain the persistent environmental pollutant cyclopentasiloxane and needless alumina? Hawaiian Tropic Baby Crème and Stick say they contain fewer chemical sunscreens, but lo and behold, they're made with oxybenzone, cancer-linked retinyl palmitate, as well as loads of parabens, BHT and two eco no-no siloxanes. Tsk, tsk. No wonder Hawaiian Tropic Baby is in Environmental Working Group's sun-screen Hall of Shame.

So what are some genuinely natural picks that provide top sunscreen protection? Saunter down to your local health store and stock up on natural brands such as **Badger Baby Sunscreen, Goddess Garden Kids** and **Green Beaver Certified Organic Kids**, which are all great picks. They offer top protection with all-natural and high organic content, but Green Beaver is hands-down the sheerest followed by Goddess Garden (Badger is pretty whitening—fine for your young-est). Yes, Green Beaver's original formula is a little oilier but that helps make it really water-resistant (which Goddess Garden Kids is not). All are free of controversial nano zinc and nano titanium dioxide (see page 46 for more info). Toronto-based **Matter Company** also makes a good zinc-based baby sun cream (though it does have sesame oil in there, so those with allergies take note). I'm not crazy about Lavera's baby sunscreen since it's made with nano titanium dioxide (actually, almost anything with titanium dioxide will be nano). For more sunscreen info and full product testing, see page 44.

Lice Treatments: It's every parent's nightmare. So what happens when these clingy little buggers have made themselves at home in your child's hair? I know you're tempted to reach for the many chemical remedies on drugstore shelves (lice is one area where chemicals might really be needed, right?), but you're just setting yourself up for repeat chemical baths and potential overdoses. According to a study published in the *Journal of Cutaneous Medicine and Surgery*, 97% of Canadian lice are resistant to the main chemicals used to combat lice: pyrethrin- and permethrin-based treatments. And if you want to avoid a chemical that's been banned in 50 countries and hasn't been allowed on crops in Canada since 2004 steer clear of lindane like the plague. It's still allowed on young infested heads. So what's a frustrated parent supposed to do to quash the little bastards? You need to look up Lice Squad pronto and order their **Lice Squad 2 in 1 Nit Kit** complete with all their effective enzyme-based products (licesquad.com). These guys get the thumbs-up from all kinds of daycares, junior schools and camps. What else helps? A study published in the *International Journal of Dermatology* found tea tree oil repelled lice more than other botanical substances tested (including lavender, peppermint and coconut oil), but it wasn't effective enough to be endorsed (plus, it's very drying with prolonged use).

DIAPERING

The children's book is right: everybody poops. Canadian babies just happen to go through 4 million disposable diapers a day doing so, according to Environment Canada. Yes, I said per day. That's about 250,000 tons of diapers going to landfill every year in this country—and that doesn't even factor in the impact of the millions of trees axed and barrels of oil drilled to make the bum wraps. Not that cloth diapers are without impact. So who wins?

Cloth vs. Disposables: Ask any tree hugger which is the greener way to swaddle a baby's behind and the answer will be swift and decisive: cloth. Well, the British government decided to do a full life-cycle assessment study in 2005, and the results surprised—and peeved—a lot of people. It concluded that cloth diapers are as damaging to the environment as the plastic type. This study kicked up such a fuss that the government issued an update in 2008. The original government-funded report looked at the life-cycle costs of three options: home-laundered cloth, commercially laundered cloth and disposables. The 200-page paper weighed everything from manufacturing of plastics involved in making disposable diapers, and the water and pesticides used in growing cotton, to the electricity needed to iron fold-'n'-pin types. In the end, the study concluded that all three are neck and neck. Enviros freaked out about how greener cleaning techniques hadn't been taken into consideration, so the updated 2008 report concluded: washing nappies in a fuller load, air-drying them and reusing cloth nappies on a second child (or passing them on to a friend, neighbour or pregnant cousin) would lower the global warming impact by 40% (200 kg of carbon dioxide equivalents, over two and a half years of diapering). The U.K.'s Women's Environment Network also noted that warm-water washes in energy-efficient machines, for instance, reduce climate-changing pollutants by 17% (Energy Star washing machines use 37% less energy and 50% less water than a run-of-the-mill washer). Okay, yes, many moms have complained that getting diapers clean in water-efficient front-loaders can be more challenging than in water-hogging top-loaders, but many have found success with an extra rinse cycle (on cold). By the way, using eco laundry detergent will help keep your cloth diapers greener, plus investing in diapers made with unbleached, pesticide-free fibres such as organic cotton, hemp or bamboo puts you even further ahead, especially if they're stitched locally.

Environment Canada says your choice should really depend on the resources where you live. "If landfill space is an issue in your community, it may be better to wash cloth diapers. Disposable diapers may be a better choice in communities where water quality and quantity is a concern."

Here's some info on making the best of both disposables and cloth. FYI, if forgoing diapers altogether sounds tempting to you, read up on **elimination communication** at diaperfreebaby.org. By the way, it's said cloth diapers actually give kids the incentive to get potty-trained earlier than disposables since disposables keep them a lot drier and more comfortable.

Greener Disposable Diapers: All disposable "green" diapers contain chlorine-free wood pulp fluff, but guess what? These days, mainstream brands aren't far off, since they've stopped using old-school elemental chlorine that produced super-toxic, bioaccumulative, carcinogenic dioxins and have switched to alternatives. They're now officially "elemental-chlorine free." Now, keep in mind that the natural brands all tend to be what's called "totally chlorine free," which is the greenest method, but still, unless a green diaper has some other redeeming feature, it's not a whole lot better than major conventional brands. Much to my surprise, I discovered that Seventh Generation falls into this category, and actually dyes its diapers browny-beige to make them *look* different from regular diapers (you may have seen me kvetch about this on CBC's *Marketplace*). Even Seventh Generation admits their diapers aren't as green as the rest of their products (at least their menstrual pads contain renewable content). This will be a big shocker to a lot of parents who've paid top dollar for Seventh Generation diapers.

But don't worry, there are several health store brands that go the extra mile with renewable content. Keep in mind that biodegradable plastics don't belong in your backyard composter and that most composting municipalities don't accept diapers. If, like Toronto, your municipality does accept diapers in its composting pickup, they immediately filter the plastic part out, even if it's certified compostable, because they can't tell the difference, but at least renewable materials have been used to make the diapers in the first place. It puts us one step closer to ditching our petroleum habit.

I know some parents worry about petrochemical-based SAP gels (Super Absorbent Polymer made of sodium polyacrylate) irritating their baby's skin. And yes, there are rumours that SAPs were associated with toxic shock syndrome in tampon users in the '80s, but the extended-wear Rely tampon was the real culprit. There is no evidence that sodium polyacrylate is dangerous to kids when absorbed through the skin. Still, some parents will tell you it gives their baby a rash. Others say it helps keep skin dry and rash free. If you'd prefer to avoid it, your diapers won't be nearly as absorbent, but there are one or two health store diapers that offer SAP-free versions. Better to just go for cloth.

By the way, these diapers were tested on my niece, Abbey, and my editor Kendall's son, Luke, and the reviews also incorporate readers' input as well as green cred.

HUGGIES PURE & NATURAL	How vague can a product be about its green credentials? Outer cover "includes" an undisclosed percentage of organic cotton though when pressed, Huggies did say lining is 50% corn plastic. Turns out the rest is petrol-based polypropylene, but we want details spelled out. Reliable performance but lose a point for cred.	
SEVENTH GENERATION	Little difference between this brand and conventional brands thanks to all the petrol-based plastic and conventional SAP. They actually add brown pigment to their plastic so it looks earthier. Yes, their wood pulp is totally chlorine free, but their certifier, PEFC, has been slammed by Greenpeace as a joke. Reliable performance but lose a point for cred.	

WHOLE FOODS 365 These are just like Seventh Generation. Other than being chlorine and fragrance free, no distinguishing green factor. Reliable performance but lose a point for cred. 👍👍

PC GREEN Perhaps the cheapest of the greener diapers and comes with stretchy tabs. Some parents love 'em, many scream about leaks, but PC is vague on who certifies their wood pulp as sustainable. An unspecified portion of the plastic and SAP is plant based. 👍👍👍

NATURE BABYCARE These Swedish diapers are chlorine free and made with 60% GMO-free renewable content. Quite absorbent. Some parents love 'em, others had mixed reviews. **naty.com** 👍👍👍👍

DELORA Seems a little boxy but totally leak-proof. Tested to biodegrade in landfill in 90 days, which is a feat. Outer cover made from organic, GMO-free plant starch. Cellulose core from well-respected FSC-certified forestry. Contains SAP. Huge in Germany. Cons: loose sizes and tabs don't always stick. 👍👍👍👍

EARTH'S BEST Chlorine free partly wheat/corn SAP, top/back sheet made from pesticide-free corn. Performs better than basics like Seventh Generation, better for newborns and held up overnight and through some messy poops. **earthsbest.com** 👍👍👍👍

MAMA ZONE	Greener than most with 100% plant-based, biodegradable outer layer, chlorine-free wood pulp, compostable packaging, all made in 100% wind-offset factory in Germany (their pulp is even FSC-approved). No overnight leaks. Contains SAP. **babyecodiapers.com**	
❦ **BROODY CHICK**	Love this B.C.-headquartered line! Super-soft lining is made of 100% corn-based Ingeo fabric that also happens to be certified compostable depending on your town, as is the waterproof outer layer (plant-based biofilm). Plus, it comes in a box, not a plastic bag. No overnight leaks! Contains SAP. A bit pricier. **broodychick.com**	

Green Thumb legend   1 = Might as well stick a Band-Aid on baby's bum   2 = Sorry excuse for a diaper   3 = Decent bum mop   4 = Great, green product   5 = Pampers' green sister

Cloth Diapers: Your most affordable cloth diapering system involves old-fashioned pre-folds. But they're not all cut from the same cloth. **Bummis Organic Cotton Prefolds** and harder-to-find **Cloth-eez** organic pre-folds both get rave reviews from parents for absorbency and top performance (bummis.com.ca, clotheez.com). Gerber cloth diapers, on the other hand, are total crap, according to reviewers.

Next step up in ease and expense involves fitted hemp/organic-cotton diapers with elastics, snaps or Velcro fittings combined with separate waterproof diaper covers. **Eco Posh One Size Fitted Pocket Diapers** are actually made of recycled water bottles, bamboo and organic cotton and should be used with a wool cover; kanga-care.com. Whatever you do, stay far away from generic PVC/vinyl diaper covers (Kushies makes some vinyl-coated cloth diapers, for instance). The granddaddy villain of plastics has been at the centre of lead scandals and it's consistently softened with hormone-disrupting phthalates. As of mid 2011, Health Canada is restricting three phthalates from all child care articles, including diaper covers, but three other phthalates of concern are only being restricted in child care articles likely to be mouthed by infants (diaper covers aren't included).

Wool diaper covers would be your greenest choice, followed by fleece, polyester, nylon and finally polyurethane. Those last three offer the most waterproofing but not every Ecoholic parent is going to like the plastics involved.

If you can afford the upfront cost, you'll definitely go gaga over the convenience and leak-busting powers of true pocket-style diapers since they're almost all in one (with a polyester/nylon outer layer and micro-fleece inner layer often available in bamboo/organic-cotton fleece). You just stuff these with an absorbable insert made of hemp, bamboo, cotton/organic cotton. Finally, the Cadillac of cloth diapering is a true all-in-one (like **bumGenius Elemental One-Size All-In-One** organic diapers; bumgenius.com). AIOs are also the priciest of the bunch.

You'll need to buy two dozen of any system upfront, which seems painfully expensive until you amortize the costs over two and a half years or so, and/or more than one kid. Compare it to the cost of buying two years' of disposable diapers and it begins to make sense. Remember, you can buy all of the above in various combinations of fabrics, including organic cotton, hemp and bamboo as well as unbleached conventional cotton and more.

Cleaning Cloth Diapers: The baby's pooped. Now what? Getting cloth diapers clean can seem like a massive headache from the outside, but it doesn't have to be. First shake any solid poop into the toilet. If you're smart, you'll run out and invest in a handy diaper sprayer that attaches to the toilet. Next you've got to choose your own adventure. Both involve tossing used diapers in a pail (one with a good lockable lid) until you're ready to wash them, but the wet route means throwing them in a locking pail that's half filled with water plus ¼ cup (60 mL) of baking soda and/or ¼ cup (60 mL) of vinegar (a few drops of tea tree oil is a good idea too). The second, more popular, option is the dry route. You basically toss the diaper into your pail, sprinkle a little odour-eating baking soda on the bottom of the pail and wash a whole pile at once every three days. For more tips, check out diaperjungle. com and diaperpin.com.

How can you keep your cloth cleaning green?

- Only flush poop-filled liners (put peed-on liners in garbage or compost, depending on the liner).
- Rinse in cold and wash in warm.
- Bleach and pure detergents such as Ivory Snow will break down your cloth nappies faster. Others will give your babe a rash. Good laundry products for diapers include unscented **Bio-Vert** and **Seventh Generation Natural 2X Concentrated Laundry Liquid Free & Clear**—both of which are top stain fighters. **Eco-Max** liquid and **Natureclean 3X** also get good scores at pinstripesandpolkadots.com/detergentchoices.htm, which gives a detailed breakdown of which laundry soaps are compatible with cloth diapers. Just be sure to use a quarter to a half of the recommended dose. Having trouble getting your diapers stink free in soft or hard water? Check out unscented **Rockin' Green Laundry Detergent,** designed for your very woes (rockingreensoap.com; buy some in Canada at abbeysprouts.com).
- Toss ¾ cup (175 mL) of vinegar into the final rinse since it's great at washing out soap residues and acts as a natural fabric softener. Avoid other fabric softeners, since they reduce absorbency and will irritate your baby's bottom.
- Hang-dry as much as possible. Air-drying nappies will not only save a lot of energy but also make them last longer (though you will need to buy more diapers when you factor in drying time, as our grandmothers did). If you want to soften up basic cotton pre-folds, toss them in the dryer for 10 minutes, though this won't be necessary for pocket-style, all-in-one, fleece or terry diapers.
- If you're too busy or pooped out to clean your own reusables,

consider a diaper service. Check your phone book for listings in your area. Just note that it can be impossible to find a service that doesn't use harsh bleach, but it doesn't hurt to ask.

THE REUSABLE/DISPOSABLE HYBRIDS

Hate the idea of tossing away a plastic diaper every time your baby has a body function but not ready to commit to the work involved in cloth diapering? Time to test-drive some hybrids. You've got a few choices these days to pick from. **gDiapers** come with a nylon outer pant/cover and your choice of washable cloth inserts or certified-biodegradable/flushable diaper linings made of wood pulp from farmed trees. (No old-growth trees are axed, the company insists, but trees are chopped to make the cellulose pulp lining, as they are for disposable diapers.) They're free of nasty bleaches, perfumes and dyes, and are made extra absorbent through SAPs (see page 380). Many parents will use the cloth inserts at home and the biodegradable linings when they're out and about. By the way, those linings were certified biodegradable by the respected folks at Cradle to Cradle (see **mbdc.com** for more on them).

GroVia's hybrids have a one-size cloth shell that you can use either with a cloth soaker pad or compostable GroVia Bio Soaker Pad that are plastic free (gro-via.com). The **Flip Diaper System** comes with a one-size cloth cover (with a built-in waterproof shell) and you've got three choices for inserts: a washable organic-cotton insert, a washable, overnight-ready micro-suede insert called Stay-Dry, or disposable ones made of bamboo viscose, wood pulp, SAP and starch-based glues (**flipdiapers.com**).

Soft shells of the latter two win over a lot of parents. Conversely you can actually put pee-soaked gDiaper and GroVia Bio liners in your backyard compost bin, where they should degrade within 150 days. (Never put liners soiled with number two back there, though some municipal composters can handle them.) Both GroVia and gDiapers' disposable liners can be flushed. If you have a powerful toilet, you might be able to get by with one flush, which would put you more on a par with cloth diaper users who shake their baby's business into the loo before they wash them. But gDiaper actually says you're likely to have to flush twice to get the liner down. You'll have to do your own calculation to compare how much water your toilet uses per flush and the amount of water your washer would need to do a load of dirty diapers. I ran the idea of flushing these liners by a municipal waste manager and, let me tell you, he was not pleased. He'd rather not see anything that doesn't come out of our bodies go down there, since the city just scoops it all out and sends it to landfill. Even the poop. No kidding.

Another thing to keep in mind is that you'll be doing a load of laundry just to wash your soiled "little gPant pouch," formerly called gSnap-in liner. The good thing is that you can wash these in cold water, and in fact they shouldn't be washed in hot (unlike what gDiapers recommends for its cloth diapers). Line-dry them so they'll last longer. Make sure to keep a dry pail on hand so you can keep your pouch/liners/covers together until you wash them all at once.

 So all this to say, they're not dirt free, but are hybrid diapers a greener compromise for parents who'd rather bypass cloth and don't want to support the corporate landfill cloggers? No doubt about it. You'll just have to decide which option suits you best.

Baby Wipes: I know parents love their wipes, but watch out for mainstream baby wipes that tuck parabens and formaldehyde-releasing preservatives such as DMDM hydantoin in with "natural" ingredients. Heck, both of these Mean 15 ingredients are in Huggies Natural Care Baby Wipes. What makes them natural? Nothing really, other than a lack of fragrance and a hint of aloe and vitamin E. That's pretty weak. And even unscented wipes like Pampers Natural Aloe Unscented contain masking fragrances, and you can bet your baby's bottom that those fragrances contain a few hormone disruptors (see Perfume, page 83). Seventh Generation has better ingredients, but what they don't tell you on the label is that the wipes are made with a mix of conventional rayon (it's just not chlorine bleached; see page 301 for more on rayon/viscose) and petroleum-based polyester. Pretty disappointing. **Jackson**

Reece wipes are made with straight viscose/rayon from unspecified European trees; they're also certified compostable/biodegradable. Some are flushable. **JR** contains certified-organic ingredients.

If you want genuinely natural disposable wipes, **Natracare** makes some from organic cotton and certified-organic plant and essential oils, though they're pricier. **Bum Boosa** wipes are made from bamboo.

$$ To be honest with you, though, natural baby wipes are pretty expensive. You'd be wiser and greener if you gave washable cloth wipes a try. You can buy some hemp or organic-cotton ones, but really, you could just cut up old T-shirts or sheets and moisten either with plain water or with an all-natural bum-cleaning spray.

NOT SO WILD ABOUT WET ONES WIPES

I swear that every minivan in town has a wipes dispenser somewhere in it, and chances are good it's a bottle of Wet Ones. Wet Ones don't contain the notorious eco-villain triclosan; instead, they get their antibacterial power from benzethonium chloride. Is that dangerous? Truth is, Health Canada is very clear that you should be washing with plain soap and water for 20 seconds and, if need be, use an alcohol-based hand sanitizer only. Any other antibacterial could be contributing to antibiotic-resistant germs. If you're looking for a wipe to clean your little one's face or hands after eating/drinking/playing, skip the totally unnecessary antibacterial kind and use an old-fashioned washable face cloth or keep some all-natural baby wipes on hand.

Baby Powder: There's a commonality that unites many Canadians. We've pretty much all had our butts dusted with Johnson's Baby Powder at some point in time. The classic formula, on shelves to this day, contains a hot-button ingredient: talc. While talc mining is incredibly destructive wherever it's done (especially when it's mined in wildlife reserves in, say, India, as has been documented; see page 59 for more on talc's enviro record), the lingering controversy has more to do with talc's link to ovarian cancer. Epidemiological studies definitely suggest that using talc "down there" might be associated with ovarian cancer. One Harvard study concluded that while they found little support for the link between talc use and ovarian cancer risk overall, "perineal talc use may modestly increase the risk of invasive serous ovarian cancer." In 2010, a U.S. federal judge refused to toss out the case of a woman who'd dusted with talc her whole life and contracted ovarian cancer. We're still waiting on the verdict. Of course, the feds and industry say talc is safe since they screen for asbestos contamination (a problem that was most recently brought to light in not-so-well-screened Korean and Chinese baby powder in 2009).

These days, even J&J sells versions of their baby powder made with cornstarch (as do alt health brands), but they add synthetic fragrance, so I'd still keep it away from my babe. I'm not mad about Burt's Bees' Baby Bee Dusting Powder since it contains "fragrance." Burt's discontinued it in late 2011 but you might still find some on shelves. You could buy a number of natural brands that use a mix of cornstarch and arrowroot powder and a few essential oils, but really, you're wasting your loonies.

Just buy a box of plain cornstarch (preferably organic) and/or some arrowroot flour from the health store and dust away for pennies without the plastic bottle waste. And if you're a busy new mom who hasn't had time to wash your hair in days, dust some cornstarch on your roots while you're at it, then brush it out well to take away any greasy evidence. Seriously.

CLOTHING

Kids are like dandelions. They grow like weeds. In light of that, it just makes sense to maximize hand-me-downs and pre-loved finds over brand spanking new duds for every day of the week. Second-hand clothes also happen to be the most environmentally conscious and budget-friendly choice in baby town. Don't you love it when a plan comes together? But if you're looking to buy a few new pieces, stick with the organic kind free of the formaldehyde finishes found on mainstream threads (that's what that new-clothes smell and wrinkle-resistant finish is; see page 305). Hemp and organic cotton are your best choices, followed by Tencel (see page 304), then equally supple soy (made of soy industry by-products) and rayon/viscose from bamboo (both soy and bamboo are heavily chemically processed, so they're not quite as green as claimed; see page 301 for more details). Now, you can find organic-cotton and eco kids' clothing at megashops like Walmart, but keep in mind that someone in China, Cambodia or Bangladesh was underpaid to make those.

Canadian Kids' Clothes: Who offers a trusty selection of planet-and-people-friendly clothing? Go for Canadian-made goods first, followed by Canadian-designed stuff that's certified fair trade and made abroad. Check out sites like **Innocent Earth**, which has a good selection of eco-clothes for babies, kids and moms (innocentearth.ca). Mylittlegreenshop.com has tons of super-cute stuff for young ladies/gents as well as maternity, and the colourful printed baby/junior styles at boutique.oom.ca are really fun. Ecocentrikapparel.com is good for kids/babies/men/women. **Mini Mioche** has sweet made-in-Canada basics (minimioche.com). A good U.S.-based source is stylish **Kate Quinn Organics**—all organic cotton and fair-trade certified at great prices for babes and kids (katequinnorganics.ca). Check out your local green and indie kids' stores too (see Directory of Green Baby/Kids' Shops, page 432).

Regardless of what you buy and where you buy it, always wash everything at least once before your kids wear it. If it's Oeko-Tex certified, though, at least you know there are no surface chemical residues to worry about (see page 415).

Pyjamas: Whether your kids sleep in Justin Bieber PJs or footed onesies, those pyjamas are actually regulated by Health Canada. Why? Well, the government department says approximately 21 children per year used to suffer from serious burn injuries, with two dying from them, as a result of PJs catching on fire before flame-retardant rules

ONE, TWO, TOSS OUT MY SHOES

Does your child waddle around in cute plastic sandals or rubber clogs? Kids might love 'em for their bright colours and parents may love their great price, but a 2009 report published by the Danish Environmental Protection Agency found wearing them with bare feet is a bad idea. The study, which looked at exposures of two-year-olds to chemical substances in all sorts of consumer products, discovered three types of phthalates in a variety of children's rubber/plastic footwear (DBP, DIPB, DEHP). The report concluded: exposures to "a high content of an endocrine-disruptor, such as that of DBP in rubber clogs, may result in a critical risk for the two-year-old" (see page 390 for more on sandals). By the way, the feds are restricting six phthalates in kids' toys, but shoes aren't affected by the ban.

So what shoes are safe for your little ones? We don't love that Crocs won't tell us what they're made of beyond it being a "cross-linked resin," but they do say they're free of phthalates. Hope we can trust them. Any sandals made of EVA should be phthalate free too, including kids' Keen's, Teva and iPlay sandals. If you're unsure, call the company and ask what kind of plastic they use. Without firm facts about what kind of plastic they're made of, it's generally best to toss them. Sorry. By the way, if you're looking for cool kids' shoes, Simple makes some awesome sneaks and Mary Janes for infants, toddlers and older kids out of organic cotton and recycled PET (**simpleshoes.ca**).

were introduced in the late '80s. Since 1998, there've been no burns or deaths reported. More good news: Health Canada says flame retardants aren't necessary to meet their guidelines. But guess what? Synthetics such as polyester have flame retardants built in; otherwise, they'd quite horrifically melt like a marshmallow if your child got close to a candle (they are plastic fibres, after all). Nylon blends are treated after the fact. By the way, while one type of flame retardant—neurotoxic, mutagenic, cancer-linked retardant chlorinated Tris—was banned from pyjamas in the 1970s, it's shockingly still turning up in foam child care products such as nursing pads. A 2011 study published in the journal

Environmental Science & Technology found that of 101 products tested, 36% contained chlorinated Tris and 80% contained worrisome halogenated flame retardants. In California, products with Tris will now have to come with warnings.

- You can get away from flame retardants if you buy cotton pyjamas that are labelled as snug-fitting (loose-fitting, untreated cotton sleepwear/robes are illegal; in the United States, Macy's was slapped with record fines of $850,000 for selling some).
- Avoid PJs with PVC plastic cartoons. PVCs are softened with hormone-disrupting phthalates, six of which are now banned from kids' toys but not from their clothing.
- Look for snugly-fitting organic PJs. Hannaandersson.com and Newjammiesshop.com (carried in Canada by Kaikids.com and Mylittlegreenshop.com), or stop by the green kids' retailer nearest you (see Directory of Green Baby/Kids' Shops, page 432).

JEWELLERY, CHARMS AND TRINKETS

What is it about kids' jewellery that screams, "Let's make this with a neurotoxin"? Every year, a whack of children's jewellery and trinkets get recalled because of high lead and carcinogenic cadmium levels, including stuff from cheap accessory stores such as Ardene and Claire's as well as major chains like Walmart and giveaways from companies like Reebok. But you're not necessarily safe buying from stores that haven't been involved in recalls. That's why Health Canada issues blanket warnings that high levels of lead continue to be found in a wide variety of children's jewellery products sold in Canada. The chairman of the U.S. Consumer Product Safety Commission had probably the safest and smartest advice: "I have a message for parents, grandparents and caregivers: Do not allow young children to be given or to play with cheap metal jewelry, especially when they are unsupervised." Lead is extremely toxic to kids even at low levels. As Health Canada says, "Children can ingest harmful amounts of lead

when they chew, suck or swallow jewellery items containing lead."
By the way, these items aren't considered a risk unless they're being
chewed or sucked on, but even teens are likely to put pendants and
such in their mouths as they daydream. I know I used to.

Here are some Health Canada safety tips:

- Jewellery with a very high lead content may be thicker and less
  delicate than jewellery made from a stronger metal. Items high
  in lead often leave a greyish mark when rubbed against a piece
  of white paper, but that's not always the case since many
  products have a decorative coating.

- If you suspect your child's jewellery may contain lead or cadmium,
  toss it. (Health Canada says to trash it with regular waste, though
  the household hazardous waste depot may be smarter.)

- Don't give young children adult jewellery to wear or play with.

- Don't allow children to suck or chew on *any* jewellery.

- If your child has sucked or chewed regularly on jewellery that
  you think may contain lead or cadmium, ask your doctor to test
  your child's blood for lead and/or cadmium.

- If you think your child swallowed jewellery that might contain
  lead or cadmium, contact emergency medical services.

- Stay on top of product recalls at healthycanadians.gc.ca.

- To be safest, don't give your kids cheap metal jewellery. Period.

HEALTH

Keeping your kids healthy doesn't always come naturally. Literally.
A lot of the drugstore remedies we buy for colds, flus and beyond are
loaded with some of the same chemicals you'd expect to see in dodgy
cosmetics, including parabens, phthalates, sodium laureth sulphate,
not to mention pharmaceuticals that end up polluting waters downstream and coming right back up to haunt us in our tap water. Check
out my health chapters (7 through 10) for all kinds of sustainable
natural solutions to family ailments, from ear and eye infections to
allergies and asthma, as well as discussions around the environmental
pollutants linked to ADHD, autism, asthma and more.

Kids' Supplements: There are lots of low-grade supplements marketed for children. Swiss Children's Choice chewable multi with iron has aspartame and artificial dyes in it. iFlora Probiotics for Kids (by Sedona Labs) had a piddly 21% of the claimed probiotics when tested by consumerlab.com, while Dr. D Chocolate Flavoured Probiotics bears had just 7% of what they promised to contain. Shouldn't companies be extra vigilant about what we give our kids, not less?

Quality Kids' Supplements: Here's a rundown of some of the better brands with kids' lines. Keep in mind that, for instance, a multivitamin for children might be cool for older kids but the dose might be too high for younger ones, so do a little digging before you dole them out.

Nature's Plus Source of Life Animal Parade: Kids' line with excellent, sometimes food-sourced multis, greens, probiotics, vit C, zinc, calcium, vit D3, ear support, warm milk sleep aid, immune support and more. Naturesplus.com

SISU: This quality B.C. brand offers a chewable kids' line including multis, super fruits, Ester-C, baby and kids' probiotics, a D tablet, teen multis and an okay calcium, all in a fruit juice base. Too bad their chewable Omega 3 Bursts are made from tuna oil when marine ecologists will tell you it's best to leave the big fish in the sea (see Fish Oils, page 245). Sisu.com

Progressive: A quality Toronto-based line with a partly food-sourced chewable multivitamin for kids sweetened with organic maple syrup, birch-based xylitol and herbal stevia, a well-rounded calcium, and top-notch PhytoBerry for Kids vitamins/minerals/phytonutrients from 32 fruit concentrates, plus probiotics and DHA. Don't love that their fish oil has tuna mixed into it. progressivenutritional.com

Natural Factors: This B.C. company offers a liquid D3 and mid-grade Big Friends Children's Chewable multis, probiotics and a C. naturalfactors.com

Nordic Naturals: These guys specialize in fish oil products, including kids' versions, but stick to the chewable Fishies or Gummies made with small sardines and anchovies over other kids' omegas from big cod liver oil, though Norway's Arctic cod stocks are quite healthy now. Nordicnaturals.com

Renew Life: U.S. brand with a few good digestive health products for kids, including FloraBEAR (chewable) and FloraBaby (powder) probiotics, Buddy Bear fibres, enzymes and Gentle Lax (with magnesium, prune and fig). Renewlife.com

Carlson: A good American brand with a kids' line that includes chewable C, multi, and kids' and baby D drops. Best known for their fish oils. Offers kids' Norwegian cod liver oils and **Carlson for Kids Very Finest Fish Oil** made from mackerel, sardines and anchovies, all tested for contaminants. Carlsonlabs.com

Greens + Kids: Squeeze in hidden greens with purple berry-flavoured powder you can add to water or juice smoothies. Made with 25 organic fruits and veg, plus antioxidants, minerals and probiotics, with no added sugar. genuinehealth.com

Sambuguard for Kids and **Sambucol for Kids** are two children's elderberry extracts for squashing flu symptoms (see page 184). **St. Francis Herb Farm Kids' EchinaSera** with certified-organic echinacea is great for colds, as is their **Deep Immune for Kids**.

Climate Change: Curing the Global Fever   397

Tar Sands: The Oil-Free Diet   399

Chemicals: Detoxing a Nation   402

Boreal: Preserving Our Northern Lungs   404

Water: Thirsty for Protection   405

BIG ISSUES

So you've made it to the end of

Ecoholic Body, which means you've figured out how to keep
your body healthy and happy without making things worse for
the planet. Now what? Sit back and switch off your worries?
Sorry, folks, there's work to be done. We can't stop at fretting
about our personal physical state when the ice caps are still
melting, the planet is still cooking and our oceans are dying.
But the two needn't be mutually exclusive. There's a direct line
between our health and the planet's. The same pollutants that
are making us sick are making the planet sick. And even for
those who are only worried about their own self-preservation,
well, let me put it this way: if we don't get our shit together and
fix the balance that we've broken on this earth, we're all going
to experience a lot more suffering. End of story. So, put on
your work boots, roll up your sleeves and let's dive into
big-picture ways you can help—all while safeguarding your
health (and your hiney) in the long run too, naturally.

CLIMATE CHANGE:
CURING THE GLOBAL FEVER

What inevitably happens when you've been overworked, undernourished and burning the candle at both ends for too long? You get sick; maybe you get a fever if you're really unwell. It's your body's way of forcing you to slow the bleep down, stay in bed and recover. Well, it doesn't take a doctor of environmental studies to see that we've been pushing the planet's immune system to the brink and the proverbial mercury is rising. Just look around. In 2010, human activity pumped more carbon dioxide into the atmosphere than ever before, and it was also the hottest year on record. And where climate change–induced weather extremes were once merely an abstract prediction for the future, meteorologists are noting what we can see with our own eyes on the nightly news, that storms are already growing more violent and more frequent. Sure, a good deal of that freaky weather is thought to be due to natural variations, but in 2011 record floods, heat waves and droughts from Australia to Alberta, Manitoba to Memphis were all being pegged on climate change.

And it's not just crops and farmland that are being affected. A 2011 report by the U.S.-based Union of Concerned Scientists entitled *Climate Change and Your Health* found that worsening climate change–induced smog could result in 2.8 million additional serious respiratory illnesses. The same year, Purdue University and the National Center for Climatic Research noted how climate change will be putting the squeeze on already stressed hospitals as heat waves spike emergency room admissions, as well as death rates. World Health Organization stats report that in the face of climate change, Lyme disease is spreading to higher altitudes (watch out, Canada), expanded pollen seasons are increasing the time we suffer from allergies (see page 265), worsening air pollution sends more of us to the ER (see page 219) and malnutrition for the rural poor is expected as more crops are already failing. Just pick up Paul Epstein and Dan Ferber's book *Changing Planet, Changing Health: How the Climate Crisis Threatens Our Health and What We Can Do About It* to get more info on the topic. And no, the health impacts aren't just a distant prophecy. A 2009 report by former UN secretary-general Kofi Annan's think tank says 300,000 people around the world are already dying every year from the impacts of climate change and 300 million are being affected by its broader impacts.

Here in Canada, the implications of a climate-stressed population on our health care system is already being mapped out by Health Canada and the Public Health Agency of Canada. Health Canada's website openly notes that those who will suffer the most from the human health impacts of climate change include "children, seniors, people who are chronically ill, low income and homeless people, disabled people, people living off the land, northern residents." Now, I hate to ask the obvious here, but, um, why isn't the federal government doing anything about it? How in-your-face does the planet's ill health and the health of its citizens need to get before Ottawa stops being part of the problem and embraces earnest solutions?

The Harper government has obstructed every set of international climate talks since it's been in power. We've refused to accept binding emissions cuts and have become notorious backroom saboteurs. We're masters at blocking out the "noise" of critics like African delegates at the Cancún climate conference who pleaded for industrialized nations to get a grip, noting that by letting Kyoto expire in 2012, we were sentencing millions of Africans to death. Said the coalition of 43 African civil society organizations, "We fear for our mothers and fathers, our sisters and brothers—your uncles, aunts and cousins. Your policy on climate change threatens not only our families but also your own." It's time Canadians rise up and say, enough is enough already. So just what are we going to do to pitch in and push for change?

Here's What You Can Do:
- Tell the prime minister that Canadian citizens support real action on climate change, not just watered-down intensity targets that let total emissions rise year after year. We need bold federal leadership today.

- Tell the PM and the environment minister to stop sabotaging and start championing international climate agreements. It's the only way forward if we want to pull the planet back from the brink of catastrophe.
- Canada needs to join the energy revolution and combat climate change by throwing its whole-hearted support behind renewable energy the way South Korea has. The Asian nation fuelled its economic recovery plan on the foundation of a new green economy. Tell the feds you don't want Canada to be left behind—and remind them that new industry means jobs for Canadians.

SEND YOUR EMAILS HERE!

Looking to share a piece of your mind?
Prime Minister: **pm@pm.gc.ca**
Environment Minister: **minister@ec.gc.ca**
Health Minister: **Minister_Ministre@hc-sc.gc.ca**
Natural Resources Minister: **Ministre.Minister@RNCan-NRCan.gc.ca**

TAR SANDS: THE OIL-FREE DIET

There's no denying humanity's got one serious oil addiction. We've injected the substance into nearly every facet of our lives, from the shampoo in your morning shower (see page 125) to the clothing we drape on our bodies (see page 293) to the laxatives we give our kids (see page 193). Instead of signing up for Celebrity Rehab, we all need to pause and genuinely consider ways to move away from oil in our daily lives (see page 401 for tips), but there's still a giant elephant in the room here. It's called the Alberta oil sands. Trying to shake off our personal oil dependency without dealing with this—Canada's fastest-growing greenhouse gas emitter—is kind of like talking about quitting smoking when you're dealing crack. Both habits need to be broken.

Now, Alberta's PR managers have been remarkably busy trying to clean up the sullied image of the notoriously dirty oil. They've been cranking out flattering TV ads on major U.S. stations and sending special envoys to Europe and south of the border, all pitching Canada as the golden child of the oil sector. Yes, we're positively brimming with "responsible," "ethical" oil, they tell the world. For one, it's extracted on friendly Canadian soil (not that dodgy Middle East) where environmental laws keep them in check and, second of all, the workers are paid exemplary wages, thank you very much. What's there to complain about?

Well, the golden goose starts to lose its sheen when you take a closer look at just how the 169.9 billion barrels of bitumen buried in Alberta are extracted from the sands. For one, two tons of topsoil and two tons of "over burden" rock/soil are removed for every barrel of bitumen (stripping ancient boreal forest and disturbing vital carbon-storing peatlands). More fun facts: processing the oil sands is so water intensive that it takes two to four barrels of fresh water to process a barrel of bitumen. Sure industry says 80% of that water now gets recycled, but the Pembina Institute says almost none of that H_2O is returned to the natural cycle. The tar sands are also the number-one reason Canada can't get a grip on its greenhouse gases. That's because oil sands fuel is 3 to 4.5 times more greenhouse gas intensive to produce than conventional oil, according to the Institute (and while industry tries to convince us that newer "in-site" techniques are more sustainable than the maligned open-pit mining, they're actually 2.5 times more CO_2 intensive). At this point, we're only squeezing roughly 1.6 million barrels a day from Alberta's sands. What happens when the industry reaches its forecasts of 4.7 million a day in 2025?

What are the health impacts of all this? Alberta keeps insisting pollution levels are perfectly safe, but an investigation by distinguished water expert David Schindler concluded "contrary to claims made by industry and government in the popular press, the oils sands industry substantially increases loadings of toxic PPEs [priority pollutants] to the Athabasca River and its tributaries via air and water pathways." About 250 kilometres from those pollutants sits Fort Chipewyan, a community whose elevated cancer rates have been clearly documented. A 2009 investigation by Alberta Health Services assessing those rates over a 12-year period found higher than expected numbers of cancers of the blood and lymphatic system, biliary tract and soft tissue. But proving that the tar sands are responsible for those tumours is another matter. A report by the Royal Society of Canada noted we'd need more monitoring of human contaminant exposures to say for sure. As it was at the time of their report, monitoring of pollutants was so problematic the RSA said we haven't been able to get a clear picture of the cumulative human and environmental impacts of the oil sands. The good news is that during the summer of 2011, the feds announced plans to improve emissions monitoring. Now let's just hope they do it right and follow up on any findings. The signs, however, aren't positive: the environment minister has already said he hopes any findings will allay American fears and speed up the approval process for an oil sands pipeline to the U.S. Gulf Coast.

Beyond the localized impacts, Canada's own Mordor (the fictitious barren wasteland made famous by *Lord of the Rings*) should certainly shoulder some of the blame for all the broader health ramifications of climate change. Call it the bitumen-drenched straw on the global camel's back. No wonder international pressure to get our tar sands pollution in check keeps mounting. So how can you help?

Here's What You Can Do:
- Tell the feds you want to see a reduction in the pace and scale of oil sands production.
- Remind the federal government that they promised to cut subsidies to the oil sands. The feds hand out $1.4 billion a year in subsidies to the oil and gas sectors. Time to pull the plug!
- Encourage more major companies to join Avon, Bed, Bath & Beyond, Levi's, the Gap and others in bringing in policies to avoid tar sands fuel wherever possible (forestethics.org).
- Join the Native resistance and tell your bank not to finance Enbridge or its Northern Gateway Pipeline, which will be

piping raw tar sands crude down the Pacific coast through traditional First Nations territory without their consent (savethefraser.ca). The Lubicon have already suffered through a 4.5-million-litre pipeline spill on their territory in April 2011. Get involved at dirtyrainbow.ca. See ienearth.org for more on indigenous tar sands resistance.

- Push for more aggressive renewable energy plans from your federal and provincial governments.
- Your lobbying shouldn't stop at the tar sands. Canada's rolling up its sleeves for more offshore drilling too. WWF Canada says a warming Arctic holds an estimated 25% of the world's remaining petroleum reserves and that Canada's regulatory framework is even weaker than that in the United States, making a spill here "almost inevitable." The WWF as well as the Council of Canadians and others have been vocal about the fact that extreme conditions in the Beaufort Sea would limit the ability of emergency responders to tackle a spill in ice-covered waters. Send a letter to the PM and the federal Natural Resources minister calling for a moratorium on drilling in the Arctic.

CHEMICALS: DETOXING A NATION

Forget material world, Madonna should have rolled around in a vat of bubbly suds, emerged in a formaldehyde-laced gown and sung about how we live in a decidedly chemical world. Yes, chemical substances have laid the foundation for modern conveniences, weaving their way into every corner of our lives (including body care, clothing fibres, health products and so much more). All wonderfully Jetsons-like really, until you start to realize how many of those are messing with our bodies.

Yes, Canada has made some good progress banning and restricting a number of chemical substances over the last few years, adding them to Health Canada's Hotlist of Prohibited and Restricted Cosmetic Ingredients. Government scientists started sorting through 23,000 existing substances that had been around since before environmental regs came into place, acknowledging no one had looked at them before to see if they posed a risk to humans or the environment. A good first step. We then prioritized about 200 of them for reassessment and have, in recent years, declared a few dozen of them toxic. Fantastic. Five years into Canada's Chemicals Management Plan, Environmental Defence issued a report card in 2011 saying, on chemical management, Canada's "at the top of its class." But this is no time to rest on our laurels. As Environmental Defence also noted, there are a hefty 2,600 "medium priority" substances that need to be assessed—though the feds have coughed up $508 million to take on the backlog. Not sure that'll include the one-third of high-priority substances from the petroleum sector that were slated for review. (See Tar Sands, above, for more on Canada's inaction on cleaning up the petroleum industry.)

We also need to overhaul the way we allow future chemicals on the market. Truth is, in this country, chemicals are still innocent until proven guilty. In Europe, it's the reverse: chemicals substances are guilty until proven innocent, and companies have to prove they're safe before they're allowed on the market. What a novel thought. The European Union is also very clear about banning from personal care products all ingredients that are known or probable human carcinogens, reproductive toxins and/or mutagens. Maybe that's why they have over 1,300 substances that are restricted in body care products while we've got maybe 500.

But hey, let's start by, at the very least, enforcing the regs we already have on our books, such as the Cosmetic Regulation that says: "No manufacturer or importer shall sell a cosmetic that contains . . . an estrogenic substance." Meanwhile, back in the beauty aisle, you'll find plenty of ingredients with estrogenic activity, including BHA, parabens, cyclomethicone and several phthalates. What's the hold up here, gang? We should be getting rid of those ASAP, and all hormone-disrupting substances, especially in products intended for kids. Yes, we banned some phthalates from some children's articles but, hell, the Danes are banning four phthalates from all consumer products that come in contact with the public and two parabens from children's personal care products. So far, we're hearing nothing but crickets from Health Canada on this front.

Here's What You Can Do:

- Tell the health minister that this is a no-brainer. Canada should follow the European Union's lead and phase out the use of all chemicals that are carcinogens, reproductive toxins or mutagens.
- In the interim, we need warning labels like California's that alert consumers "Warning: this product contains chemicals known to cause cancer or birth defects."
- Ask your MP why our Hotlist doesn't apply to by-product ingredients (see page 5 for more info on our troubled body care regs). It's time for a change.
- Push your MP and the prime minister to apply organic regulations to personal care products and not just food. We want to be able to trust that products labelled organic really are.

BOREAL: PRESERVING OUR NORTHERN LUNGS

You probably grew up hearing that the Amazon rainforests are the "lungs of the planet," but not too many people tell you that Canada's boreal forest—one of the world's largest intact old-growth forests, stretching from Newfoundland to British Columbia and north into the Yukon—shares that claim. Chop down the boreal and you remove the globe's northern lobes that quietly breathe in carbon dioxide and exhale the gift of clean oxygen for the world. The boreal, in fact, stores more carbon dioxide in its great northern expanse than the Amazon rainforest. Once you understand that, it starts to make more sense when you hear that logging our forests creates more global warming than all the emission-spewing passenger vehicles in the country, according to Forest Ethics and Environment Canada. So what's our old-growth forest worth to us? Clear-cutting the whole thing (1.4 billion acres) and selling off the sum of its dead wood would net you a good $50 billion, according to a Pembina Institute report entitled "Counting Canada's Natural Capital." Not bad, but what about its non-market value? Once the think tank factored in the inherent carbon storage, flood control, water filtering and myriad natural services offered by the boreal ecosystem, that forest is worth 14 times as much: roughly $700 billion. I'm happy to report in 2010, 9 enviro groups and 21 forest companies signed the historic Canada Boreal Forest Agreement protecting an area twice the size of Germany from logging. Still, it only covers a small percentage of the allocated boreal forest in Canada and environmentalists say there's more work to be done.

Here's What You Can Do:
- Reduce your use of disposable tissue products such as facial tissues, and choose only 100% recycled paper products. See tissue.greenpeace.ca.
- Tell your member of provincial parliament to do more to protect endangered species such as woodland caribou and grizzlies, and to enforce existing regulations for species at risk (protecting them protects our forests).
- We need to save more forest already allocated for logging. Tell your MP and provincial rep.
- Lobby the feds to put a stop to illegally logged forest imports. We don't want our global lungs collapsing, too.

WATER: THIRSTY FOR PROTECTION

Water. It's the most abundant compound on this planet and without it, well, we'd be Mars. The life-giving element is so paramount to human health and survival that you can see why access to clean water and sanitation was recently declared a human right (though Canada, shamefully, voted against the move). Already, nearly 2 billion people live in water-stressed areas (no wonder the UN special adviser on water, Maude Barlow, said that access to clean water is the most violated human right), but bodies worldwide are expected to face even graver thirst over the next 20 years. A World Bank–backed Water Resources Group report noted that by 2030, global water demand will exceed supply by, oh, a mere 40%. But whoa, back up, freshwater threats are a global problem. Canada's got so much fresh water that we've got nothing to worry about, right? Well, on too many reserves, access to clean water and sewage services are on par with the poorest countries of the southern hemisphere, much to our global embarrassment. The auditor general has repeatedly called on the feds to rectify the situation ASAP, and still nada. The federal government can spend $2 million on a fake lake to impress G20 leaders but can't seem to find the funds to get clean water to First Nations communities.

Making sure we keep the fresh water we do have clean and abundant is another essential big issue. Yes, Canada holds a whopping 20% of the world's fresh water, but only 7% is renewable and half of that drains north into the Arctic Ocean or Hudson Bay, where 85% of us can't get at it. That's why the supply we do have gets pretty heavily stressed and overused. Without serious conservation efforts, we're basically shooting ourselves in the cistern and setting ourselves up for serious long-term problems. Especially if we keep flushing endocrine-disrupting chemicals down the drain every time we take a shower and don't invest in water treatment plants that can break all those chemicals down.

We're also facing devastating threats to our oceans. A 2011 UN-sponsored study by the International Programme on the State of the Ocean (which involved 27 scientists from 18 organizations in 6 countries) came to a sobering conclusion that should get us all choking on our tuna fish. They warned that the world's oceans are teetering on "entering a phase of extinction of marine species unprecedented in human history." That's right, a perfect storm of factors from overfishing, climate change, ocean acidification, fertilizer runoff, massive dead zones, and plastic and chemical pollutants are creating a combination of stressors that could quite easily kick off the next mass extinction on this planet—all within one generation. The report notes that entire oceanic ecosystems, such as coral reefs, could be wiped out before the end of your lifetime.

What will this mean for us humans and our health? Widespread fisheries collapse would spell global disaster, as 200 million people in coastal communities lose their livelihood and 1 billion lose this vital food source. Also, the oceans actually produce 70% of the oxygen that sustains life on this planet and play a vital role in climate change thanks to their carbon dioxide absorption, notes WWF. If our oceans grow so acidic from having sopped up too much CO_2 and the seas simply can't absorb any more of our carbon emissions, as scientists are predicting, we've got to be prepared for the impacts of climate change—including sweeping health consequences (see Climate Change: Curing the Global Fever, page 397)—to seriously accelerate.

Here's What You Can Do:

- Tell the feds it's time for them to recognize water as a human right in this country by bringing in a National Water Policy that, amongst other things, introduces legally enforceable drinking water standards. For more on the Council of Canadians' vision for such a policy, see canadians.org/water.
- We need greater protection of our seas on all levels. Push our politicians to close fisheries that aren't being sustainably managed and to establish a network of marine protected areas that safeguard at least 30% of our coastal waters.
- Tell the feds you want substances deemed harmful to aquatic organisms removed from our shelves and tougher sewage treatment standards that actually do something about breaking down chemicals of concern.
- Tell your local councillor and mayor you'd like your town to become an official "Blue Community"—a municipality passes a resolution banning the sale of bottled water in public facilities and at municipal events, recognizes water as a human right, and promotes publicly owned and operated water and waste-water services. canadians.org/water/issues/blue_communities/.

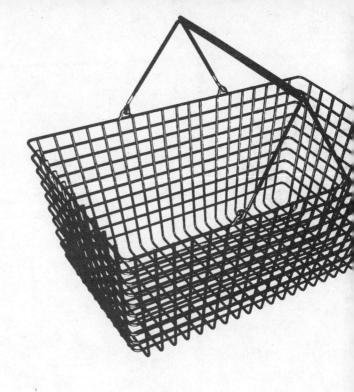

Label Decoder   411

Plastics Guide   418

Green Plastics Guide   420

Directory of Green Clothing Stores   422

Directory of Green Baby/Kids' Shops   432

RESOURCES

I've got to admit, I'm an obsessive

label reader. Drugstores and health stores can swallow me in their aisles for hours, it seems, before I'm done reading all the fine print behind the marketing hoopla. Since I don't expect the world to have the same oddball passion for decoding, let me take the guesswork out of it for you with my trusty label decoder guide.

LABEL DECODER

Biodegradable: Don't bank on products that claim to be biodegradable without coughing up third-party certification, such as the Scientific Certification Systems. But even that doesn't tell you a product is 100% biodegradable, it just means it will biodegrade by 70% within 28 days. Look for products with better specs, like "Biodegrades 99% within 28 days according to OECD test #301D."

CFC-Free: Nice that your hairspray tells you it's CFC free but, honey, everything's been free of ozone-depleting chlorofluorocarbons since, like, the mid-'90s (in North America, anyway). This label in no way means the chemicals used in a CFC-free product are good for the planet or the people in your home. CFC replacements, such as HCFCs, have also been found to be detrimental to the ozone layer. (See also HCFC-free.)

Compostable: If your diapers or the packaging on your personal care product are certified by the Biodegradable Products Institute/US Composting Council, you can trust this to mean that a product has been tested to biodegrade at the same rate as yard trimmings and food scraps. But it doesn't mean it can be put in your backyard composter. bpiworld.org

Cradle to Cradle: The cutting-edge peeps behind this label certify products as Cradle to Cradle Basic, Silver, Gold or Platinum based on the use of green chemicals and the perpetual recyclability of the materials used to make them. Nearly 200 products have been certified, including shampoo, textiles and more. The end products aren't necessarily perfect (no item has received Platinum certification, for instance, and not all have upcycling infrastructure in place), but the certifiers are trying to keep the trajectory moving ahead to a brighter, greener future. mbdc.com

EcoLogo/Environmental Choice: This respected Canadian label was founded in '98 by Environment Canada. The logo can now be spotted on over 7,000 products North America–wide, from personal care to paint, with comprehensive set standards for each. These guys actually require independent verification of product claims, which too few do. EcoLogo products should be greener than roughly 80% of the products in any given category. ecologo.org

Eco-friendly: Says who? No one's policing this term.

Eco-safe: Totally meaningless. No regulation of this term.

Elemental chlorine free: Products with this label (such as tampons and diapers) have been bleached without old-school elemental chlorine gas, a process that notoriously releases carcinogenic, bioaccumulative dioxins. ECF processes use chlorine dioxide instead. (See also Totally Chlorine Free.)

Fair Trade Certified: You'll find this label on a couple of natural body care products, such as shea butter, as well as ingredients such as sugar, coffee, or vanilla that can turn up in body care products. It can also appear on cotton and new standards are coming in for apparel that certify a garment from field to factory. This seal tells you workers are paid a decent wage and the premiums you fork out for that fair-trade lotion or whatnot also fund health care and education. Dangerous pesticides are banned and organic practices are encouraged, but unless it comes with the certified-organic seal as well, there are no guarantees.

FSC **FSC** **Mixed Sources** Product group from well-managed forests and other controlled sources www.fsc.org Cert no. SW-COC-867 © 1996 Forest Stewardship Council **Forest Stewardship Council (wood/ paper):** You may see this on the paper packaging of body care labels or in reference to wood-based fabrics such as Tencel. It's still considered the best wood label we have, but critics say the FSC's global monitoring of forests has major gaps and that tropical old-growth trees aren't well protected from the axe. To avoid chopping old-growth rainforests, it's best to stick to domestic FSC lumber. FSC Pure means it's 100% certified; the FSC Mixed Sources label, on the other hand, means it contains up to 30% non-certified sources, which gets a little dodgy. fsccanada.org

Good Manufacturing Practices (GMP): A set of manufacturing guidelines from Health Canada for licensed facilities that manufacture your supplements, drugs, medical devices and more. They have to meet regs around sanitation, raw materials, quality control, packaging material, finished product testing, stability, sterility and more. The Health Products and Food Brand Inspectorate program inspects facilities to see if they're in compliance with GMP. Some bodies certify facilities for GMP, and you may see a GMP seal on supplements and more.

GOTS (Global Organic Textile Standard): On top of making sure the fabric is grown, processed and dyed in an environmentally preferred way, this standard calls for decent worker rights (i.e., right to collective bargaining, 48-hour workweek with max 12 hours voluntary overtime) with unannounced third-party inspections. Clothes have to be 95% organic, unless they say "made with organic," when they have to contain at least 70% organic fibres. global-standard.org

Green Seal: You used to see this seal only on cleaning products and at home reno stores, but they now have certification for personal care products. This non-profit org has comprehensive certification schemes that, in the case of personal care, address health, environmental labelling and worker rights concerns. A body care product with this seal will be free of carcinogens, endocrine disruptors, neurotoxins, reproductive toxins, animal testing and more. Air-polluting VOCs and asthma triggers and lead contaminants are restricted, and biodegradability and aquatic toxicity

413

standards must be met. Plus, it verifies accuracy in labelling terms such as "natural" and "organic." These guys actually visit the factory floor and do annual monitoring, and they insist on independent verification of product claims. greenseal.org

HCFC-Free: Now we're getting somewhere—this label is way more relevant than CFC-free. Though hydrochlorofluorocarbons were originally brought in as a greener replacement for CFCs, HCFCs also turned out to be an ozone-depleting greenhouse gas. Whoops. In 2007, at a United Nations Environment Programme meeting, 200 countries agreed to phase out HCFC production by 2013.

Hypoallergenic: The FDA in the United States says it "does not know of any scientific studies that prove whether 'hypoallergenic' products produce fewer allergic reactions than products that don't have the claim." Sorry to disappoint.

Includes Biodegradable Surfactants: Okay, so the surfactants (wetting agents that help lift dirt and oil away) might be biodegradable, but don't be fooled into thinking this applies to the product as a whole. This claim has no real third-party monitoring.

 Krav: Trusted Swedish certifier that covers organic cotton, wool, silk, linen, leather and hides. krav.se

Leaping Bunny: One of the only certified "no animal testing" logos around. Unless you see this exact bunny with stars in the logo, it probably wasn't certified (most companies just stick any old rabbit image on their product and call it a day). This one's on a lot of cleaning products, as well as personal care goods, and tells you the company has officially pledged to the Coalition for Consumer Information on Cosmetics that neither it nor its suppliers conduct or commission animal testing, though they might have in the past.

leapingbunny.org

Made with organic ingredients: According to the USDA, a product bearing these words on the front of its packaging must be at least 70% certified organic.

Non-toxic: Think someone's overseeing the use of this term on your personal care or baby product? Think again. Health Canada told me this is an "industry-devised marketing term." No universal meaning.

NSF (National Sanitation Foundation): This non-profit is considered the world leader in setting standards for product safety, including vitamins and other supplements (NSF does product testing and Good Manufacturing Practices inspections required by Health Canada). You can find the seal on millions of products. nsf.org

NSF Contains Organic Ingredients: A personal care labelling standard that tells you a product contains at least 70% certified-organic content.

Oeko-Tex 100: Clothes certified to this global standard are tested to make sure there's no discernible presence of formaldehyde, flame retardants, pesticides, phthalates, dye allergens, extractable heavy metals that come out when you sweat, or other harmful chemicals on the finished fabric itself. It doesn't mean the cotton for a shirt wasn't, say, grown with pesticides, but the textile won't have any meaningful residues. The International Oeko-Tex Association is a grouping of 14 textile and test institutes in Japan and Europe that's responsible for the independent Oeko-Tex tests. oeko-tex.com

Oeko-Tex 1000: This beefed-up version of Oeko-Tex is way more holistic in making sure the factory that makes your clothes is green. Besides not using harmful dyes on the textiles, the factory has to minimize its energy use, noise and dust pollution as well as waste water and exhaust air. There are safety standards for workers and a policy to prevent child labour. Monitored by independent auditors. oeko-tex1000.com

Organic: This doesn't mean anything on a product unless it's accompanied by a recognized certified-organic label/logo. Canada doesn't have any requirements for minimum organic contents for personal care. Why? The feds choose to only certify food and avoid personal care altogether. Shame.

Processed Chlorine Free (PCF): Spot this logo on recycled paper and you'll know the recycled content wasn't bleached with chlorine-containing compounds. This label is third-party certified (chlorinefreeproducts.org). Since original materials being recycled may have once been bleached, it doesn't qualify as totally chlorine free.

SFI (Sustainable Forestry Initiative): You might see this on paper packaging. This industry-run program of the American Forest and Paper Association doesn't get much R-E-S-P-E-C-T from enviros. Not only do they allow clear-cuts of up to 120 acres, but they green-light genetic engineering and the axing of old-growth forests. sfiprogram.org

Skal: This is the Netherlands' organic certifier; you might see it on European-made brands. skal.nl

Soil Association: This is a good British organic certifier that you might spot on organic cosmetics and apparel made in the U.K. soilassociation.org

Totally Chlorine Free (TCF): When this logo appears on virgin (non-recycled) paper/wood pulp products (i.e., diapers and tampons), it guarantees that the pulp that went into them wasn't bleached with chlorine or chlorine-containing compounds. chlorinefreeproducts.org

USDA Biobased: New label identifies products made of renewable resources that are entirely or in part biological—namely, renewable plant, animal, marine and forestry ingredients. Part of its aim, according to the USDA, is "facilitating increased U.S. energy independence by reducing the use of petroleum in manufactured products." Truth is, a product only needs to be 25% renewable to qualify and it doesn't have to fess up to what percentage of its content is renewable, so it's pretty sucky. The label's already been accused of promoting greenwashed products. The label stems from an older federal program called BioPreferred, which encouraged federal agencies in the United States to buy bio-based products, thereby supporting the agricultural sector.

USDA Organic: If you see a natural health product or body care product with this seal on the front, it's at least 95% certified organic. Since there is no separate standard for personal care products, shampoo or lotion that carries this label actually meets the USDA food standards for organic. Certified-organic ingredients come from farms where no chemical inputs have been used for at least three years and where the focus is on using natural pest control, crop rotation and boosting the soil's fertility without synthetics. Note that "organic" doesn't mean the workers were fairly paid; only "fair trade" means that.

PLASTICS GUIDE

You've got to hand it to the plastic people. They've cleverly managed to finagle their way into literally every move we make. Just look around. They've infiltrated our water supply (PVC pipes, water mains, bottles), our clothing (nylon, polyester, spandex), our electronics (casings, wiring), our food supply (packaging and fossil fuel fertilizers) and pretty much everything in our bathrooms (including the bottles and the petrochemicals inside them)—and the list goes on. Truth is, unless you've built your own off-grid cabin free of modern amenities, it's virtually impossible to entirely separate yourself from petroleum's offspring (not to mention the children of Monsanto's corn), but we can certainly try to give ourselves a little distance from them. Especially in light of recent findings published in *Environmental Health Perspectives* which concluded that an astounding 71% of over 500 plastics sampled released estrogenic chemicals. Yes, you heard me. The researchers tested all types of plastic that came in contact with food (including "safer" plastics such as PET and HDPE), and that estrogenic percentage jumped to 90% when those plastics were stressed under hot water (simulating dishwashing), UV light or in a microwave. The fact that 10% of plastics were unaffected indicates that plastics can be manufactured so they're not estrogenic, but when Ecoholic contacted the researchers to get a list of safe plastics, they noted that no single plastic could be clearly identified by consumers as free of estrogenic concerns. Yikes. Now, you're not eating out of the plastics in your bathroom or bedroom closet, but until we know more about totally estrogen-free plastics, it's useful to know which plastic may be better or worse and which is most recyclable (those little triangular recycling logos are there for a reason).

Polyethylene Terephthalate (PET): Found in shampoo bottles, soda bottles and water bottles. Probably the most commonly recycled plastic. Contains UV stabilizers and flame retardants, but has fewer harmful additives that will leach into landfills and your meal. PET disposable water bottles have been known to leach antimony, however. In 2008, a *Milwaukee Journal Sentinel* investigation found that even some No. 1 containers leached bisphenol A in the microwave. The news didn't spread. And no, despite the "phthalate" in "terephthalate," this plastic doesn't contain phthalates.

High-density Polyethylene (HDPE): Shampoo bottles, milk jugs, cleaning-product bottles, shopping bags (which aren't necessarily recycled in municipalities that recycle No. 2 plastic—best to check). Most municipalities accept narrow-nose containers, but not all take wide-lipped ones such as margarine tubs even if they're No. 2 (again, best to ask). HDPE is not a bad plastic, compared to the others—though the 2008 *Milwaukee Journal Sentinel* investigation found that even some No. 2 containers leached bisphenol A in the microwave.

Polyvinyl Chloride (PVC): Greenpeace ranks this one as the biggest eco-villain of all plastics. This is the plastic wrapped up in all the toy recalls, as well as shower curtain scares. PVC, or vinyl, is made with vinyl chloride, a known human carcinogen. It's said to emit persistent dioxins in both its manufacture and its incineration (especially in crappy municipal incinerators). Hormone-disrupting phthalates added to soften it have been found to off-gas from the plastic. Lead and cadmium are commonly used as stabilizers and have also been found to migrate from the plastic (think lead in toys or venetian blinds). It's the basis of fake leather, many screen-printed T-shirts, as well as rubber coats, sandals and more. If your plastic bottle has the number 3 or a V on the bottom, it's PVC. Rarely labelled and recycled.

Low-density Polyethylene (LDPE): Like its high-density sibling, No. 4 plastic isn't as toxic to manufacture as other plastics are, but it's less commonly recycled.

Polypropylene (PP): Not recyclable in every municipality, but it's considered the safest plastic with regard to leaching potential. Shocker of all shockers, in the *Milwaukee Journal Sentinel* investigation, some No. 5 containers were also found to leach bisphenol A when microwaved.

Polystyrene (PS): A category best known by the trade name Styrofoam, which is often used to refer generically to the whole PS category, though Styrofoam specifically applies to one type of PS, namely extruded polystyrene. Either way, PS is tied with polyurethane for second-worst plastic, because making the stuff involves carcinogenic benzene; plus, it's very rarely recycled.

Basically, any plastic other than Nos. 1 to 6. Not recyclable by municipalities since they have no idea what type of plastic it is.

Polycarbonate: Not readily recyclable. This clear, hard plastic is famous for containing estrogen-mimicking bisphenol A. It used to be marketed as non-leaching, not to mention indestructible. Boy, were they wrong. Actually, the *Environmental Health Perspectives* study as well as research by Health Canada found even bisphenol A–free baby bottles released various estrogenic chemicals. Health Canada says the trace levels of estrogen-mimicking bisphenol A detected in their own studies on non-polycarbonate (a.k.a. BPA-free) baby bottles are "much lower than those that could cause health effects." Not that we have any idea what that threshold might be.

Polyurethane: It's also a No. 7, and though considered greener than PVC, it still emits toxins such as methylene chloride during production.

GREEN PLASTICS GUIDE

Green plastic used to mean plastic that was some shade of celery, avocado or lime, but now the environmentally inclined kind are turning up everywhere. You'll find them in body-related goods from lipstick tubes to shoe soles. Are they really as earth-friendly as they claim to be? It depends. The very greenest, most cutting-edge plastics are being made from waste, including milk curd, cashew shells and plant stems. Conventional corn-based plastic is definitely less impressive, though much more common since it's also a lot more affordable. Conventional corn is highly energy intensive to grow (thanks to fossil fuel fertilizers used in industrial farming) and is commonly genetically modified.

Here's a breakdown of some eco-plastics. Warning: (Almost) none of these should be placed in conventional recycling bins! They can damage the durability of recycled plastic goods such as recycled plastic Muskoka chairs or carpeting.

Bioplastic: Broad term for plastics made from plant-based oils, starches or fibres. Could come from genetically engineered crops, so it's always best to ask.

Biodegradable Plastic: Unless it's certified biodegradable, this doesn't mean much. Biodegradable plastic is generally made of some sort of plant-based material such as cornstarch, potato starch or sugar cane (though scientists have tinkered around with plastics made from garbage such as orange peels and chicken feathers too). If it ends up in a dark, airless landfill, it's unlikely to break down fully, given that decades-old hot dogs can still be found in dumps. For that reason, as well as the possibility that biodegradable plastics could be made with genetically modified ingredients, many feel these plastics do not deserve the green hype they get. Critics also charge that food crops should be left for hungry bellies rather than feeding our appetite for disposable plastic products. One company makes an additive called Bio-Batch that is said to make regular plastic biodegradable and recyclable. To ensure a plastic is legitimately biodegradable, make sure it's certified by a third party (see Label Decoder, page 411).

Compostable Plastic: If these are certified compostable, they're greener than plain biodegradable plastics since they biodegrade much more readily (the plastic is often flimsier as a result). Certification basically tells you it'll break down in a municipal composter as fast as other compostable goods, with no toxic residue, but it doesn't necessarily mean it'll disintegrate in your backyard composter, so read the fine print. Look for the certified-compostable seal (see Label Decoder, page 411).

Degradable or Oxo-degradable Plastic: Often petroleum based but designed to decompose when exposed to UV light or oxygen—both of which are rarely found in landfills. Don't believe claims that oxo-degradable plastics are comparable to a fallen leaf. Oxo-degradable plastics can go in the recycling bin, unlike bio-degradable and compostable plastics, but this can be pretty confusing for the consumer to keep track of. Check with your municipality before you recycle it.

DIRECTORY OF GREEN CLOTHING STORES

Looking for a place to buy green threads near you? Here's a breakdown of your online and regional options (often the bricks-and-mortar stores have good websites too). By the way, hemp general stores often carry hemp clothing but there are just too many of these in Canada to mention. If you know of any great green clothing stores that we didn't include in this directory, please email the details to eco@ecoholic.ca. By the way, if you're wondering why I don't have a directory of stores that carry natural body care products and supplements, truth is, there are far too many of them in this country to mention here (so use trusty Google to find health stores and pharmacies near you). See page 122 for a listing of some of the top online retailers of natural/organic body care.

ONLINE STORES

So many earth-conscious designers and green clothing stores have e-boutiques now, I can't mention them all here, but here's a sampling of some online sources for green clothing that sell a good cross-section of eco designers.

Legend: Men = 🚹   Women = 🚺   Kids = 👶

notjustpretty.ca 🚺 BC
chartreusestyle.com 🚺 ON
ecocentrikapparel.com 🚹🚺👶 QC
hempandcompany.com 🚹🚺👶 BC
mudsharkstreetwear.com (not all eco, but carries a wide range of eco-brands) 🚹 ON
fashionandearth.com 🚹🚺👶 PEI
rawganique.com 🚹🚺 BC
stilleagle.com 🚹🚺👶 ON
ethicalocean.com 🚹🚺👶
terra20.com 🚹🚺👶 BC

REGIONAL STORES
ALBERTA

Elements
135 8th Avenue SW
Calgary, AB
(403) 266-6463
elementsinc.ca

Eleven Eleven Boutique
233 10 Street NW
Calgary, AB
(403) 452-5285
elevenelevenboutique.com

Riva's The Eco Store
1237 9th Avenue SE
Calgary, AB
(403) 452-1001
rivasecostore.com

Lucid Lifestyle Eco Apparel
10406 82 Avenue
Edmonton, AB
(780) 953-4376
lucid-lifestyle.com

Natural Attractions
145 Spokane Street
Kimbley, AB
(250) 427-4349
(no online presence)

Sundara Transformational
Centre and Ethical Boutique
11 Elma Street
Okotoks, AB
(403) 995-9395
sundaraonline.com

BRITISH COLUMBIA

The Lakes Hair Studio and
Eco Boutique
7356 Sheridan Frontage Road
100 Mile House, BC
(250) 593-4987
(no online presence)

All Things Being Eco
105–7388 Vedder Road
Chilliwack, BC
(604) 824-9442
allthingsbeingeco.ca

Be Clothing
113–255 6th Street
Courtenay, BC
(250) 331-0588
beclothing.ca

Ziva Spa and Natural Fibre
Fashions
512 5th Street
Courtenay, BC
(250) 871-8701
zivaorganicspa.ca

Radway Studio
1759 Cowichan Bay Road
Cowichan Bay, BC
(250) 746-8444
radway.ca

Prudence Organics
7–225 Canada Avenue
Duncan, BC
(250) 597-1188
prudenceorganics.vpweb.ca

Lilikoi
471 Baker Street
Nelson, BC
(250) 352-3382
lilikoiclothing.com

Still Eagle
557 Ward Street
Nelson, BC
(250) 352-3844
stilleagle.com

Shades of Green
117 Craig Street
Parksville, BC
(250) 248-2501
shadesofgreenmindbodyhome.com

Agnes Jean Boutique
38018 Cleveland Avenue
Squamish, BC
(604) 892-9181
agnesjean.com

Devil May Wear
198 E 21st Street
Vancouver, BC
(604) 216-2515
devil-may-wear.ca

Little Dream
The Net Loft @ Granville Island
Unit 130, 1666 Johnston St.
Vancouver, BC
(604) 683-6930
dreamvancouver.com

Twigg & Hottie
3671 Main Street
Vancouver, BC
(604) 879-8595
twiggandhottie.com

Adhesif Clothing
2202 Main Street
Vancouver, BC
(604) 568-4905
adhesifclothing.com

Body Politic
208 12th Avenue East
Vancouver, BC
(604) 568-5528
bodypolitic.ca

Dream
311 W Cordova St.
Vancouver, BC
(604) 683-7326
dreamvancouver.com

Riot
1395 Commercial Drive
Vancouver, BC
(604) 254-5073 ·
riotinbc.ca

Two of Hearts
3728 Main Street
Vancouver, BC
(604) 568-0998
two-of-hearts-clothing.com

Not Just Pretty
1036 Fort Street
Victoria, BC
(250) 414-0414
notjustpretty.com

Salts Organic
105–561 Johnson Street
Victoria, BC
(250) 590-6961
saltsclothing.com

Shift Natural Fashion
547 Lower Johnson Street
Victoria, BC
(250) 383-7441
shiftfashion.ca

MANITOBA

Five Two Sustainable Lifestyle Boutique
52 Adelaide Street
Winnipeg, MB
(204) 975-2880
fivetwoboutique.com

Hempyrean
213–1 Forks Market Road
Winnipeg, MB
(204) 947-5223

Sew Dandee
105 Osborne Street
Winnipeg, MB
(204) 453-5110
sewdandee.blogspot.com

NEW BRUNSWICK

Earth Threadz
Moncton Market Complex
120 Westmorland Street
Moncton, NB
(506) 204-7293
earththreadz.ca

NEWFOUNDLAND

Johnny Ruth Integrity In Style
181 Water Street
St. John's, NL
(709) 722-7477
johnnyruth.com

Model Citizens
183b Duckworth Street
St. John's, NL
(709) 722-2777
modelcitizens.ca

Twisted Sisters Boutik
175 Water Street
St. John's, NL
(709) 722-6004
twistedsistersboutik.blogspot.com

NOVA SCOTIA

Flow Lifestyle Boutique
127 Victoria Street
Amherst, NS
(902) 660-3569
flowboutique.ca

Aigle
5507 Spring Garden Road
Halifax, NS
(902) 406-7495
aigle.ca

Love, Me Boutique
1539 Birmingham Street
Halifax, NS
(902) 444-3668
lovemeboutique.ca

P'lovers
Park Lane Mall
5657 Spring Garden Road
Halifax, NS
(902) 422-6060
plovers.net

Luvly in Lunenburg
230 Lincoln Street
Lunenburg, NS
(902) 640-4100
luvly.ca

P'Lovers
The Old Station
3 Edgewater Street
Mahone Bay, NS
(902) 624-1421
plovers.net

ONTARIO

Awear Eco Boutique
161 Hurontario Street
Collingwood, ON
(705) 293-1008
awearecoboutique.com

Ecomystic
136 James Street South
Hamilton, ON
(289) 389-4788
ecomystic.ca

The Green Goose
25 Main Street West, Unit 2
Kingsville, ON
(519) 733-2713
greengoosekingsville.com

Noinkees
168b Broadway
Orangeville, ON
(519) 942-4456
noinkees.com

Kania
145 York Street
Ottawa, ON
(613) 695-4171
kania.ca

Footprints Eco-Store
46 Carden Street
Guelph, ON
(519) 763-3337
footprintsecostore.ca

**P'lovers The
Environmental Store**
123 Princess St
(613) 544-1230
Kingston, ON
ploverskingston.ca

The Earth Collection
114B Queen St.
Niagara-on-the-Lake, ON
(905) 468-3987
theearthcollection.com

Green Tree Eco Fashion
358 Richmond Road
Ottawa, ON
(613) 695-8733
greentreeecofashion.ca

**P'Lovers Environmental
Store**
180 Queen Street
Port Perry, ON
(905) 982-0660
planetlovers.com

Heartsong World Boutique
18 Renfrew Avenue West
Renfrew, ON
(613) 433-7346
heartsongyogapilates.ca

Anami Organic Luxuries
87 Avenue Road
Toronto, ON
(647) 347-8263
anamiorganicluxuries.com

Earth Collection
143–207 Queen's Quay
Toronto, ON
(416) 363-8154
theearthcollection.com

**Fashion Takes Action
Showroom**
55 Mill Street, Building 74, studio 202
Toronto, ON
fashiontakesaction.com

Grassroots
408 Bloor Street West
Toronto, ON
(416) 944-1993
grassrootsstore.com

P'lovers
56 Ontario Street
Stratford, ON
(519) 271-3883
plovers.ca

Chartreuse Style
1692 Queen Street West
Toronto, ON
(416) 901-2800
chartreusestyle.com

Ecoexistence
766 St. Clair Avenue West
Toronto, ON
(416) 652-0808
ecoexistence.ca

**Freedom Clothing
Collective**
939 Bloor Street West
Toronto, ON
(416) 530-9946
freedomclothingcollective.com

Grassroots
372 Danforth Avenue
Toronto, ON
(416) 466-2841
grassrootsstore.com

Mariclaro
457 Roncesvalles Ave.
Toronto, ON,
(416) 533-9161
mariclaro.ca

Nathalie-Roze
1015 Queen Street East
Toronto, ON
(416) 792-1699
nathalie-roze.com

Preloved
881 Queen Street West
Toronto, ON
(416) 504-8704
preloved.ca

Shop Eco
624 Chilver Road
Windsor, ON
(519) 973-8400
shopeco.ca

Thieves
1156 Queen Street West
Toronto, ON
(647) 435-4880
thieves.ca

PRINCE EDWARD ISLAND
Fashion & Earth
(888) 868-5567
fashionandearth.com (online only)

QUEBEC
Atelier boutique Émilie
Desmeules
201, rue St-Louis Est
Alma, QC
(418) 720-0335
emiliedesmeules.com

Arthena-art & écodesign
205, chemin Old Chelsea
Chelsea, QC
(819) 827-8885
arthena.ca

Boutique Le Local
140, rue Eddy
Gatineau, QC
(819) 205-1905
boutiquelelocal.com

Aigle
2070, rue de la Montagne
Montreal, QC
(514) 903-8836
aigle.ca

Belle et Rebelle
6321, rue St-Hubert
Montreal, QC
(514) 315-4903
belleetrebelle.ca

Boutique Cokluch
410a, rue Villeray
Montreal, QC
(514) 273-5700
cokluch.com

Folle Guenille
4236, rue Ste-Catherine Est
Montreal, QC
(514) 845-0012
folleguenille.com

Eco-Boutique Un
Monde à Vie
1075, montée Masson (125 Nord)
Mascouche, QC
(450) 474-5078
mondeavie.ca

Atelier B
5758, boulevard Saint-Laurent
Montreal, QC
(514) 769-6094
atelier-b.ca

Boutique 4 éléments
4326, rue St-Denis
Montreal, QC
(514) 564-0410
boutique4elements.wordpress.com

Boutique Ethik BGC
6050, rue St-Hubert
Montreal, QC
(514) 656-6929
ethik-bgc.ca

La Gaillarde Boutique
Mode Écologique
4019, rue Notre-Dame Ouest
Montreal, QC
(514) 989-5134
lagaillarde.ca

Modeco
1827, avenue Mont-Royal Est
Montreal, QC
(514) 527-3699
modeco.ca

Rien à Cacher
4141, rue St-Denis
Montreal, QC
(514) 907-6187
rienacacher.com

Code Vert
586B, rue Saint-Jean
Quebec, QC
(418) 524-4004
codevert.ca

Boutique Equinoxe
2309, de l'Église
Val-David, QC
(819) 322-3121
boutikequinoxe.com

SASKATCHEWAN

Seed Sustainable Style
3100 13th Avenue
Regina, SK
(306) 924-5426
seedsustainablestyle.com

The Better Good
640 Broadway Avenue
Saskatoon, SK
(306) 242-4663
thebettergood.com

YUKON

Climate Clothing
124–1116 1st Avenue
Whitehorse, YT
(867) 633-3177
climateclothing.ca

DIRECTORY OF GREEN BABY/KIDS' SHOPS

Green baby websites and shops seem to be multiplying like embryos at a fertility clinic. Here's a listing of bricks-and-mortar shops that offer up a large selection of green baby/kids' goods (they often have great online boutiques too) as well as some of the many online-only green kids' stores from coast to coast. If you know of any retail storefronts not mentioned here, let us know!

ONLINE STORES

These green baby/kids' stores offer up everything from diapers to toys,
personal care products to food supplies, and more. To make it easier
for you to order locally, I've listed the provincial base for each.

rockprettybaby.ca (AB)

trovekids.com (AB)

bumblebeebaby.ca (AB)

naturalurbanmamas.com (AB)

diapersupply.ca (AB)

bellybuttonbaby.ca (AB)

abbysprouts.com (BC)

raspberrykids.com (BC)

organicallyhatched.com (BC)

lavishandlime.com (BC)

mylittlegreenshop.com (BC)

thegreensheep.ca (BC)

newandgreen.com (BC)

cozybums.ca (BC)

bootyboutiqueclothdiapers.com (BC)

babybellhop.com (BC)

babygreensprout.com (MB)

littlelamb.com (MB)

clothdiapermom.com (MB)

tinytreehuggerdiapers.com (MB)

enchanted-forest.ca (NS)

fluffybottombabies.ca (NS)

eastcoastdiapers.com (NS)

bynature.ca (ON)

greencollection.ca (ON)

kaikids.com (ON)

ecobebeboutique.com (ON)

theclothdiapershop.com (ON)

ottawaclothdiapers.com (ON)

sogreenbaby.com **(ON)**

peatoes.com **(QC)**

enfantstylediapers.com **(QC)**

mybabybumblebee.com **(QC)**

bebekolo.com **(QC)**

fuzzibunzquebec.ca **(QC)**

babyluvboutique.com **(SK)**

teenytinytotshop.com **(SK)**

sweetlildimplesbabyshop.com **(SK)**

REGIONAL STORES
ALBERTA

Babes in Arms
130–6707 Elbow Drive SW
Calgary, AB
(403) 835-4614
babesinarms.ca

Nature Babies
Calgary Farmers Market
Calgary, AB
naturebabies.ca

Carbon Environmental Boutique
10184 104 Street
Edmonton, AB
(780) 498-1900
www.carbonboutique.com

Edamame Kids
1911 34 Avenue SW
Calgary, AB
(403) 453-0454
edamamekids.ca

Riva's The Eco Store
1237 9th Avenue SE
Calgary, AB
(403) 452-1001
rivasecostore.com

Earth's General Store
9605 82nd Avenue
Edmonton, AB
(780) 439-8725
www.egs.ca

BRITISH COLOMBIA

Bumbletree
1117 Baker Street
Cranbrook, BC
(250) 489-4499
bumbletree.ca

Huckleberry Baby Shop
12A–4376 Boban Drive
Nanaimo, BC
(250) 585-5552
huckleberrybabyshop.com

Dandelion Kids
Suter Brook Village
1–101 Morrissey Road
Port Moody, BC
(604) 949-1862
dandelionkids.ca

Crocodile Baby
2156 West 4th Avenue
Vancouver, BC
(604) 742-2762
crocodilebaby.com

Hip Baby
2110 West 4th Avenue
Vancouver, BC
(604) 736-8020
hipbaby.ca

Lizzie Bits Baby Co.
Kampoops, BC
204–450 Lansdowne Street
(250) 374-8706
lizziebaby.ca

Back to Nature Baby
3329 Henry Street
Port Moody, BC
(778) 840-3344
backtonaturebabystore.com

Crocodile Baby
Shops at Morgan Crossing
108–15775 Croydon Drive
South Surrey, BC
(604) 542-8860
crocodilebaby.com

Dandelion Kids
1206 Commercial Drive
Vancouver, BC
(604) 676-1862
dandelionkids.ca

Jack and Lola
135 West 1st Street
North Vancouver, BC
(778) 340-5225
jackandlola.ca

Pebble
2675 Arbutus Street
Vancouver, BC
(604) 568-6923
pebblebaby.com

Abbey Sprouts
3011 Gosworth Road
Victoria, BC
(250) 294-8978
abbeysprouts.com

The Good Planet Company
764 Fort Street
Victoria, BC
(250) 590-3500
goodplanet.com

Hip Baby
104A–560 Johnson Street
Victoria, BC
(250) 385-8020
hipbaby.com

MANITOBA

AMP Diaper Store
1660 St. James Street
Winnipeg, MB
(204) 779-2683
ampdiaperstore.com

The Baby Bin Boutique
1444 Corydon Avenue
Winnipeg, MB
(204) 487-4687
babybin.ca

NEWFOUNDLAND

Bellies & Bundles
Maternity & Baby
Coaker's Meadow Plaza
286 Torbay Road
St. John's, NL
(709) 237-6262
belliesandbundles.ca

NOVA SCOTIA

Fiddleheads Kids Shop
300 Prince Albert Road
Dartmouth, NS
(902) 405-8801
gofiddleheads.com

Fluffy Bottoms
629 Bedford Highway
Halifax, NS
(902) 818-2223
fluffybottombabies.ca

Nurtured
2571 Robie Street
Halifax, NS
(902) 405-4367
nurtured.ca

P'lovers
3 Edgewater Road
Mahone Bay, NS
(902) 624-1421
www.plovers.net

P'lovers
5657 Spring Garden Road
Halifax, NS
(902) 422-6060
www.plovers.net

ONTARIO

Mixed Greens
3 Francis Street West
Fenelon Falls, ON
(705) 887-3326
mixedgreens.ca

Sustain
8 Crescent Road
Huntsville, ON
(705) 787-0326
sustainecostore.com

Go Green Baby
293 Division Street
Kingston, ON
(613) 344-0390
go-greenbaby.ca

Citizen Kid
188 Locke Street South
Hamilton, ON
(905) 963-1265
citizenkid.ca

Belly Laughs
Kanata Centrum Plaza
300 Earl Grey Drive
Kanata, ON
(613) 963-0711
bellylaughs.ca

Cheeky Monkey
590 Oxford Street East
London, ON
(519) 645-6706
cheekymonkey.ca

Ecoinhabit
26–121 Old Highway
Meaford, ON
(888) 538-0777
ecoinhabit.com

3 Little Monkeys
1150 Bank Street
Ottawa, ON
(613) 733-3993
3littlemonkeysottawa.com

Extraordinary Baby
1131 Wellington Street West
Ottawa, ON
(613) 321-7249
extraordinarybabyshoppe.com

Little Lamb
264 Third Avenue
Timmins, ON
(705) 264-2225
littlelamb.ca

Baby on the Hip
786 College Street
Toronto, ON
(647) 427-1484
babyonthehip.ca

Parenting by Nature
5 Ontario Street
Orillia, ON
(705) 325-0506
bynature.ca

Arbour Environmental
Shoppe
800 Bank Street
Ottawa, ON
(613) 567-3168
arbourshop.com

P'lovers
56 Ontario Street
Stratford, ON
(519) 271-3883
plovers.ca

Baby on the Hip
969 Queen Street East
Toronto, ON
(416) 465-4141
babyonthehip.ca

EcoExistence
766 St. Clair Avenue West
Toronto, ON
(416) 652-0808
ecoexistence.ca

Grassroots
372 Danforth Avenue
Toronto, ON
(416) 466-2841
grassrootsstore.com

Grassroots
408 Bloor Street West
Toronto, ON
(416) 944-1993
grassrootsstore.com

Hello Sunshine
5 High Park Avenue, Suite 1
Toronto, ON
(416) 763-4799
hello-sunshine.com

Little Peeps
768 Queen Street East
Toronto, ON
(416) 406-5437
littlepeeps.ca

Extraordinary Baby
24–26 Regina Street North
Waterloo, ON
(519) 342-0867
extraordinarybabyshoppe.com

**Sweetheart Diapers &
More**
4782 Wyandotte Street East
Windsor, ON
(519) 800-3963
sweetheartdiapers.com

QUEBEC

Boutique Bummis
4302, boulevard St-Laurent
Montreal, QC
(514) 289-9415
boutiquebummis.com

Calins et Popotin
2160A, rue Beaubien Est
Montreal, QC
(514) 670-3131
calinsetpopotin.com

La Loba
6252, Plaza St-Hubert
Montreal, QC
(514) 509-2818
laloba.ca

Le Baby Shop
Plaza Pointe-Claire
245B, boulevard St-Jean
Pointe-Claire, QC
lebabyshop.com

Le Nid de la Cigogne
268, rue Saint-Viateur
Montreal, QC
(514) 276-6262
leniddelacigogne.ca

Le Baby Shop
Club Piscine Complex
493 Harwood Blvd., #130
Vaudreuil-Dorion, QC
(450) 319-6008
lebabyshop.com

SASKATCHEWAN

Groovy Mama
3206 13th Avenue
Regina, SK
(306) 347-2229
groovymama.net

A Soft Landing
112–120 Sonnenschein Way
Saskatoon, SK
(306) 229-0934
asoftlandingsask.blogspot.com

GLOSSARY

1,4-Dioxane: A petroleum-derived contaminant considered a probable human carcinogen by the U.S. Environmental Protection Agency (EPA), and a definite animal carcinogen. It's a by-product of chemical processing called ethoxylation that's used to soften certain ingredients found in many sudsy products, including shampoo and bubble bath. Potentially contaminated chemicals include polyethylene, polyethylene glycol (PEG), polyoxyethylene, polyethoxyethylene and polyoxynolethylene.

adaptogen: Term used by herbalists and naturopaths to refer to a plant/herb that's thought to increase the body's resistance to stress.

bioaccumulation: The buildup of chemicals in the tissues of a living thing, whether human, wildlife or plant. (Chemicals enter our bodies through the food we eat, the air we breathe and the water we drink.) Bioaccumulation explains why larger, older fish have higher levels of mercury, for instance, than smaller, younger ones.

bioavailability: The degree to which a nutrient, supplement or drug is actually absorbed by and active in the body.

biocompatible: Something that can be implanted in the body without causing harm. Often used in the context of medical devices, dental materials and prostheses.

biodegradable: The insinuation is that a product called biodegradable will fully break down and return to nature (hopefully in the form of CO_2 and H_2O), but the label isn't policed. Be your own sheriff. Look for certification symbols and details about biodegradability testing standards, and do your own research. Under what conditions does the product degrade (only in full sun or also in dark, airless landfill piles)? And just how long does it take to return to nature?

441

biodynamic: Certification standards for this label are similar to those for "organic" but go one step further by requiring farmers to be in sync with the rhythms of nature and the cosmos and to use specially prepared herbs and minerals in compost and field sprays. Biodynamic farming embraces a philosophy focused on healing the earth. Certifiers include Demeter.

bisphenol A (BPA): See Plastics Guide, page 418.

cadmium: A metallic element found in far too much children's jewellery, especially since it's considered a probable human carcinogen.

carbon footprint: Nothing to do with your foot size. This has to do with the total greenhouse gas emissions directly and indirectly attributable to a product you buy, your house, your car, your vacation, you name it.

carbon neutral: Some companies and products (including condoms) are marketed as "carbon neutral," which means they're supporting enough greenhouse gas–abating projects that they can claim to have a carbon footprint of zero.

carbon offset: Companies can mitigate the greenhouse gases they produce in their activities by supporting a greenhouse gas–saving project (such as a wind farm or a tree farm).

carcinogen: Anything that may cause cancer.

chemical sensitivities (a.k.a. multiple chemical sensitivities): A chronic syndrome caused by a person's intolerance to chemicals. Even a low dose of an offending chemical can stimulate a negative reaction. Symptoms vary but can include headaches, a runny nose, aching joints, confusion, fatigue and sore throat.

Symptoms generally improve or disappear when the chemicals are removed.

chlorinated Tris: A carcinogenic fire retardant banned from children's PJs 30 years ago but still used on furniture foam. Deemed a health hazard by the World Health Organization, the National Cancer Institute and the National Research Council.

closed-cell: Used in reference to plastics found in products such as yoga mats and Croc shoes, as in "100% closed-cell PVC mat." The term may imply that the product doesn't off-gas, but all it really means is that its plastic cells are sealed within their own little bubble, making the object highly water resistant.

coal tar dyes: Dyes derived from carcinogenic coal tar and petroleum. May be contaminated with heavy metals. Several coal tar dyes are on Health Canada's Hotlist (see page 5).

Competition Bureau: The Competition Bureau is an independent Canadian law enforcement agency set up by the government of Canada. It investigates consumer complaints about false advertising and unfair pricing.

contraindication: Condition/factor that makes taking a supplement or drug inadvisable (e.g., pre-existing heart condition, pregnancy).

Cradle to Cradle: See Resources: Label Decoder, page 411.

DEHP: See phthalates, page 453.

dioxins (a.k.a. furans): Carcinogenic, endocrine-disrupting neurotoxins. There are lots of different types of dioxins, but they all contain chlorine, and they're all bad. The largest source of dioxins in Canada is the burning of municipal and medical waste (mainly from burning PVC products). Dioxins build up in animal tissues, so the main way humans ingest dioxins is by eating meat, milk products and fish. The pulp and paper processing biz was historically also a big source of dioxins (they were also found in chlorine-bleached tampons and diapers), but the industry says it has dramatically reduced its dioxin pollution.

EcoLogo: See Resources: Label Decoder, page 412.

EMF (electromagnetic field): Electric and magnetic fields are invisible lines of energy created by the production and transmission of electricity. Electric fields are kick-started whenever an electronic object is plugged into a socket (even if it's not turned on). Magnetic fields are created when that device is flicked on. The closer you are to the source, the stronger the EMFs. EMFs are given off by everything from household wiring and lighting to anything plugged into a wall. In those with electro-hypersensitivity (EHS), EMFs can trigger nausea, headaches, chronic fatigue, chronic pain, tinnitus, rashes and more. Health Canada says, "There is no conclusive evidence of any harm caused by exposures at levels normally found in Canadian living and working environments." Sweden, with an estimated 250,000 EHS sufferers, leads the pack by recognizing EHS as a full-on disability.

endocrine disruptors: Chemicals that interfere with the endocrine system, which secretes development-guiding and reproductive hormones. See also hormone disruptors, page 447.

Environment Canada: The federal government department in charge of conserving natural resources, protecting water resources, predicting the weather and co-ordinating environmental policies and programs.

Environmental Working Group (EWG): Founded in 1993, this non-profit D.C.-based group is responsible for extensive research and advocacy on toxic chemicals in consumer products and farming as they relate to health, food and water pollution, and more. Lately, they're best known for their extensive product testing and research. ewg.org

EPA (Environmental Protection Agency): The American equivalent of Environment Canada. The EPA develops and enforces environmental regulations, gives grants to state and non-profit enviro programs, researches environmental issues and educates the public on green subjects.

estrogen: Hormone naturally produced by the ovaries, responsible for menstruation, breast development and other secondary sex characteristics. About 80% of breast cancers are hormone sensitive and feed off estrogens to grow. Birth control pills are by and large made with synthetic estrogen.

estrogenic: Something that has the properties of estrogen.

estrogen-mimicking: Describes a chemical or ingredient that mimics the female hormone estrogen. Estrogen mimickers can interfere with the normal metabolism of estrogen in the body. They have been known to spawn intersex fish. In addition, they've been linked to decreased sperm counts in men and elevated endometriosis and breast cancer rates in women.

ethoxylation: Process by which ingredients are made gentler. Commonly creates carcinogenic contaminant 1,4-Dioxane. Ethoxylated ingredients can be purified (stripped) to remove the contaminant.

Forest Stewardship Council: See Resources: Label Decoder, page 412.

formaldehyde: Commonly found in pressed woods (particleboard and medium-density fibreboard), permanent press fabric (clothing and curtains) and numerous body care preservatives. Formaldehyde may cause cancer in humans (it's classified as a known human carcinogen by the International Agency for Research on Cancer and as of 2011 by the U.S. EPA), as well as wheezing, fatigue, rashes, and eye, nose and throat irritation. Some people are especially sensitive to it. It's also a major component of smog.

Green Seal: See Resources: Label Decoder, page 413.

halogenated flame retardants: Family of flame retardants widely used in electronics; includes brominated/chlorinated/fluorinated flame retardants. Considered widespread environmental contaminants. Banned from plastics in Europe as of 2006.

HCFC: When ozone-depleting CFCs were phased out in the mid-1990s, HCFCs (hydrochlorofluorocarbons) were brought in as their greener alternative. We soon realized that HCFCs are also ozone-depleting substances, as well as greenhouse gases. HCFCs were banned from consumer aerosol products (such as hairspray, mousse, deodorant) in 1994, but they were still allowed in refrigerants used by the air conditioner and fridge sector (now being phased out).

HFC: Can be used as a greener alternative to HCFCs and CFCs in consumer aerosol products like, say, hairspray, since it doesn't affect the ozone layer, but it's still an extremely potent greenhouse gas. Since the '90s, Greenpeace International has been trying to convince companies to avoid HFCs and use natural gases instead.

high-density polyethylene (HDPE): See Resources: Plastics Guide, page 419.

homeopathy/homeopathic: A system of alternative medicine developed in Germany 200 years ago. It basically works on the principle that like cures like and that highly diluted doses of what is making a person unwell can cure a condition. In homeopathy's case, the more diluted the medicine, the stronger it's considered and the process of making the homeopathic remedy is said to impart it with an energetic memory. It has prompted criticism that homeopathic remedies are "sugar pills." Health Canada's Natural Health Products Regulation requires that all homeopathic medicines be licensed.

hormone disruptors: Chemicals that mimic or block hormones, potentially throwing off normal body functions and triggering behavioural, reproductive and developmental problems. See also endocrine disruptors, page 445.

integrative medicine: The combination of conventional medicine with alternative medicine.

integrative practitioner: A health care professional dedicated to integrative medicine.

leaching: The process by which a chemical or toxin is transferred from one surface to another.

lead: A highly toxic metal. This neurotoxin has been found to trigger changes in a child's mental and physical behaviour (lowering IQ performance, reducing hand-eye co-ordination and slowing fine motor function), even at low levels. High lead exposure can cause lead poisoning and neurological disorders.

low-density polyethylene (LDPE): See Resources: Plastics Guide, page 419.

mercury: The shiny neurotoxin found in old thermometers, and the only metal that's liquid at room temperature. Mercury is used in dental fillings and batteries and as a preservative in some vaccines. It's also commonly found in fish and is a contaminant in fish oils, though most fish oils are purified to reduce mercury levels. How do fish get so full of mercury to begin with? Emissions from coal plants and other factories send mercury up into the air, where it can travel great distances on wind currents and come down with rain or snow over bodies of water. It then collects in the bodies of aquatic animals and moves up the food chain. See also bioaccumulation, page 441. Developing fetuses are most at risk and can develop severe disabilities from exposure.

multiple chemical sensitivities: See chemical sensitivities, page 442.

nanotechnology: Nanotechnology essentially creates and manipulates molecules or atoms that are one-billionth of a metre in size (that's 100,000 times narrower than a human hair follicle). Industry swears that nano-mania is revolutionizing everything from makeup (see Mineral Makeup, page 100, and Sunscreens, page 44) to stain-repellent clothes (see Wrinkle- and Stain-Resistant Finishes, page 305), but critics say it's the next GMO (genetically modified organism) and cautionary lessons should be learned from our experience with genetically engineered seeds. Health Canada says it's evaluating the potential risks and benefits of nanotechnology, and Environment Canada says new nanotech must undergo a risk assessment of its potential effects on the environment and human health.

Natural Resources Defence Council: One of America's most powerful environmental orgs. nrdc.org

neurotoxin: A toxin that affects the central nervous system, harming neural tissue.

nickel-metal hydride (NiMH): A type of rechargeable battery similar to old-school nickel cadmium rechargeable batteries (including those found in toothbrushes and sex toys), but made with much less toxic materials. These batteries don't hold a charge as long and they release their charge even when not in use more readily than nickel cadmium, but that's the price you pay for reducing toxins in the environment.

octinoxate (octyl methoxycinnamate): A UVB-absorbing sunscreen chemical. There's strong evidence that it's an endocrine disruptor and has weak estrogenic properties.

Oeko-Tex: See Resources: Label Decoder, page 415.

off-gassing: Not a bodily function, but the release of chemicals such as phthalates from vinyl shoes/purses/clothing and volatile organic compounds (VOCs) into the air.

Organic Consumers Association: This grassroots public interest org aggressively battles to maintain and elevate the integrity of organics. They have ongoing campaigns about phony organic body care, supplements, food safety, genetic engineering, fair-trade issues and much more. organicconsumers.org

oxybenzone: Chemical found in 60% of sunscreens. It's a suspected hormone disruptor readily absorbed by the skin. No wonder the U.S. Centers for Disease Control have found it in 97% of Americans. Linked to low birth weight babies and allergic reactions. Scientists at University of California, Riverside reported that two-thirds of the male turbot and sole gathered near a sewage pipe a few kilometres off Huntington Beach had ovaries growing. The prime suspect estrogenic chem they found in the gender-bending fish was, you guessed it, oxybenzone. Luckily, from 2008 to 2009, 19% fewer sunscreens contained oxybenzone.

parabens: All types of parabens (methyl-, ethyl-, etc.) have been found to be estrogenic — meaning they mimic female hormones. They have been found in breast tumour samples but haven't been conclusively linked to cancer. Butyl and propyl parabens were banned by Denmark from children's personal care products.

paraffin: A petroleum by-product. Canada produces 32,700 barrels of kerosene, a.k.a. paraffin, each day. In liquid form, you'll know it from your body care products as mineral oil. It also makes micro-crystalline waxes.

PBDEs: A family of flame retardants used for decades in a broad range of consumer goods. Skyrocketing levels of these have been found in everything from Arctic animals, lake trout, whales and water birds to human breast milk. PentaBDE and octaBDE production in North America ceased at the end of 2004, but they might still be found in imported products. The government pissed off a lot of onlookers when it continued to allow neurotoxic decaBDEs in electronics and upholstery, but Canada has since arranged for a voluntary phase-out by 2013.

PCB (polychlorinated biphenyl): An extremely persistent environmental contaminant. This industrial chemical was introduced in 1929 and used in the making of electronic equipment. Canada banned the substance in 1977, but it's still turning up in human tissue and farmed salmon.

permethrin: A suspected hormone disruptor and possible carcinogen. Permethrin is toxic to fish and tadpoles and can cause all sorts of physical reactions in humans, from nausea to asthma attacks.

persistent: Referring to a chemical that does not readily biodegrade but instead accumulates in the environment and living tissues. See also bioaccumulation, page 441.

petrochemical: Any chemical derived from petroleum, coal or natural gas. According to the government of Alberta, petrochemicals make up 10% of all the products we buy and use each and every day, from clothing, shoes, health and personal care products, cleaning products and paint to the foods we eat (think food additives and packaging). All of the ecological problems that arise from fossil fuel excavation, processing and shipping are also associated with its offshoots, plus the extra pollution created by refining and manufacturing each chemical.

PFCs (perfluorinated chemicals/compounds, a.k.a. perfluorochemicals): A family of chemical substances composed of fluorine and carbon, responsible for making raincoats waterproof and clothing stain resistant. PFCs have been found to be extremely persistent in the environment around the globe, and many have been tied to serious health problems. Brand name incarnations of PFCs include Teflon, Gore-Tex, Stainmaster and Scotchgard. For a shopper's guide to what products contain PFCs and detailed reports on the topic, check out ewg.org.

PFOA (perfluorooctanoic acid): An ingredient used to make Teflon (a.k.a. PTFE) but also used in manufacturing breathable, all-weather clothing as well as personal care products including certain dental flosses, eyeshadows and more (avoid anything with ingredients containing "fluoro-" and "perfluoro-"). It does not break down in the wild (even DDT breaks down eventually) and has reportedly accumulated in 95% of Americans' tissues and in high levels in wildlife, including polar bears. Eight major manufacturers have committed to eliminate PFOA altogether by 2015, but the pact is totally voluntary and there are no repercussions if they don't meet the target. Plus, not a single company from China is participating. PFOA is part of a slippery and persistent class of chemicals called PFCs (perfluorinated chemicals).

PFOS (perfluorooctanesulphonate): A chemical commonly found on older stain-repellent carpets, furniture and clothing. PFOS was the basis of Scotchgard's and Stainmaster's original formulation until 3M stopped production of the chemical in 2002 after the EPA threatened it with regulatory action. Studies found that PFOS was turning up everywhere in the environment, and that it killed some rat pups even though it was their mothers that had been exposed while the pups were in the womb, not the pups themselves. PFOS use has been phased out in Canada. PFOS is part of the persistent PFC (perfluorinated chemicals) family.

Pharmaceuticals and Personal Care Products as Pollutants (PPCPs): Any personal care product or drug used by individuals or agriculture, from veterinary antibiotics to ladies' perfume. PPCPs are known environmental contaminants that are turning up in rivers, lakes, groundwater, and downstream from sewage treatment plants.

phenols: A broad class of chemical compounds that includes hormone-disrupting bisphenol A and the estradiol in birth control pills. Phenols are used in slime-fighting chemicals, disinfectants, mouthwashes, lozenges and more. According to the U.S. Agency for Toxic Substances and Disease Registry, short-term exposure to phenol in the air can cause respiratory irritation, headaches and burning eyes. High skin exposure can cause skin burns, liver damage and worse. Some phenols are also naturally occurring in plants.

phthalates: Chemicals often added to PVC plastic as softeners, found in everything from kids' toys to sex toys, as well as all sorts of personal care products and perfumes (though they're not listed on labels). The industry insists they're safe, but Canada has finally restricted six phthalates from children's toys and some child care items, but not from personal care products. One type of phthalate in particular, DEHP, has been found to cause birth defects in lab animals and is classified as a probable human carcinogen. Harvard researchers found that another, DEP, can cause DNA damage in the sperm of adult men. Phthalates are also found in water, household dust, breast milk and wildlife—clearly showing that they migrate from their source.

Denmark has announced it is banning four phthalates from all products in direct contact with consumers.

polycarbonate: See Resources: Plastics Guide, page 420.

polyethylene: Without getting into a lot of scientific mumbo-jumbo, polyethylene is a polymer that contains carbon and hydrogen. It forms the basis of PET (see polyethylene terephthalate, below), HDPE (see high-density polyethylene, page 419) and LDPE (see low-density polyethylene, page 419).

polyethylene terephthalate (PET): See Resources: Plastics Guide, page 418.

polypropylene (PP): See Resources: Plastics Guide, page 420.

polystyrene (PS): See Resources: Plastics Guide, page 420.

polyvinyl chloride (PVC): See PVC, page 455.

proprietary: Something that's privately owned and operated. Proprietary information is often a reference to trade secrets, as in: "We own the formula, so we don't have to share the ingredients list with you people."

PTFE: The trade name for PTFE, owned by DuPont, is Teflon. You'll find it in all kinds of body-related products, from cosmetics (check your powder, eyeshadow, lotion, mascara, shaving gel) to your Gore-Tex jacket (basically PTFE with micropores). Gore-Tex swears its gear is so stable it'll never break down, but you wouldn't want to, say, accidentally throw your rain gear in a fire. PTFE-coated heat lamps used to warm ducklings were found to kill 23.3% (over 400 chicks) in five days. Generally considered a PFC (perfluorinated chemical), though a chemist might argue the point and say it's in the fluoroplastic family.

PVC (polyvinyl chloride, a.k.a. vinyl): See Plastics Guide, page 419.

Scientific Certification System (SCS): Founded in 1984 as a third-party certification system based in California, SCS provides environmental, sustainability and food-quality certification, auditing, testing and standards development.

SFI (Sustainable Forestry Initiative): See Resources: Label Decoder, page 416.

sodium laureth sulphate (a.k.a. sodium laurel ether sulphate, or SLES): Similar to sodium lauryl sulphate (see below), but somewhat gentler. Its processing creates harmful 1,4-Dioxanes, by-products found in many products.

sodium lauryl sulphate (SLS): A sudsing surfactant found in shampoos, soaps and toothpaste, and a known skin and eye irritant that may aggravate dandruff and mouth ulcers. Rumours of it being a carcinogen are considered urban myths. Health food products often contain SLS made from coconut oil.

surfactant: A type of chemical found in shampoos and body washes. Surfactants make these products lather, spread and penetrate well. Hundreds of surfactants are in existence, many petroleum based. Many surfactants biodegrade in sewage treatment plants, but some, like nonylphenol ethoxylates (NPEs), are of environmental concern because they don't really biodegrade, are toxic to algae and aquatic life, and have been associated with hormone-disrupting effects.

sustainable: If it's sustainable, you can keep doing it again and again without messing up the planet for future generations. Simple as that.

sweatshop: A factory where workers put in long hours at abusively low wages, often under oppressive conditions. Avoid these like the plague by supporting fair trade–certified products.

Teflon: See PTFE, page 454, and PFOA, page 452.

toluene: A common solvent used in paints, glues, disinfectants and rubber, as well as in tanning leather and manufacturing polyurethane foam (synthetic leathers). Inhaling toluene regularly over time can lead to brain and kidney damage. Even low doses can cause confusion, as well as memory, hearing and vision loss. Pregnant women should minimize exposure. Toluene is a petroleum by-product.

tonifying: Term used by herbalists and traditional Chinese medicine referring to something that boosts your ch'i, or vital life force energy.

triclocarbon: A chemical disinfectant found in some antibacterial soaps, though it's less common than triclosan. Triclocarbon is persistent and has been known to survive the sewage treatment process and turn up in lakes, rivers and streams.

triclosan: The active ingredient in many antibacterial soaps, deodorants and toothpastes. Beyond accumulating in fatty tissues (it's been found in fish and in breast milk), it has made its way into lakes, rivers and streams (the U.S. Geological Survey found triclosan to be one of the top 10 stream contaminants). Researchers at the University of Minnesota found that when these chemicals are exposed to sunlight in water, they create a mild dioxin (a carcinogenic hormone disruptor that accumulates in the food chain, even at low levels). And when you throw chlorinated water into the mix, it could turn into a much nastier dioxin. Research from the University of Victoria says it also acts as a harmful endocrine disruptor in aquatic life, particularly frogs. As well, research from Tufts University found that *E. coli* that survived being treated with triclosan became resistant to 7 of 12 antibiotics.

U.S. EPA: See EPA, page 446.

vinyl: See PVC, page 419.

volatile organic compounds (VOCs): Found in all sorts of personal care products, such as nail polish/fragrance/aerosols, as well as being released by certain clothing finishes. Don't be fooled by the word "organic" in the name — VOCs aren't good for us. They're carbon-containing gases and vapours that evaporate readily into the air, contributing to air pollution. VOCs can even off-gas from non-liquid sources that contain formaldehyde, such as office furniture, leading to serious indoor air pollution. Exposure can cause dizziness, headache and nausea. Some VOCs are more toxic than others and are tied to cancer and kidney and liver damage. Some react with nitrogen oxide to form smog-inducing compounds.

wildcrafted: Term used for herbal products sourced from the wild. The term may seem to imply that herbs were carefully collected, suggesting sustainability, but the fact that a product was wildcrafted does not guarantee it isn't threatened or at risk.

ACKNOWLEDGEMENTS

Growing up in a household of body 'n' soul–conscious health enthusiasts, it was inevitable—*Ecoholic Body* was going to be a family affair. Especially my chapters on health. How could they not be? I've been surrounded by siblings in the field, each with their own complementary insights on healing the body: Nick, the holistic nutritionist/chartered herbalist (whose article on Travel Health is featured on pages 186–87); Lisa, the family doctor with a focus on orthomolecular medicine; and Mark, the supplements advisor–turned–health store educator.

Then, a short while before the first draft of this very book was originally due, discussions of health and failing bodies were no longer musings tied to the page. Within the span of six months, my father had a severe, disabling stroke and my brother Nick passed away. *Ecoholic Body* was indefinitely postponed as I took time to heal with my family.

To be honest, the only thing that motivated me to go back to writing after nearly a year off was knowing how *Ecoholic Body* was really an ode to my family and their love, and to my big brother in particular. Nick was my family's original environmentalist, writer and health guru. He taught us all how to tune in to our bodies and how to heal any maladies with nature's gifts. To my mind, his web of environmental sensitivities also transformed him into the proverbial canary in the coal mine, signalling that the world around us needs to change. His guiding light showed me and my family the way forward in so many ways and continues to. I hope, in turn, his influence is passed on to you, through the pages of this book.

Of course, there are so many others whose love made this book possible. First and foremost, my true love, my rock, my sunshine in the storm, Brad. My dad, for being such a loving father, even through all his recent challenges, and for long ago teaching me that love is all you need. My mom, for being such a graceful pillar of strength and daily support. Mark, who patiently spent days on end hashing out ideas with me and talking shop on supplements. And of course Lisa, who shared her medical expertise via countless long-distance phone hours and who combed through my health chapters, making corrections. Then there's my extended tribe of soul brothers and sisters, all my amazing friends—thanks for keeping a smile on my face and a laugh in my belly.

A heartfelt thanks to the many health practitioners who offered me input and guidance, especially my naturopathic consultant Alexandra Triendl. (And an extra hug to all those pros who've helped me research treatments on my own body woes!) Speaking of research, I brought back my dynamo research assistant, Tonya Stanislawska, to help me cope with the mound of research tasks at hand. Couldn't have done it without you. Nor could the book have been written without my volunteer product testers and scouters from coast to coast including Brianne, Abbey, Mark, Melissa, Sierra, Manon, Sarah, Linda, and particularly Sarika, who not only tested DIY recipes in my kitchen (turning herself a ghastly shade of white for my sunscreen trials) but also helped with research and publicity photos in a pinch. I can't talk about friends who are both handy at product reviews and photography without plugging my amazing photographer pal Dustin Rabin (who took the shot of me that appears on the book cover, one sweaty summer day in my backyard). Then there are the generous minds I picked again and again, including cosmetics know-it-all, holistic aesthetician and pro makeup artist Margot Keith, and green fashion queen Kelly Drennan as well as everyone in Big Carrot's body care department, Joy and the gang at Whole Foods Oakville, and the team at Grassroots, past and present (this book was, after all, a few years in the making), including Meredith, Michelle, Amanda and of course, Rob.

I've got to send a big shout-out to my entire NOW family, especially Ellie Kirzner, my amazing Ecoholic column editor, as well as Alice Klein and Michael Hollett for eternally supporting the weekly column that spawned these books. This book wouldn't even exist without my wonderful (and understanding) Random House/Vintage Canada team (Kendall Anderson, Marion Garner, Pamela Murray, Sharon Klein, Kelly Hill, Amanda Lewis, Deirdre Molina, Erin Cooper, Carla Kean, Matthew Sibiga and Anne Collins)—you guys rock. Thanks also to my literary agent, Denise Bukowski, for having my back and to my posse at Lavin, including Warren Campbell and Charles Yao, for helping me get my message out to the nation. That message wouldn't be complete without online transmission, so big thanks to Clayton Partridge and Caroline Bright at One Pixel Off for all their Ecoholic.ca support.

And finally I have to thank you, yes, I'm talking to you there holding this book, as well as all the other Ecoholic readers who may have followed me from the beginning, or who just discovered Ecoholic Nation last week, and everyone in between. I can't ever thank you enough for all the enthusiasm, support and tips you've sent my way. You keep me motivated and inspired. As long as you're around doing your part to be greener, I know I'm doing the right thing.

INDEX

acai berry, 240–41
acetone
    replacements for, 118
acne, 192–95
    washes and gels, 33–36
acrylic resins
    in dental devices,
        285–86
activewear, 319
acupuncture, 196
    for pain relief, 200, 202,
        203
ADHD, 274–77
aerosols
    deodorant, 59
    hairsprays, 143, 145–46
air pollution, 265
    and infertility, 160
algae, blue-green, 245
allergies, 263, 265–67
    and climate change,
        267
aluminum
    in deodorants, 59
animals
    endangered, 257
anti-aging creams, 36–42
    acids in, 39
    collagen and, 40
    cosmeceuticals, 40–41
    DMAE in, 39
    efficacy of, 36–37
    retinol A in, 40
anti-aging face mask
    homemade, 42
anti-aging tips, 41–42
antibacterials
    bee propolis, 180, 197
    garlic, 179–80
    goldenseal, 180, 197
    hand soap, 79–80
    olive leaf, 180
    ointments, 197
    oregano oil, 180
    toothpaste, 69–70
antibiotics
    alternatives to, 179–95
    overuse of, 177–79

antidepressants, 209–10
    and autism, 279
antifungals
    in shampoos, 133
anti-inflammatories, 198
antimicrobials, 187
antimony
    and autism, 278
antiperspirants. See
        deodorants/
        antiperspirants
anxiety, 213–16
    supplements for, 214–15
    techniques for
        managing, 216
    therapy for, 213–14
arnica cream, 231
    for pain relief, 199
arousal gels, 169
arthritis
    pain relief for, 205–9
asthma, 263–65
athletic shoes, 348–49
attention deficit hyperac-
        tivity disorder,
        274–77
attitude
    and immune system,
        187
autism, 270, 278–79

baby powder, 387–88
baby wipes, 386–87
bags, 363–65
balms, 27–28
bamboo
    clothing, 310
    fabric, 301–3, 309
barberry
    for yeast infections, 192
BDIH Certified Natural
        Cosmetics, 18
bee propolis
    as antibacterial, 180,
        197
benzethonium chloride
    in grapefruit seed
        extract, 194

BHA, 9
BHT, 9
bio-identical hormone
        replacement
        therapy, 222–23
birth control, 155–63
    cervical caps, 159–61
    condoms, 155–56,
        162–63
    diaphragms, 159–61
    estrogen in pills,
        156–58
    fertility awareness
        method, 160–61
    IUDs, 158–59
    patch, the, 156–58
    pill, the, 156–58
    progestin in pills, 158
    sponges, 159–61
    withdrawal method,
        162
bismuth oxychloride
    in makeup, 101
bisphenol A
    in canned food, 269
    in cash register
        receipts, 221
    in dental braces, 285
    in dental fillings, 284
    and infertility, 160
black cohosh
    and menopause
        symptoms, 223
blueberries
    pesticides in, 242
blush
    heavy metals in, 99
body care products
    disposing of conven-
        tional, 56
body washes, 23–24
boric acid suppositories, 192
boswellia
    and lung health, 265
bracelets for pain relief,
        203
braces, dental, 284–85
breathing exercises, 264

bromelain
    as pain reliever, 196
bronchitis, 263–65
bronzer
    heavy metals in, 99
bronzing lotions, 54
brown seaweed extract, 256
bubble bath
    children's, 370–72
bug spray, 87–90
    homemade, 90
    and DEET, 51
butterbur
    for allergies, 266
    and lung health, 265
    as pain reliever, 202

cadmium
    in children's jewellery,
        391–92
calcium
    for menstrual pain, 204
    sources, 250–54
calendula ointment, 197
camu camu berries, 241–43
cancer, 267–69
candles, 168
capsaicin cream
    for pain relief, 199
castor oil, 33
catnip oil, 89
cervical caps, 159–61
chasteberry
    and menopause
        symptoms, 224
chemical sensitivities,
        272–73
    clothing for people
        with, 338–39
chemicals
    restrictions on, 402–4
cherries
    pesticides in, 242
Chinese pharmaceuticals
    in ecosystem, 173
chiropractic, 200
    as pain reliever, 202–3
chocolate
    pesticides in, 243
chondroitin
    for arthritis pain, 206

chronic obstructive
    pulmonary disease,
        263–65
citronella, 88–89
cleaning products
    for footwear, 349–51
    in hospitals, 289
climate change, 397–99,
        401, 406–7
    and allergies, 267
    and depression, 211
clothing, 298–300. See also
        fabrics
    activewear, 319
    for chemically sensitive
        people, 338–39
    children's, 388–91
    consignment, 313
    donating, 335
    environmental
        footprint of,
        328–29
    formal, 335–37
    fur, 324–25
    homemade, 315–16
    jeans, 316–18
    lingerie, 325–27
    maternity, 329
    men's, 330–33
    organic brands, 308–12
    plus-sized, 318
    for proms, 335–37
    reconstructed vintage,
        314–15
    suits, 332–33
    swap party, 330
    thrift, 313–14
    T-shirts, 320–22
    underwear, 325–27,
        331–32
    vintage, 313
    wedding dresses,
        333–35
    winter coats, 322–24
coal tar
    in soaps and shampoos,
        133
coats, 322–24
cocamide DEA, 9
codeine
    in ecosystem, 173

coenzyme Q10
    and heart health, 218
colds
    natural remedies,
        182–88
    over-the-counter
        remedies, 183
collagen, 40
colognes, 83–86
concealer, 105–7
conditioners, 126–32
    testing of, 127–32
condoms, 155–56, 162–63
constipation, 193
copper bracelets, 203
corn fabrics, 303–4
cosmeceuticals, 40–41
cosmetics. See also
        makeup
    database for, 20
    grow your own, 34
    lead in, 101
    palm oil in, 9
    parabens in, 101
    preservatives in, 7–9
    regulations and, 5–6
COSMOS, 17
cotton
    Better Cotton, 297
    clothing, 308–10
    fair-trade, 310–12
    organic, 296–97
    pesticide use in
        cultivation, 295
    T-shirts, 321
counselling
    for anxiety, 213–14
    for depression, 213
cradle cap, 134, 373–75
cranberry extract pills
    for urinary tract
        infections, 190
creams
    anti-aging, 36–42
    body, 25–27
    eye, 32
    facial, 29–31
CT scans, 289–90

dairy products
    and acne, 195

and calcium, 253
and ear infections, 189
dandruff shampoos, 132–35
homemade treatments,
134–35
database for ingredients,
20, 48, 122, 236
DEA (diethanolamine), 9
DEET, 51, 88
dental care
braces, 284–85
dentures, 286–87
fillings, 283–84
flossing, 78
mouthguards, 285–86
mouthwash, 77–78
retainers, 285–86
toothbrushes, 72–75
toothpaste, 68–72
tooth whitening, 75–76
X-rays, 287
dentists, holistic, 283
dentures, 286–87
deodorants/antiperspirants,
59–67
homemade, 60
testing, 60
depression
treating, 210–13
DHA (dihydroxyacetone),
54
diamonds, 358–60
diaper rash, 373–75
diapers, 375, 377–88
cloth, 378–79, 382–85
disposable, 378–82
hybrids, 385–86
testing, 380, 382
diaphragms, 159–61
diet
and ADHD, 277
and cancer prevention,
269
Ecoholic weight loss
plan, 258–59
for healthy heart,
217–18
hospital food, 288
and infertility, 160
and lung health, 265
organic food in, 270–71

weight loss, 254–56
dildos, 165
disinfectants
used by hospitals, 289
DMAE
in anti-aging creams,
39
douching, 92–93
drugs. See also antibiotics;
pharmaceuticals
dry cleaning, 273

ear infections, 188–89
echinacea
for colds and flu, 182–83
for immune strength-
ening, 186
Ecocert, 16
recommended
makeup, 97–98
elderberry
as cold and flu remedy,
184
electric shavers, 140–41
electromagnetic
sensitivities, 273–74
emphysema, 263–65
emu oil, 29
endocrine disruptors, 9
in black hair care
products, 149
in children's shoes, 390
and infertility, 160
in nail polish remover,
118
in shaving cream, 142
in sunblock, 108
triclosan as, 80
environmental sensitivity,
271–74
estrogen
in birth control pills,
156–58
in hair care products,
149
and health, 220–24
and hormone
replacement
therapy, 221–22
in waterways, 220–21
eucalyptus, 304

exercise
and ADHD, 277
and anxiety, 216
and weight loss, 259
eye creams, 32
eye infections, 189
eyeliner
heavy metals in, 99
eyeshadow
heavy metals in, 99

fabrics, 295–300. See also
clothing
bamboo, 301–3
corn, 303–4
cotton, 295–97, 321
fair-trade cotton, 310–12
finishes, 305–7
hemp, 296, 321
linen, 296
Lyocell, 302–4
modal, 304
from pop bottles, 320
rayon, 301–3
silk, 298
soy, 303
synthetic, 295, 300–304
viscose, 301–3
wool, 297–98, 323
face creams, 29–31
facial cleansers, 32–33
fair-trade clothing, 310–12
feverfew
as pain reliever, 202
fibromyalgia
and environmental
sensitivity, 271
pain relief, 204–5
first aid
for children, 373–75
natural first aid, 197
fish oils, 207–8, 245–49
and ADHD, 277
and lung health, 264
sustainability of,
246–47
5-HTP, 205
as depression
treatment, 212
and menopause
symptoms, 224

flame retardants
    and ADHD, 276
    and autism, 278
    in children's pyjamas,
        389–91
flax oil, 248
flossing materials, 78
flu
    natural remedies,
        182–88
    over-the-counter
        remedies, 183
fluoridation
    of toothpaste, 68–69
foaming agents
    sodium laureth
        sulphate, 11
footwear
    athletic shoes, 348–49
    children's, 390
    leather, 343–46
    protection, 349–51
    vegan, 346–48
forests, 404–5
formaldehyde
    in baby wipes, 386, 387
    in children's personal
        care products,
        370–72, 375
    in cosmetics, 9
    in hair straighteners,
        144–45
    in wrinkle-resistant
        fabrics, 305–6
forskolin, 255
foundation (makeup)
    heavy metals in, 99
    liquid, 102–3
    mineral, 100–104
    recommended brands,
        103–4
fragrance
    and allergies, 10
    in body care products,
        83–86
    in deodorant, 60
    effects of, 10
    homemade, 85
    in "natural" products,
        84
    tips about, 84–86

fucoxanthin, 256
fungal infections
    oregano oil and, 187
fur, 324–25

garlic
    as antibacterial, 179–80
    as cold and flu remedy,
        185
    for ear infections,
        188–89
    and heart health, 218
ginger
    and pain relief, 201
ginkgo biloba, 231
ginseng
    as cold treatment, 188
gloss. See lipstick
glucosamine
    for arthritis pain, 206
glycine
    for anxiety, 215
goji, 243–44
gold
    production, 355–56
    recycled jewellery, 356,
        360
goldenseal
    as antibacterial, 180
    for eye infections, 189
    for wounds, 197
    for yeast infections, 192
grapefruit seed extract, 194
"greenness"
    assessing brands, 65–67
"greenwashers," 86–87
green tea
    pesticides in, 242
guggul, 195, 235–36

hair
    donation of, 146
hair care products. See also
        conditioners;
        shampoos
    for black hair, 148–51
    detanglers for children,
        373
    dandruff treatments,
        132–35
    henna, 138

hot oil treatments,
        homemade, 136
    shampoo, homemade,
        132
    straighteners/relaxers,
        144, 148–49, 150
    styling aids, 135–36,
        145–46
hair dyes, 136–40, 146–47
    highlights, 140
    natural, 138
    PPD in, 10–11, 137–38
    recommended brands,
        139
    resorcinol in, 138
    testing, 139
hair removal, 140–43
hair salons, 144–48
    healthy, 145–47
hairstyling aids, 135–36
hand sanitizers, 81
    homemade, 82
hand soap
    antibacterial, 79–80
    homemade, 82
    liquid, 82
hay fever. See allergies
headaches
    relief for, 202–3
health
    and climate change,
        398
heart health, 216–20
    and lifestyle, 217–18
    and pollution, 219
    supplements for,
        218–20
heavy metals
    in makeup, 99
hemp fabrics, 296
    T-shirts, 321
    for winter jackets,
        323–24
hemp oil, 31, 33, 248
henna, 138
herbs, 229–36. See also
        specific herbs
    endangered, 230
    endangered Ayurvedic,
        235–36
    at risk, 233, 235–36

homemade products
  anti-aging face mask,
    42
  body care, 34
  bug spray, 90
  dandruff treatments,
    134–35
  deodorant, 60
  dry shampoo, 133
  hand sanitizers, 82
  hand soap, 82
  hot oil treatments for
    hair, 136
  jewellery, 363
  lip balm, 111
  lubricants, 168
  menstrual pads, 91
  mouthwash, 78
  perfume, 84
  scar treatment, 43
  shampoos, 132
  shaving oil, 143
  for skin care, 35–36
honey
  in anti-aging mask, 42
  as cough remedy, 185
  as first aid ointment,
    197
hoodia, 255
hormone disruptors, 6
  and autism, 270, 278
  in baby wipes, 386
  in dental devices,
    285–86
  in footwear, 346, 390
  in fragrance, 83–86
  in hair dye, 138
  in hair styling aids, 135,
    144
  in hand sanitizer, 81
  in hand soap, 80
  in medical devices,
    288–89
  in nail polish, 117
  on pyjamas, 391
  in sex toys, 164
  in sunscreen, 36, 44,
    45, 127, 376
hormone replacement
  therapy, 221–22
  bio-identical, 222–23

hormones
  in anti-aging creams, 36
  in birth control, 157–59
  in black hair care
    products, 149
  disruption in teens,
    104–5
  in hydrocortisone, 27
  synthetic, pollution,
    220–21
  in wild yam, 223
hospitals, 287–91
  cleaning products, 289
  food in, 288
  medical devices,
    288–89
  medical imaging,
    289–90
  nuclear tests, 289–90
hydrogen peroxide, 197
hydroquinone, 43

immune system, 187
immune tonics, 186
infertility, 160
ingredients
  database for, 20, 48,
    122, 236
inhalers, 263–64
insect repellant, 51, 87–90
interstitial cystitis, 190
itch relief, 90
IUDs, 158–59

jeans, 316–18
jewellery, 355–63
  children's, 391–92
  do-it-yourself, 363
  engagement rings,
    359–61
  gems, 358–60
  homemade, 363
  natural and repurposed,
    361–62
jojoba oil, 33

kale
  pesticides in, 243
ketoconazole
  in shampoos, 133
konjac root, 256

labelling
  complaints about, 15
  decoder, 411–17
  definitions of terms,
    13–19
laundry
  cloth diapers, 383–85
laxatives
  petroleum in, 193
lead
  and ADHD, 276
  and autism, 278
  in children's jewellery,
    391–92
  in calcium, 251–52
  in cosmetics, 99, 101
  in diaper covers, 383
  in handbags, 363–64
  and infertility, 160
  in lipstick, 107–8
  in tattoos, 120–21
  in water, 269
leather
  footwear, 343–46
  purses, 365
lice treatments, 377
lifestyle
  and heart health,
    217–18
linen fabric, 296
lingerie, 325–27
lip balm
  homemade, 111
lipstick
  heavy metals in, 99
  lead in, 107–8
  recommended brands,
    108–10
lip tints. See lipstick
lubricants, 166–69
  homemade, 168
  and sex toys, 164
lungs
  breathing exercises,
    264
  foods that affect
    breathing, 265
  supplements for
    healthy, 264–65
Lyocell, 302–4, 308–10

magnesium
for constipation, 193
gel, for muscle cramps, 199
and lung health, 265
for menstrual pain, 204
as pain reliever, 198, 205
magnetic bracelets, 203
makeup, 97–105, 336–37
bismuth oxychloride in, 101
heavy metals in, 99
mineral, 100–104
natural brands, 97–100
permanent, 120–21
recommended brands, 103–4
removers, 116
malic acid
for pain relief, 205
manuka honey
for wounds, 197
mascara
chemicals in, 112
heavy metals in, 99
lash-growing, 115
natural, 112
recommended brands, 113–14
testing, 112–13
massage oil, 168
maternity clothing, 329
MEA, 9, 137, 147
medical devices
mercury in, 288
phthalates in, 286, 289
medical imaging, 289–90
meditation
and anxiety, 216
for pain relief, 201–2
menopause
relief from symptoms, 223–24
men's clothing, 330–33
menstrual cup
and IUDs, 159
menstrual pads, 90–91
menstrual pain, 203–4
menstrual products, 90–93
mental health, 209–16

and activity, 211
antidepressants, 209–10
anxiety, 213–16
anxiety, natural supplements for, 216
depression, natural supplements for, 210–13
mercury, 43
and autism, 278
in dental fillings, 283–84
in fish oil, 246, 248
in jewellery, 355, 360
in medical devices, 288
in skin-lightening creams, 43
in tattoos, 121
in vaccines, 291–92
methyl acetate
in nail polish remover, 118, 120
MI (methylchloroisothia-zolinone), 7, 8
mineral makeup, 100–104
mineral oil
in beauty products, 10
as laxative, 193
minerals, 249–54. See also specific minerals
mink oil, 29
in black hair care, 149
in footwear cleaning products, 350
in nail products, 119
MIT (methylisothia-zolinone), 7, 8
modal, 304, 308, 310
for underwear, 326
moisturizers, 25–32
for children, 372–73
ingredients in, 25–26
and sunscreen, 51–54
mouthguards, 285–86
mouthwash, 77–78
homemade, 78
MRIs, 289–90

N-acetylcysteine
and respiratory infections, 182

nail bars, 119
nail care, 116–20
hardener, 118
polish, almost natural, 117–18
polish remover, 118–20
nano minerals, 101–2
nanotechnology, 306–7
"natural,"
defined, 14
"naturally derived"
defined, 14–15
Naturally Sephora, 18
Natural Products Association Certified, 15
recommended makeup, 98
neem oil, 89
to combat dandruff, 134
neti pots
for allergy relief, 266
as cold and flu remedy, 184–85
for sinus infections, 182
niacinamide
for anxiety, 215
nipple cream, 7
nonoxynol-9 spermicide, 156, 161
nuclear tests, 289–90

OASIS Organic, 17
octinoxate
in hair conditioners, 127
in sunscreens, 9
oil cleansing method, 33
oil sands, 26, 399–402
oils
for children, 372–73
fish, 207–8, 245–49, 277, 278
fish-free, 248
shark, 248–49
ointments, 27–28
for pain relief, 198–200
olive leaf
as antibacterial, 180
for yeast infections, 192

olive oil, 33
omega-3 fatty acids
    and ADHD, 277
    and depression, 212
    in fish oil, 245
    and muscle pain, 198
    in salmon, 242
    and skin care, 135
    sources, 248
    for vegetarians, 248
1,4-Dioxane
    in children's personal
        care products,
        370–71
    in shampoos, 125
oregano oil, 180, 187
    as antibacterial, 180
    as antimicrobial, 187
    and fungal infections,
        187
    manufacturing
        sustainability of,
        232–35
    strength of, 234–35
    for yeast infections, 192
"organic"
    defined, 16, 18–19
"organic ingredients"
    defined, 17
osteoarthritis, 205–6, 208
osteopathy, 200
oxybenzone, 44–45
    in hair conditioners,
        127
    in sunscreens, 9

PABA, 47
pain relief, 195–209
    acupuncture, 196, 200,
        202, 203, 205
    for arthritis, 205–9
    bodywork, 200–201
    chiropractors, 200,
        202–3
    for fibromyalgia, 204–5
    ginger, 201
    for headaches, 202–3
    meditation, 201–2
    for menstrual pain,
        203–4
    ointments, 198–200

osteopathy, 200
physiotherapists, 200
    shiatsu, 200
    supplements for,
        196–98
    tai chi, 205
    ultrasound, 200
    yoga, 200
palm oil, 9, 12–13
parabens, 9–10
    in children's products,
        369–70, 373–76,
        386
    in cold and flu
        remedies, 183
    in cosmetics, 38, 45,
        54, 65–67, 86, 92,
        101–3, 113
    Danish ban of, 369–70,
        403
    in sexual lubricants,
        166, 169
    in teenagers, 104
paraffin
    in beauty products, 10
parfum. See also fragrance
patch (birth control),
    156–58
pau d'arco, 232
PBDE flame retardants,
    160
PEGs
    effects of, 10
penicillin
    in ecosystem, 173
perfume, 83–86. See also
        fragrance
    homemade, 85
permanent makeup, 120–21
pesticides
    and ADHD, 276
    foods containing,
        242–43
    use in cotton
        cultivation, 295
    in yards, 270
petrochemicals
    avoiding, 24, 26
petroleum distillates
    in beauty products, 10
PET scans, 289–90

PFOA
    in clothing, 322–23
    in fabrics, 306
    in shoes, 350
PGX, 256
pharmaceuticals
    disposing of, 176, 191
    in ecosystem, 173–76
phthalates, 11
    and ADHD, 276
    and autism, 278
    in children's footwear,
        390
    in children's personal
        care products, 369
    in dental devices,
        285–86
    in fragrance, 83–86
    in medical devices, 289
    in sex toys, 164–65
physiotherapy, 200
pill (birth control), 156–58
placenta
    in hair care products,
        149
"plant-based"
    defined, 14–15
planting
    at home, for body care,
        34
platinum production,
        355–56
political action, 398–99,
        401–2, 404, 405, 407
pollution
    and heart health, 219
    and infertility, 160
    and lung health, 263,
        265
    and oil sands, 400
    pharmaceutical,
        173–76
polycarbonate plastic
    in dental devices,
        283–86
polyurethane (PU)
    in footwear, 346
polyvinyl chloride. See
        PVC
powders
    heavy metals in, 99

PPD
  in hair dyes, 10–11,
    137–38, 147
preservatives
  in cosmetics, 7–9
probiotics
  as cold and flu remedy,
    184
  for constipation, 193
  and immune system,
    187
  regulation of, 253
  treatment for
    respiratory
    infections, 181
  for yeast infections, 192
progestin
  in birth control pills,
    158
  in IUDs, 159
propylene glycol
  in arousal gels, 169
  in cold and flu
    remedies, 183
  in yeast infection
    meds, 191
Prozac
  in ecosystem, 174
purses, 363–65
PVC
  and ADHD, 276
  and autism, 270
  in dental retainers, 286
  in diaper covers,
    382–83
  in faux leather, 346,
    363
  in inks, 320
  in medical devices,
    288, 289
  on pyjamas, 391
  in sex toys, 164
pyjamas
  children's, 389–91

quercetin
  for allergies, 266

radon, 270
rayon, 301–3
razors, 141–42

red yeast rice extract
  and heart health,
    219–20
regulations
  for cosmetics, 5–6
renovation tips, 270
resorcinol, 138
respiratory infections
  treatment of, 180–82
retainers, dental, 285–86
retinol A, 40
retinyl palmitate
  and skin care products,
    11, 12, 27, 101, 104,
    376
  and sunscreen, 47
rhapontic rhubarb root
  and menopause
    symptoms, 224
rheumatoid arthritis. See
    arthritis
rhodiola, 232
rubbing alcohol, 197

St. John's wort
  for anxiety, 204
  for depression, 210–11
salicylic acid
  in acne wash, 34
  in shampoos, 133
saline water
  for sinus infections,
    182
salmon
  pesticides in, 242
salves, 27–28
SAM-e
  for arthritis pain, 207
  for depression, 211–12
  for fibromyalgia pain,
    205
  as pain reliever, 198
scars, treating, 43
scents. See also fragrance
screen-printing inks,
    320–21
seaweed/kelp, 244–45
selenium, 208
  in dandruff shampoos,
    134
self-tanning, 54

sewage
  in ecosystem, 175
sex toys, 164–66
  dildos, 165
  lubricants, 164
  phthalates in, 164
  vibrators, 164–66
  VOCs in, 164
shampoos, 125–35
  baby's, 370–72
  for dandruff, 132–35
  dry, 133
  dry, homemade, 133
  homemade, 132, 133
  1,4-Dioxane in, 125
  recommended brands,
    128–32
  shark oil, 248–49
  sodium lauryl/laureth
    sulphate in, 125, 134
  testing of, 127–32
  in vaccines, 292
shaving, 140–43
shaving cream, 142–43
shaving oil, 143
  homemade, 143
shiatsu therapy, 200
silicone
  in hair conditioners,
    126–27
  in sex toys, 165
silk, 298
siloxanes, 11
  in hair conditioners,
    126–27
  in hairstyling products,
    135
silver production, 355–56
sinus infections
  treatment of, 182
skin
  lightening, 43
smoking, 271
soap
  hand, homemade, 82
  ingredients in, 23
  palm-free, 13
sodium laureth sulphate
  in baby shampoo, 371
  in diaper rash cream,
    373–74

and ethoxylation, 125
as foaming agent, 11
plant-based, 14–15
in shampoos, 134
sodium lauryl sulphate
in body care products,
6–7
in shampoo, 125, 134
soy
fabrics, 303
phytoestrogens in, 224
spas, 54–55
spermicide
in condoms, 156
natural, 157, 161
spirulina, 245
for allergies, 266
stain-resistant finishes,
305–7
strawberries
pesticides in, 243
sugaring, 142
sunscreens
for children, 376–77
ingredients, 9, 44–47
with moisturizers,
51–54
recommended, 48–51
testing of, 48
superfoods, 239–45
supplements
for anxiety, 214–15
for children, 393–94
for depression, 210–12
for heart health, 218
for lung health, 264–65
for menopause, 224
for pain relief, 196–98
sustainable, 229
vitamins, 236–39
weight loss, 255–56
sweatshops, 311, 312, 333, 363

tai chi
as pain reliever, 205
talc
in deodorants, 59–60
tampons, 91–92
tanning, 337. See also
sunscreens
tar sands. See also oil sands

tattoos, 120–22
TEA (triethanolamine), 9
Teflon
in fabrics, 306
Tencel, 304, 310
thimerosal, 291–92
thrift clothing, 313–14
titanium dioxide, 46–47
tobacco use
and ADHD, 276
toothbrushes, 72–75
electric, 74–75
toothpaste, 68–72
antibacterial, 69–70
children's, 68–69
fluoridated, 68–69
testing guide, 70–72
tooth whitening, 75–76
toxicity
database for cosmetics,
20
travel
preparation for, 186–87
trees, 404–5
triclocarban, 11. See also
triclosan
triclosan, 11
in deodorants, 59
in ecosystem, 174
in grapefruit seed
extract, 194
in shaving cream,
142–43
triphala
for constipation, 193
tropics
trip preparation,
186–87
T-shirts, 320–22
men's, 330–31
turmeric
for arthritis, 208
as pain reliever, 196–97

ultrasound
as pain reliever, 200
underwear, 325–27, 331–32
urinary tract infections,
189–90
USDA Organic, 16

vaccines, 291–92
vacuum cleaners, 271
vegan diets, 208
vegan footwear, 346–48
vibrators, 164–66
vintage clothing, 313
viscose, 301–3
vitamin A, 40, 195
vitamin B
for anxiety, 215
vitamin C
and arthritis, 208
as cold and flu remedy,
185
and lung health, 264
vitamin D
and menopause
symptoms, 224
for pain relief, 205
as pain reliever, 198
and respiratory
infections, 181
vitamin E
for pain relief, 204
synthetic, 218
vitamins, 236–39. See also
specific vitamins
for children, 393–94
food-sourced, 239
synthetic, 236–38
VOCs
in aerosols, 143,
145–46
in footwear cleaning
products, 350
in sex toys, 164

warfarin
in ecosystem, 173
wastewater
in ecosystem, 175
water
bottled, 175
filtered, 175–76,
269–70
scarcity of, 405–7
tap, 175
waxing, 142
wedding dresses, 333–35
weight loss, 254–56
Ecoholic plan, 258–59

whale oil, 29
wheat
    and inflammation, 209
white willow bark
    as pain reliever, 196, 202
wild yam, 223
wolfberry, 243–44
wool, 297–98, 323

wrinkle-resistant finishes,
    305–7

X-rays, 287

yeast infection, 190–92
yoga
    for pain relief, 200

zinc
    as cold and flu remedy,
        184
zinc oxide, 46–47
zinc pyrithione
    in shampoos, 132–34

The Production of Ecoholic Body: The paper used to print *Ecoholic Body* is FSC-certified (Forest Stewardship Council), 100% post-consumer recycled and Processed Chlorine–Free. It's manufactured using biogas energy. The cover for *Ecoholic Body* is FSC-certified, 10% recycled and Elemental Chlorine–Free. To avoid using non-recyclable lamination, the cover was strengthened using UV processes. Vegetable-based inks were used for the two-colour interior and on the cover. The book was perfect bound and the glue used is recyclable and emits negligible VOCs.

Corrections and Additions: If you have found an error in *Ecoholic Body* or if you are a producer or retailer who would like to be considered for upcoming editions of this indispensable guide, please contact the author at her website — www.ecoholic.ca.

For Adria's weekly column, as well as book updates, event listings and more, please visit www.ecoholic.ca.

Also, be sure to join the official Ecoholic fan site on Facebook — facebook.com/ecoholicnation. Follow her on Twitter at twitter.com/ecoholicnation.

Adria Vasil is the acclaimed and bestselling author of *Ecoholic* and *Ecoholic Home*. She has been writing the feisty and informative Ecoholic advice column for *NOW Magazine* since 2004 and has covered environmental issues for *NOW*'s news section for over a decade. Adria's been on pretty much every TV and radio station in the country, demystifying all things green, and gives talks to audiences across Canada on the topic, too. Adria lives in Toronto with her partner and cat.